His

He will claim his secret love-child!

**Three glamorous, passionate
romances from three beloved
Mills & Boon® authors!**

In October 2008 Mills & Boon bring
you two classic collections, each
featuring three favourite romances
by our bestselling authors...

HIS CHILD

The Mistress's Child
by Sharon Kendrick
Nathan's Child by Anne McAllister
D'Alessandro's Child
by Catherine Spencer

PAPER MARRIAGES

Wife: Bought and Paid For
by Jacqueline Baird
His Convenient Marriage by Sara Craven
A Convenient Wife by Sara Wood

His Child

THE MISTRESS'S CHILD
by
Sharon Kendrick

NATHAN'S CHILD
by
Anne McAllister

D'ALESSANDRO'S CHILD
by
Catherine Spencer

MILLS & BOON
Pure reading pleasure™

*Harlequin Mills & Boon Limited,
Eton House, 18-24 Paradise Road, Richmond, Surrey TW9 1SR*

HIS CHILD © by Harlequin Enterprises II B.V./S.à.r.l 2008

The Mistress's Child, Nathan's Child and D'Alessandro's Child
were first published in Great Britain by Harlequin Mills & Boon
Limited in separate, single volumes.

The Mistress's Child © Sharon Kendrick 2001
Nathan's Child © Barbara Schenck 2003
D'Alessandro's Child © Kathy Garner 2001

ISBN: 978 0 263 86135 8

05-1008

*Printed and bound in Spain
by Litografia Rosés S.A., Barcelona*

THE MISTRESS'S CHILD

by

Sharon Kendrick

100 Reasons to Celebrate

We invite you to join us in celebrating
Mills & Boon's centenary. Gerald Mills and
Charles Boon founded Mills & Boon Limited
in 1908 and opened offices in London's Covent
Garden. Since then, Mills & Boon has become
a hallmark for romantic fiction, recognised
around the world.

We're proud of our 100 years of publishing
excellence, which wouldn't have been achieved
without the loyalty and enthusiasm of our
authors and readers.

Thank you!

Each month throughout the year there will
be something new and exciting to mark the
centenary, so watch for your favourite authors,
captivating new stories, special limited
edition collections…and more!

Sharon Kendrick started story-telling at the age of eleven and has never really stopped. She likes to write fast-paced, feel-good romances with heroes who are so sexy they'll make your toes curl!

Born in West London, she now lives in the beautiful city of Winchester – where she can see the cathedral from her window (but only if she stands on tip-toe). She has two children, Celia and Patrick, and her passions include music, books, cooking and eating – and drifting off into wonderful daydreams while she works out new plots!

Don't miss Sharon Kendrick's exciting new novel, *Sicilian Husband, Unexpected Baby*, available in November 2008 from Mills & Boon® Modern™.

To the enigmatic Signor Candice.
And to the horse-riding Thomas Hietzker
(Ave Maria).

CHAPTER ONE

HE WALKED into the office and all her dreams and nightmares came true.

Lisi felt giddy. Sick. But maybe that was just the effect he was having on her heart-rate.

Up until that moment it had been a perfect day—her last afternoon at work before she finished for Christmas. There had been nothing bigger on her mind than the arrangements for Tim's birthday party the following day and wondering, along with everyone else, whether the threatened snow would fall.

She stared up into the cool, chiselled features and her fingers—which had been flying furiously over the keyboard—froze into stillness. But so did the rest of her—heart, body and soul. For one long, timeless moment their eyes met and she wondered what on earth she could say to him, but just the sight of him was making speech impossible.

He was as devastating as he had always been, but his body looked leaner, harder—all tight, honed muscle which even the elegant winter coat couldn't disguise.

Instinct made her want to stand up and demand what he was doing there, to ask him how he had the nerve to show that heartbreaking face of his, but the stakes were much too high and she knew that she could not afford to give into instinct.

'Hello, Philip,' she said at last, astonished to hear how steady her voice sounded.

He should have been expecting it, but her effect on him took him completely off guard and the sound of her low, husky voice ripped through his defences. Damn her, he thought bitterly as he recalled her soft white thighs wrapped around his body as he had plunged deep, deep inside her, unable to stop himself even though every fibre of his being had tried. Damn her!

He felt the leap of blood, like a fountain to his senses, and it felt like being resurrected. Months which had moved into years of living in an emotional and physical wasteland and she had vanquished his icy indifference simply by the lilting way she said his name. His normally lush, sensual mouth was thin and unsmiling.

'Why, for a moment there I thought you didn't remember me, Lisi,' he mocked softly.

Not remember him? She would have to be dead not to have remembered him, even if she hadn't had the living proof to remind her every single day of her life.

She kept her face impassive, but in reality she was greedily registering every detail of that arrogantly beautiful face. Thinking of her son's face and searching for heartbreaking signs of similarity—but thank God there was none. His lightly tanned golden skin was so very different from her son's natural pallor, as were Philip's startling emerald eyes. They made the aquamarine hue of Tim's look so diluted in comparison.

And then her heart began to race and the inside of her mouth turned to sandpaper as painful questions began to buzz silently around her head. Why was he here?

Did he *know*?

The foundations of her world threatened to rock on their axis, but she kept her face as calm as his. He couldn't know. He couldn't possibly know!

'Not remember you? Of course I remember you,' she said, in as bland a voice as she could manage—she even tacked on a weak attempt at a smile as she met the emerald ice of his stare. 'I always remember—'

'All the men you've slept with?' he challenged, unable to resist the taunt, cruelly pleased by the sting of colour which brought roses to the whiteness of her skin.

She felt heat flaring across her cheeks, but that was her only outward reaction to his remark. How blatant, to say something as provocative as that, she thought indignantly—especially when you considered *his* track record. And all the while looking at her with that cold, studied insolence which did nothing to mar the sheer beauty of his face.

She bit back the temptation to remind him that there had been no sleep involved. He had not wanted to sleep with her—and for very good reason. She repressed a shudder as she was reminded of what a gullible fool she had been.

Far better to change the subject completely. To find out what he wanted and to see the back of him.

'I was about to say that I always remember clients—' She wished that she could bite the word back. It seemed so cold and unfeeling in view of what she had shared, until she reminded herself that they had shared nothing—except their bodies.

'Clients,' she continued valiantly, 'who have involved this company in as many deals as you once did. You brought us a lot of business, Mr Caprice. We sold a lot of properties through you.'

So she remembered his surname, too. Philip didn't know whether to be flattered or not, though he was certainly surprised. He suspected that he had been just one in a long line of men she had enticed into her bed—a woman who looked like that would have no trouble doing so. Did she have a photographic memory for *all* their names?

He studied her—taking all the time in the world to do so—and why not? Hadn't she haunted his memory with bitter-sweet recall? Given him the acrid taste of guilt in his mouth every time he'd thought of her in nearly four years?

Even though he had tried his hardest not to think of her. Tried and failed every time.

But Lisi Vaughan had been a fever in his blood for far too long now.

His eyes skimmed over her. Time had not made much of a mark—certainly not on her face, which was probably the most beautiful he had ever seen. A face completely devoid of make-up, which gave it an odd kind of purity which seemed so at odds with her innate sensuality.

The eyes he remembered because they were icy and aquamarine—unique. Slanting, siren's eyes, half shielded by a forest of thick, dark eyelashes, which made her look so minxy. The darkness of her lashes was echoed in her hair—deep, dark ebony—as black as the coals of hell itself and made even blacker by its dramatic contrast to the whiteness of her skin. She looked like a witch, he thought, a beautiful temptress of a witch with a body which few men would see outside paradise.

He knitted his eyebrows together almost imperceptibly. Not that her body was on display much today, but some things you couldn't disguise—even though she had done her level best with some plain black skirt and high-necked blouse which made her look almost *dowdy*.

No. On second thoughts—certainly not dowdy. Philip swallowed as she moved her head back, as if trying to escape his scrutiny, and the movement drew attention to the unforgettable swell of her breasts. Her waist was as tiny as ever, but her breasts were slightly fuller, he thought, and then was punished with the heavy jackknifing of desire in response.

Lisi could feel her heartbeat growing thready and erratic. She wished he wouldn't look at her that way. It reminded her of too much she would rather forget. Of tangled limbs and the sheen of sweat, the sweet, fleeting pleasure of fulfilment followed by the shattering pain of rejection. He had no *right* to look at her that way.

She quashed down the desire to tell him to get out, and forced a pleasantry out instead. He was not the kind of man to be pushed. If she wanted him out of there—and she most certainly did—then he must come to the conclusion that it had been his idea to leave and not hers.

Keep it cool and keep it professional, she told herself. 'Now. How can I help you?'

He gave her a grim smile, not trusting himself to answer for a moment, and then he lifted his eyebrows in mocking question. 'What a sweetly expressed offer,' he murmured.

'Why, thank you,' she said demurely.

'Do you say that to all the men?'

'Most of them are grown-up enough not to read anything into it.' She matched his remark with a dry tone of her own and then fixed her eyes on his unwaveringly, trying not to be distracted by that dazzling green gaze. 'So. Are you interested in a property for sale, Mr Caprice?'

Her unemotional attitude was having precisely the wrong effect on him. 'Oh, what's with all this ''Mr'' stuff?' Again he felt the sting of life to his senses, but ruthlessly he subdued them and gave a short laugh instead. 'Come on, Lisi,' he purred. 'I think we can dispense with the formalities, don't you? Surely we are intimate enough with each other to use first names?'

'*Were* intimate,' she corrected, and the heat in her face intensified as she was forced to acknowledge it aloud. 'Past tense. Remember?'

How could he possibly forget? And wasn't that why he had come here today—to change the past back to present? To rid himself of her pervasive and unforgettable sensual legacy. Wouldn't a whole night lost in the scented curves of her siren's body mean that he would be free of the guilt and the longing for ever? Sensations which had somehow chained him to her, and made him unable to move on.

He looked around the office, where the Christmas decorations were glittering silver and gold. In the corner stood a small artificial tree which was decked with shining crimson-red baubles and tiny white fairy lights.

He found Christmas almost unbearable—he had forgotten its poignant lure while he had been away. You could tell yourself that it was corny. Commercial. That all its true values were forgotten these days—but it still got to you every time.

And this was his first Christmas back in England since working in Maraban, where of course they had not celebrated the feast at all. He had not even had to think about it.

He was slowly beginning to realise that living in the Middle East had protected him from all the things he did not want to think about. And Christmas brought with it all kinds of things he would rather not think about. Feelings, mostly. Feelings of remorse. The pain of loss and the pain of wanting. Or, rather, of not wanting. For too long now, his body had felt as unresponding as a block of ice until he had walked in here today and seen her, and now his groin was on fire with need. Damn her, he thought again. Damn her!

He gritted his teeth, his gaze moving to her hand. She wore no wedding ring, nor any pale sign that one might have been recently removed, either. But women these days lived with men at the drop of a hat and he needed to find out if she was involved with someone. But even if she *did* have another man—would that honestly prevent him from doing what he intended to do?

He sat down in the chair opposite her desk, spreading out his long legs and not missing the thinning of her mouth as she watched him do so. He coolly crossed one leg over the other and felt a jerk of triumph as he saw her eyes darken. She wants me, he thought and his heart thundered in his chest. She still wants me.

'I must say that I'm surprised to see you still working here,' he observed, looking around the office of the small estate agency.

Lisi stiffened, warning herself not to get defensive. It was none of his business. She owed him nothing, least of all the truth.

'I just happen to like selling houses,' she said.

'I guess you do.' It had been another aspect of her character which he had been unable to fault—her unerring ability to match the right property to the right client. It had been what had brought him back to this small English village time after time as he'd sought valuable property for a clutch of wealthy buyers. In the beginning he had always dealt with Jonathon, the owner and senior negotiator, but after a while Lisi had taken over. Beautiful Lisi, with her ready smile and soft, sympathetic manner.

Part of him had not expected to find her here. He had imagined that she would be running her own place by now—and it was more than a little disconcerting to see her at the same desk, in the same office. As if time had stood still, and she with it. He gave her a questioning look. 'Most people would have moved on by now—to bigger and brighter things.'

And leave her safety net? Her cushion?

Her job had been the one familiar constant in those dark, far-off days when she had wondered just how she was going to cope—how could she ever have left it? 'Not me,' she said staunchly.

'Why ever not?' he asked quietly, bemused—because she had not only been good at her job, she had been ambitious, too.

She didn't break the gaze, even though her stomach was

churning over with anxiety, as if he somehow knew her
secret and was just biding his time before he confronted
her with it. Distract him, she thought. 'Why on earth should
my job prospects interest you?'

'Call it curiosity,' he told her softly. 'Ex-lovers always
interest me.'

Lisi repressed a shudder. She didn't feel like his ex-
lover—she felt like a woman who had shared his bed under
false pretences before he had disappeared dramatically from
her life. But she didn't want to analyse *that*—not now and
not with him here. Instead she took his question at face
value.

'I love my job,' she said staunchly. 'It's convenient and
it's local—and there's no reason why I should travel miles
to find something which is already on my doorstep, is
there?'

'I guess not.' But he couldn't help wondering why she
had settled for such steady small-town life when she was
still so young and beautiful. His eyes were drawn irresistibly to the lush lines of her mouth, knowing that he would
never be satisfied until he got her out of his system one last
time.

For good.

He gave a conventional smile as he forced himself to
make conventional conversation. 'And of course Langley
is a very pretty little village.'

Lisi was growing uncomfortable. She wished he would
go. Just his proximity was making the little hairs on the
back of her neck stand up like soldiers and she could feel
the prickle of heat to her breasts. She remembered the light-
ning feel of his mouth as it caressed all the secret places
of her body and thought how sad it was that no other man
had ever supplanted him in her memory.

She cleared her throat. The last thing she wanted was to
antagonise him and to arouse his suspicions, but she could

not tolerate much more of him sitting across the desk from her while she remembered his love-making, the unmistakable glint in his eyes telling her that *he* was remembering, too.

'You still haven't told me how I can help you,' she asked quietly.

Philip narrowed his eyes. He didn't know what he had expected from her today. More anger, he guessed. Yes. Much more. And more indignation, too. Lisi looking down her beautiful nose at him for daring to reappear without warning and after so long. Particularly after the last words he had ever said to her.

Yet there was an unexpected wariness and a watchfulness about her rather than the out-and-out anger he might have expected, and he wondered what was the cause of it. Something was not as it should be.

He ran a long, reflective finger along the faint shadow which darkened his jaw. 'You mean am I here today on business? Or pleasure?'

She gave a thin smile. 'I hope it's the former! Because I don't think that the atmosphere between us could be described as pleasure—not by any stretch of the imagination.'

Oh, but how wrong she was! You didn't have to like a woman to want her. He knew that. Liking could die, but lust seemed to have a much longer shelf-life. 'Then maybe we should try and put that to rights.'

'By placing as much distance as possible between us, you mean?'

'Not exactly.' He leaned back in the chair and narrowed his eyes in provocative assessment. 'Why don't I take you for a drink after work instead?'

His audacity left her reeling, and yet there had been weeks and months when she had prayed for such a proposition, when she'd tried to tell herself that what had happened between them had all been one big misunderstanding

He shook his head. 'No, you're not. Don't pretend. You didn't know her.'

'Of course I didn't know her! I didn't even know *of* her, did I, Philip? Because if I had...if I had—' She chewed frantically on her lip.

'What?' he interjected softly. 'Are you trying to say that you wouldn't have gone to bed with me if you'd known she existed?'

'No,' she whispered. 'Of course I wouldn't.'

'Are you so sure, Lisi?'

She bent her head to gaze unseeingly at all the property details she had been typing up. Of course she wasn't sure. She wasn't sure of anything other than the fact that Philip Caprice had exercised some strange power over her—the power to transform her into the kind of wild, sensual creature she hardly recognised, and certainly didn't like.

'Just go away,' she said, her voice very low. 'Please, Philip. There's nothing left to say, and, even if there was, we can't have this conversation here.'

'I know we can't.' He leaned forward and the movement caused his trousers to ride and flatten over the strong, powerful shafts of his thighs and he heard her draw in a tiny breath. 'So let's have that drink later and catch up on old times. Aren't you interested to compare how the world has been treating us?'

Something in his words didn't ring true and again she felt a frisson of apprehension. Why would Philip suddenly reappear and want to *catch up on old times*?

'I don't think so.'

'Oh, come on, Lisi—what have you got to lose?'

Her freedom? Her sanity? Her *heart*? She shook her head. 'I'm busy after work,' she said, despising herself for being tempted all the same.

But there was something in her body language which told a conflicting story, something which put his senses on in! What is the point of you being here? Do you honestly think you can just waltz back in here after all this time, and pick up where we left off?'

'Is that what you'd like, then?' he asked softly. 'To pick up where we left off?'

Yes! More than anything else in the world!

No! The very *last* thing she wanted!

Lisi stared distractedly at the hard, angular planes of his face and—not for the first time—wished that she had more than one beautiful yet unsatisfactory night to remember this man by. And then reminded herself that she had a whole lot more besides.

Imagine the repercussions if he were to find out!

She gave a humourless laugh. 'I outgrew my masochistic phase a long time ago!' She looked down deliberately at her watch. 'And now, if you'll excuse me, I really do have work to do!'

He remembered her as uncomplicated and easygoing, but now he heard the sound of unmistakable frost in her voice and he found himself overwhelmed by the urge to kiss the warmth back into it. And it was so long since he had felt the potency of pure desire that he found himself captive to his body's authority. Compelled to act by hunger and heat instead of reason—but then, that was nothing new, not with her.

A pulse began to beat at his temple. 'You don't look too busy to me.'

Like an onlooker in a play, Lisi stared with disbelief as she saw that he was moving around to her side of the desk, with a look on his face which told its own story.

'Philip?' she questioned hoarsely as he bent towards her.

'Answer me one thing and one thing only,' he demanded.

His voice was one of such stark command that Lisi heard herself framing the word, 'What?'

'Is there a man in your life?' he murmured. 'A husband or a fiancé or some long-time lover?'

This truth was easy to tell, but then perhaps that was because she was compelled to by the irresistible gleam of his eyes. She shook her head. 'No. No one.'

He looked down at her for one brief, hard moment and knew a moment of sheer, wild exultancy before he pulled her into his arms with a shudder as he felt the soft warmth of a woman in his arms again.

The blood roared in her ears. She wanted to push him away and yet she was powerless to move, so tantalising was his touch. Suddenly she knew just how a butterfly must feel shortly before it was impaled against a piece of card. Except that a butterfly would receive nothing but pain— while Philip could give her untold pleasure.

'What the hell do you think you're doing?' she breathed as she felt the delicious pressure of his fingers against her skin through the shirt she wore.

'You know what I'm doing.' Doing what he had been wanting to do ever since he had walked back in here again today. Doing what had haunted him for far too long now.

'You need kissing, Lisi,' he ground out and pulled her even closer. 'You know you do. You want me to. You always did. Didn't you?'

His arrogance took away what little of her breath was left, because just the sensation of feeling herself in the warm circle of his arms again was enough to make her feel as weak as a kitten.

'Get out of here! We're standing in the middle of my bloody *office*—' she spluttered, but her protest was cut short by the ringing of the doorbell and Marian Reece, her boss and the owner of Homefinders, walked in, her smile of welcome instantly replaced by one of slightly irritated bemusement as she took in the scene in front of her.

'Hello, Lisi,' she said steadily, looking from one to the other. 'I'm sorry—am I interrupting something?'

Hearing the unmistakable reproof in her boss's voice, Lisi sprang out of Philip's arms as if she had been scalded, thinking how close he had been to kissing her. Would she have let him? Surely not. But if she had…?

Her heart was crashing against her ribcage, but she struggled to retain her breath and to appear the kind of unflappable employee she usually was. 'H-hello, Marian. This is Philip Caprice. We were, um, we were just—'

'Just renewing our acquaintance,' interjected Philip smoothly and held his hand out to Marian, while smiling the kind of smile which few women would have the strength to resist.

And Marian Reece was not among them.

Lisi had known the forty-five-year-old since she had bought out the estate agency two years ago. She liked Marian, even though the older woman led a life which was streets apart from her own.

But then Marian was a successful businesswoman while Lisi was a struggling single mother.

'Lisi and I are old…friends,' said Philip deliberately. 'We go way back.'

'Indeed?' said Marian rather tightly. 'Well, call me a little old-fashioned—but mightn't this kind of fond greeting be better reserved for *out* of office hours?'

Fond? Inside, Lisi almost choked on the word. 'Yes, of course. And Philip was just leaving, weren't you, Philip?'

'Unfortunately, yes—I have some business to see to.' He glittered her a look which renewed the racing in her heart. 'But I'll be back tomorrow.'

Lisi thought it sounded more like a threat than a promise. 'Back?' she questioned weakly. 'Tomorrow?'

'Of course. You haven't forgotten that you're going to sell me a house, have you, Lisi?'

Lisi blinked at him in confusion. Had she had missed something along the way? 'A house?' He had mentioned *nothing* about a house!

'That's why I'm here,' he said gently. 'I'm looking for a weekend cottage—or something on those lines.'

Was she being offered a lifeline? In the old days he had done deals for rich contemporaries of his from university—they had valued his taste and his discretion.

'You mean you're buying for someone else?' Lisi stared up at him hopefully.

Her obvious resistance only increased his desire for her—although maybe she knew that. Maybe that was precisely why she was batting those aquamarine eyes at him like that and unconsciously thrusting the narrow curves of her hips forward. 'Sorry to disappoint you, sweetheart—but I'm looking for a country home for myself.'

Lisi's world threatened to explode in a cloud of black dust. 'Around *here*?' she questioned hoarsely.

'Sure. Why not? I know the area. It's very beautiful—and just about commutable from London.' His eyes mocked her. 'Sounds just about perfect to me.'

'Does it?' asked Lisi dully.

'Yes, of course we'll be delighted to find something for you, Mr Caprice,' said Marian crisply. 'I can look for you myself, if you prefer.'

He shook his head. 'Oh, no,' he contradicted softly. 'I'm quite happy to deal with Lisi.'

Well, I'm not happy to deal with *you*, she thought hysterically, but by then it was too late. He was charm personified to Marian as he said goodbye, and then he took Lisi's hand in his and held it for just a little longer than was necessary while he held her gaze.

'Goodbye, Lisi. Until tomorrow.'

'Goodbye, Philip.' She swallowed, while inside her heart raced with fear and foreboding.

She stood in silence with Marian as they watched him leave and Lisi's hands were shaking uncontrollably as the door clanged shut behind him.

Marian turned to look at her and her eyes were unexpectedly soft with sympathy. 'So when are you going to tell him, Lisi?' she asked softly.

Time froze. Lisi froze. 'Tell him what?'

'The truth, of course.' She placed a perfectly manicured hand on Lisi's shaking arm. 'He's the father of your child, isn't he?'

CHAPTER TWO

LISI stared at Marian. 'You can't know that!' she babbled, and now her knees really *were* threatening to give way. 'Tim looks nothing like him!'

'Sit down, dear, before you fall down.' Marian gently pushed her back down onto her chair and went and poured a glass of water from the cooler, then handed it to her. 'Now drink this—you've gone even paler than usual.'

Lisi sucked the chilled liquid into her parched mouth and then shakily manoeuvred it to a corner of her desk before raising her eyes beseechingly to her boss. 'He doesn't look anything like Philip,' she repeated stubbornly.

'Lisi,' said Marian patiently. 'Tim is your living image— but that doesn't mean that he hasn't inherited any of his father's characteristics. Sometimes a mother can blind herself to what she doesn't want to see. Sometimes it's easier for an outsider to see the true picture. I knew immediately that Philip was Tim's father.'

'But how?' Lisi demanded brokenly.

Marian sighed. 'Well, Tim is an unusually tall boy for his age—we've always said that. He has his father's strength and stature—and there's a certain look of him in the shape of his face, too.'

A chasm of frightening dimensions was beginning to open up in front of Lisi's feet. 'A-anything else?' she demanded hoarsely.

Marian shrugged awkwardly. 'Well, I've never seen you behave like that with a man before—'

'Because he was hugging me in the office, you mean?'

'*Hugging* you?' Marian raised her eyes to heaven.

'That's a new way to describe it! He looked more like he wanted to eat you up for breakfast, lunch and tea—and vice versa. Like no one else existed in the universe other than him.'

And he had always had that effect on her—even though she could have been nominated for an Oscar, so hard had she always tried to hide it in the past. Philip could do and behave exactly as he pleased and Lisi would always be there with a smile for him. No questions, Lisi. Weak Lisi. Foolish Lisi.

Well, not any longer!

'It must have been a very passionate relationship,' observed Marian.

If only she knew!

'The question is, what are you going to tell him?'

Lisi shook her head. 'I'm not. I'm not going to tell him.'

Marian screwed her eyes up. 'Oh, Lisi—do you honestly think that's a good idea?'

Lisi shook her head. 'I know it isn't ideal, but it's the only thing I can do.'

'But why, dear? Why not tell him? Don't you think he has the right to know that he has a beautiful son?'

'The right?' Lisi looked at her boss and knew that she could not tell her whole story—but part of the story would surely make her point for her. And illustrate as well as anything just how little she had meant to Philip.

'Marian—he walked out on me. He made it clear that he thought our night together was a big mistake, and that he wanted nothing more to do with me.'

Marian frowned. 'One night? That's all it was? Just one night?'

Lisi nodded. 'That's right.' She saw Marian's rather shocked face. 'Oh, it wasn't the *classic* one-night stand—believe me.' It hadn't even been meant to happen. 'I...I used to see him every couple of months or so,' she contin-

ued painfully. 'We had grown to like one another, though
I realise now that I never really knew him, or anything
about him. But the "affair" wasn't really an affair, as
such.' In fact, it hadn't lasted beyond midnight.

'But isn't it time he found out the truth—whatever has
happened between you? I have children of my own, Lisi,
and children *need* a father wherever possible. They need to
know their roots and where they come from.'

Lisi sighed. How could she possibly explain this without
sounding scheming and cold-hearted? 'Maybe I'll tell him
if he shows any sign of wanting to *be* a father, but if I just
announce it without careful consideration—can't you just
imagine the consequences? Philip demanding contact.
Philip turning up to take Tim out...' Philip taking Tim's
affection...while feeling nothing for her but lust at best,
and contempt at worst. 'Tim doesn't even *know* about
Philip!'

'But surely other people round here must know he's the
father? *Someone* must know?'

Lisi shook her head. Her night with Philip had gone un-
noticed and unremarked upon, and that was how she had
kept it. No one knew the truth except for her mother, and
that had been a death-bed secret. Even her best friend
Rachel thought that her refusal to divulge the identity of
Tim's father was down to some fierce kind of pride at having been deserted, but it went much deeper than that.

Lisi had accepted that Philip could and had just walked
out of *her* life—but she had vowed that he would never
play emotional ping-pong with that of her son. A child was
a commitment you made for life, not something to be
picked up and put down at will—especially if the father of
that child was married.

Except now that his wife was dead. So didn't that change
things?

Lisi shook her head. 'Nobody knows. Not a living soul.' She stared at Marian. 'Except for you, of course.'

'I won't tell him, if that's what you're worried about, Lisi,' said Marian awkwardly. 'But what if he finds out anyway?'

'He can't! He won't!'

'He's planning on buying a house here. It's a small village. What if he starts putting two and two together and coming up with the right answer? Surely he'll be able to work out for himself that he's the father?'

Lisi shook her head. Why should he? It was a long time ago. Months blurred into years and women blurred into other women, until each was indistinguishable from the last. 'Maybe he won't find a house to suit him?' she suggested optimistically, but Marian shook her head with a steely determination which Lisi recognised as the nine-carat businesswoman inside her.

'Oh, no, Lisi—don't even think of going down that road. This is strictly business. And if a client—any client—wants to buy a house from this agency, then we find one for him to buy. Beginning and end of story. I simply can't allow you to prejudice any sale because of some past quarrel with your child's father—which in my opinion, needs some kind of resolution before Tim gets much older.'

'An outsider doesn't know how it feels,' said Lisi miserably.

'Maybe that's best. An outsider can tell you what she thinks you *need* rather than what you think you *want*.' Marian's face softened again. 'Listen, dear,' she said gently, 'why don't you take the rest of the afternoon off? You look much too shaken to do any more work. Peter will be back from his viewing shortly—and it's always quiet at this time of the year. Think about what I've said. Sleep on it. It may be better in the long run if you just come clean and tell Philip the truth about Tim.'

Better for whom? wondered Lisi as she took off her work shoes and changed into the wellington boots she always wore to work when the weather was as inclement as it was today. It certainly wouldn't be better for *her*.

She felt disorientated and at a loss, and not just because of Philip's unexpected reappearance. Tim didn't finish nursery until four, which meant that she had nearly two hours going spare and now she wasn't quite sure what to do with them. How ironic. All the times when she had longed for a little space on her own, when the merry-go-round of work and single motherhood had threatened to drag her down—and here she was with time on her hands and wishing that she had something to fill it.

She didn't want to go home, because if she did then she would feel guilty for not putting any washing into the machine, or preparing supper for Tim, or any of the other eight million tasks which always needed to be done. And mundane tasks would free up her mind, forcing her to confront the disturbing thoughts which were buzzing around inside her head.

Instead, she turned up her coat collar against the chill breeze, and headed up the main village street, past the duck pond.

The light was already beginning to die from the sky and the contrasting brightness of the fairy lights and glittering Christmas trees which decorated every shop window made the place look like an old-fashioned picture postcard. How their gaiety mocked her.

The breeze stung her cheeks, and now and again, tiny little flakes of snow fluttered down from the sky to melt on her face like icy tears.

The weathermen had been promising a white Christmas, and, up until today, it had been one of Lisi's main preoccupations—whether her son would see his first snow at the most special time of year for a child.

But thoughts of a white Christmas had been eclipsed by thoughts of Philip, and now they were threatening to engulf her, making her realise just why she had put him in a slot in her memory-bank marked 'Closed'. She had done that for reasons of practicality and preservation—but seeing him today had made it easy to remember just why no one had ever come close to replacing him in her affections.

And now he might be here to stay.

She climbed over a stile and slid down onto wet grass, glad for the protection of her heavy boots as she set out over the field, but she had not walked more than a few metres before she realised that she was being followed.

Lisi knew the village like the back of her hand. She had lived there all her life and had never felt a moment's fear or apprehension.

But she did now.

Yet it was not the heartstopping and random fear that a stranger had materialised out of nowhere and might be about to pounce on her, because some sixth sense warned her to the fact that the person following her was no stranger. She could almost sense the presence of the man who was behind her.

She stopped dead in her tracks and slowly turned around to find Philip standing there, his unsmiling face shadowed in the fast-fading light of dusk. Out here in the open countryside he seemed even more formidable, his powerful frame silhouetted so darkly against the pale apricot of the sky, and Lisi felt the sudden warm rush of desire.

And she didn't want to! Not with him. Not with this beautiful, secretive and ultimately deceitful man who had given her a child and yet would never be a father to that child.

She had overplayed the bland, polite card in the office today and he had not taken heed of her wish to be rid of him. The time for politeness was now past.

'Do you always go creeping up on people in the twilight, Philip?' she accused.

He gave a faint smile. 'Sometimes. My last employment meant that I had to employ qualities of stealth, even cunning.'

She resisted the urge to suggest that the latter quality would come easily to him, intrigued to learn of what he had been doing for the past four years. 'And what kind of employment was that?'

He didn't answer immediately. He wasn't sure how much of his past he wanted to share with her. What if anything he wanted to share with her, other than the very obvious. And his years as emissary to a Middle Eastern prince could not be explained in a couple of sentences in the middle of a field on a blisteringly cold winter's afternoon. 'Maybe I'll tell you about it some time,' he said softly.

So he wasn't going to fill in any gaps. He would remain as unknowable as he ever had been. She looked at him in exasperation. 'Why are you really here, Philip? What brought you back to Langley after so long?'

An unanswerable question. How could he possibly define what his intentions had been, when nothing was ever as easy as you thought it was going to be? *Something* had compelled him to return and lay a increasingly troublesome ghost to rest, and yet the reality was proving far more complex than that.

He had been dreaming of her lately. Images which had come out of nowhere to invade his troubled nights. Not pin-point, sharply accurate and erotic dreams of a body which had captivated him and kept him prisoner all this time. No, the dreams had been more about the elusive memory of some far-distant sweetness he had experienced in her arms.

Part of him had wondered if seeing her again would make the hunger left by the dream disappear without trace—like the pricking of a bubble with a pin—but it had not happened like that.

The other suspicion he had nurtured—that her beauty and charm would be as freshly intact as before—had sprung into blinding and glorious Technicolor instead. His desire for her burned just as strongly as before—maybe even more so—because nobody since Lisi had managed to tempt him away from his guilt and into their bed.

Not that there hadn't been offers, of course, or invitations—some subtle, some not. There had been many—particularly when he had been working for the prince—and some of those only a fool would have turned down. Was that what he was, then—a fool?

Or was it that one night with her had simply not been enough? Like a starving man only being offered a morsel when the table was tempting him with a banquet?

He looked into her eyes—their bright, clear aquamarine shaded a deeper blue by the half-light of approaching dusk. Her face was still pale—pale as the first faint crescent of the moon which was beginning its nightly rise into the heavens. Her lips looked darker, too. Mulberry-coloured—berry-sweet and succulent and juicy—what wouldn't he give to possess those lips again?

'Maybe I wanted to see you again,' he murmured.

It sounded too much like the kind of declaration which a woman dreamed a man would make to her, but there was no corresponding gentling of his tone when he said it. The deep-timbred voice gave as little away as the green, shuttered eyes did.

'Why?' She forced herself to say it. 'To sleep with me again?'

Philip's mouth hardened. He wasn't going to lie. 'I think you know the answer to that.'

She let out a cold, painful breath as the last of her hopes crumbled. It was as she had suspected. The warm, giving

Philip whose bed she had shared—that man did not exist. It had all been an act. He was merely a seductive but illusionary figure who had let his defences down enough to have sex with her, and then had retreated to his real world—a world which had excluded her because he'd had a wife.

Not just cruel, but arrogant, too!

'And you think...' She sucked in a deep breath. 'Do you really think that I've been sitting around, just waiting for you to come back and make such a—' she almost choked on the word '—*charming* declaration as that one?'

'But I'm not telling you any lies, am I, Lisi?'

She shook her head violently, and some of the thick, dark hair escaped from the velvet ribbon which had held it captive. 'No,' she agreed. 'Lies aren't your thing, are they? You lie by omission rather than fact! Like you omitted to tell me that you were married when you seduced me!'

'*Seduced* you?' He gave a short laugh and his breath clouded the air like smoke. 'You make it sound as though we were both starring in some kind of Victorian melodrama! There was no wicked master seducing some sweet little innocent who knew no better, was there, Lisi? Quite the contrary, in fact. You were the one who stripped naked in my bed. You knew exactly what you wanted and what you were doing. So please don't play the innocent. That night you kept me delightfully and memorably entertained—something which is simply not compatible with someone who isn't...' he narrowed his eyes into hard, condemnatory slits '...*experienced.*'

Lisi swallowed. He was insulting her, she knew that—and yet it was like no insult she had ever heard. The disparaging tone which had deepened his voice did not have her itching to slap the palm of her hand against that smooth, golden cheek the way it should have done.

Instead, it seemed to have set off a chain reaction which

began with the quickened pace of her heart and ended with the honey-slick throb of a longing so pure and so overwhelming that she could have sunk down into the thick, wet clods of earth and held her arms open to him.

But she had played the fool with Philip Caprice once before, and once was too often.

She raised her eyebrows. 'You know, you really ought to make your mind up how you feel about me. On the one hand you seem to despise me for my so-called experience—while on the other you seem unable to forget what happened.'

'Can you?' he demanded as he felt the heavy pull of need deep in his groin. 'Can you forget it, Lisi?'

Of course she couldn't! But then, unlike Philip, she had a very tangible memory of that night.

Tim.

She thought of Marian's words—wise, kindly experienced Marian who had urged her to tell him, who had emphasised how much a child needed a father. But what if this particular man had no desire to be a father? What if she told him and ruined both her and Tim's lives unnecessarily? What if Philip had *children of his own*?

Was now the time to ask him? In a field on a cold December night where stars were now beginning to appear as faint blurry dots in the skies?

She steeled herself. 'What happened to your wife, Philip?'

She took him off guard with her question, though perhaps that was because these days he had schooled himself not to remember Carla more than was absolutely necessary. The living had to let go—he knew that—just as he knew how hard it could be.

He used the same words as the press had done at the time. 'She was involved in a pile-up on the motorway.'

She nodded, painfully aware of how much the bereaved

resented other people's silence on the subject. She remembered when her mother had died, and people had seemed to cross the road to avoid her. 'Was it…was it instant?'

'*No.*' The word came out more harshly than he had intended, but he did not want to discuss Carla, not now. God forgive him, but he wanted to lose the pain of death in the sweet, soft folds of living flesh. 'Can't we go somewhere warmer, if we're going to talk?'

She shook her head. Tim would be out of nursery soon enough and she had no desire to take Philip home and have him see her little house with all its childish paraphernalia, which might just alert his suspicions.

And where else to go to talk in Langley on one of the shortest days of the year—the pub would have shut by now. There was always the hotel, of course, she reminded herself, and a shiver of memory ran down her spine.

'I don't think there's any point in talking. What is there left to say?'

He watched the movement of her lips as she spoke, saw the tiny moist tip of her tongue as it briefly eased its way between her perfect white teeth, and a wave of lust turned his mouth to dust. 'Maybe you're right,' he agreed softly. 'How can we possibly talk when this crazy attraction is always going to be between us? You still want me, Lisi— it's written all over your face,' and he reached out and pulled her into his arms.

'D-don't,' she protested, but it was a weak and meaningless entreaty and she might as well not have spoken for all the notice he took of it.

He cupped her face in the palm of his hand and turned it up so that she was looking at him, all eyes and lips and pale skin, and his voice grew soft, just as once it had before. 'Why, you're cold, Lisi,' he murmured.

It was the concern which lulled her into staying in his arms—that and the masculine heat and the musky, virile scent of him. Helplessly, she stared up at him, knowing that he was about to kiss her, even before he began to lower his mouth towards hers.

The first warm touch of him was like clicking on a switch marked 'Responsive'. 'Philip,' she moaned softly, without realising that she was doing so, nor that her arms had snaked up around his neck to capture him.

The way she said his name incited him, and he whispered hers back as if it were some kind of incantation. 'Lisi.' Her mouth was a honey-trap—warm and soft and immeasurably sweet. He felt the moistness of her tongue and the halting quality of her breath as it mingled with his. Even through the thickness of his greatcoat, he could feel the flowering of her breasts as they jutted against him and he felt consumed with the need to feel them naked once more, next to his body and tickling both hard and soft against his chest. 'Oh, Lisi,' he groaned.

All she could think of was that this was not just the man she had found more overwhelmingly attractive than any other man she had ever met—this man was also the biological father of her child, and in a way she was chained to him for ever.

Just for a minute she could pretend that they had been like any other couple who had created a child together. They could kiss in a field and she could lace her fingers luxuriously through the thick abundance of his hair, and feel the quickening of his body against hers and then…and then…

Then what?

The logical conclusion to what they were starting clamoured into her consciousness like a bucket of ice-cold water being torrented over her and Lisi pulled herself out of his arms, her eyes wide and darkened, her breath coming in short, laboured little gasps.

'You thought it would be that simple, did you, Philip? One kiss and I would capitulate?'

The ache of her absence made his words cruel. He raised his eyebrows in laconic mockery. 'You weren't a million miles away from capitulation, were you?'

She drew her coat around her tightly and the reality of the winter afternoon made her aware that she was chilled almost to the bone. 'I may have had a moment's weakness,' she hissed, 'but I can assure you that I have, or *had*, absolutely no intention of letting you take me in some damp and desolate field as if I were just some girl you'd picked up at a party and thought you'd try your luck with!'

'Luck?' he said bleakly, stung by the irony of the word. Maybe it was time he told her. Maybe he owed her that much. For what kind of bastard could have walked out on a woman like Lisi with only the baldest of explanations— designed not just to hurt her but to expurgate his own guilt? 'I really do think we need to have that talk, Lisi—but not now, and not here—'

'I don't think talking is what you *really* have in mind, do you?' she enquired archly. 'So please don't dress up something as simple as longing by trying to give it a respectable name!'

'Something as simple as longing?' he echoed wryly. 'You think that longing is ever in any way simple?'

'It can be for some people!' she declared hotly. 'Boy meets girl! Boy falls in love with girl!'

'Boy and girl live happily ever after?' he questioned sardonically. 'I'm a little too old to believe in fairy tales any more, Lisi, aren't you?'

His scent was still like sweet perfume which clung to her skin, and she drew away from him, frightened by the depth of how much she still wanted him. 'I'm going home now,' she said shakily, and fought down the desire to do the impossible. 'And I'm not taking you with me.'

He nodded, seeing that she was fighting some kind of inner battle, perversely pleased that she was not going to give into what he was certain she wanted. Maybe it had all happened too quickly last time. Maybe this time he should take it real slow. 'I'll walk with you.'

Her heart missed a beat. 'No, you won't!' She didn't want him to see where she lived, or catch a glimpse of her as she left the tiny cottage to go and collect Tim. And then what? For him to observe the angel-child who was her son and to start using that clever mind of his to work out that Tim was *his* son as well?

It was too enormous a decision to make on too little information, and who knew what Philip Caprice really wanted, and why he was here? She wasn't going to take the chance. Not yet.

'I'm not letting you walk home alone,' he said imperturbably.

Was it her imagination, or had he grown more than a little *autocratic* in the intervening years? 'Philip—this is the twenty-first century, for goodness' sake! How do you think I've managed to get by all these years, without you leaping out of the shadows ready and willing to play the Knight in Shining Armour? Langley is safe enough for a woman to walk home alone—why else do you think I've stayed here this long?'

He gave her a steady look. 'I don't know, Lisi. That's what makes it so perplexing. It doesn't add up at all.'

Her breath caught like dust in her throat. 'Wh-what doesn't?'

'You. Sitting like Miss Havisham at the same desk in the same office in the same estate agency. What kind of a life is that? What's your game plan, Lisi—are you going to stay there until you're old and grey and let life and men just pass you by?'

She caught a sudden vivid image of herself painted by

his wounding words. A little old woman, stooped and bent—her long hair grown grey, her skin mottled and tired from the day-in, day-out struggle of being a single mother, where money was tight. And Tim long gone. She drew in a deep sigh which was much too close to a sob, but she held the sob at bay.

'I don't have to stay here and be insulted by you,' she told him quietly. 'Why don't you just go away, Philip? Go back to where you came from and leave me alone!'

He gave a wry smile. If only it were as easy as that. He didn't try to stop her as she turned away from him and ran back over the field, the heavy mud and the heavy boots making her progress slow and cumbersome.

But she leapt over the stile like a gazelle and he stood watching the last sight of her—her hair almost completely free of its confinement now, and it danced like crazy black snakes which gleamed in the light of the moon—while his heart pounded like a piston in his chest.

CHAPTER THREE

Lisi ran and ran without turning back, as if he were chasing her heels—and wasn't there part of her which wished that he were?

But once she was safely out onto the village street and she realised that Philip was not intent on pursuing her, she slowed her pace down to a fast walk. She didn't want to alarm anyone by looking as though the hounds of hell were snapping at her heels.

Her cottage was tucked up a little incline, three streets away from the shops, and she fumbled her key into the brightly painted blue front door, closing it firmly behind her, safe at last.

The place was small, but it was cosy and it was home and it suited the two of them just fine. Lisi had bought it once her mother's big house had been sold—a big, rambling old place which would have cost a fortune to run and maintain.

She drew the curtains and went round the room switching on the lamps and creating a warm, homely glow. Later, once she had collected Tim, she would light the fire and they would toast crumpets and play together—her son completely oblivious of the knowledge of whom she had just seen.

While down in the village his father would spend the evening doing God only knew what while she kept her momentous secret to herself.

Lisi shook her head. She felt like pouring herself a large drink and then another, but she wasn't going to start doing *that*. Instead she put on an extra sweater and made herself a cup of tea, then curled up on the sofa with her fingers curled around the steaming mug.

She looked at Tim's advent calendar which hung next to the fireplace. Only seven days lay unopened. Seven days until Christmas and only one until his birthday tomorrow.

Had fate made Philip turn up at the time of such a milestone in Tim's life? Or a cruel and bitter irony?

She remembered the birth as difficult—partly because she had gone through it all on her own. Lisi's fingers tightened around the mug. Just thinking about the long and painful labour cut through her carefully built defences, and the memories of Philip which she had kept at bay for so long came flooding out, as if her mind had just burst its banks, like a river.

It had started innocently enough—though afterwards she thought about whether there was ever complete innocence between a man and a woman. When and how did simple friendship become transmuted into lust?

The first few times he saw her he completely ignored her, his cool green eyes flicking over her with a disappointing lack of interest.

She knew exactly who he was, of course—everyone in the office did. Rich, clever, enigmatic Philip Caprice who owned a huge estate agency in North London.

He was something of a scout, too—because people seeking discretion and a home in the country flocked to him to find them the perfect place. Rich—fabulously rich—clients who had no desire for the world and his wife to know which property they were in the process of buying. According to Jonathon, he handled house sales for film stars and moguls and just plain old-fashioned aristocracy.

He always dealt with Jonathon. In fact, Lisi was the office junior, only six months into the job, and eager to learn. Jonathon had let her handle a couple of accounts—but terraced cottages and houses on the new estate on the outskirts of Langley were not in Philip Caprice's league!

And then he walked in one lunchtime, on the day after her twenty-second birthday. She had been left on her own in the office for the first time. Jonathon was at lunch and Saul Miller, her other colleague, was out valuing a property which was coming onto the market shortly.

The phones were quiet and all her work up to date and Lisi felt contented with life. She was wearing her birthday sweater—a dream of a garment in soft blue cashmere which her mother had bought—and her hair was tied back in a ribbon of exactly the same shade.

On her desk were the remains of her birthday cake and she was just wondering whether to throw it away or stick a piece of cling-film round it and put it in the fridge. Jonathon seemed to have hollow legs, and it *did* seem a shame to waste it.

The door to the office clanged and in came Philip and her heart gave its customary leap. His hair was thick and nut-brown, ruffled by the breeze, and he wore an exquisitely cut suit which immediately marked him out as a Londoner.

For a moment, words deserted her. He seemed to dwarf the room with his presence—it was a little like having a Hollywood film star walk into a small-town estate agency!

She swallowed. 'Good morning, Mr Caprice.'

He gave a curt nod. 'Jonathon not around?'

'He's not back yet. He, er—' she glanced down nervously at her watch, and then lifted her eyes to him '—he shouldn't be long. You're—er—you're a bit earlier than expected.'

'The roads were clear,' he said shortly. 'I'll wait. No problem.'

He didn't look as though he meant it and Lisi thought that his face looked bleak, as if he had had a long, hard morning—no, make that a long, hard month. There was a restless, edgy quality about him, as if he hadn't slept properly for a long time. She said the first, impulsive thing which came into her head and pointed to her desk. 'Would you like some birthday cake?'

He narrowed his eyes as if she had just offered him something vaguely obscene. 'Birthday cake?' He frowned. 'Whose? Yours?'

Lisi nodded. 'That's right. It's really quite nice—a bit sickly, perhaps, but birthday cakes *should* be sickly, I always think, don't you?' She was aware that she was babbling but something in the slightly askance question in his eyes made her babble on. 'Won't you have some?'

There was something sweet and guileless about her eager chatter which completely disarmed him. Nor was he completely oblivious to the slenderly curved figure and the white skin and black hair which made her look like some kind of home-spun Snow White. But with the ease of practice he dismissed her physical attractions and stared at the cake instead.

Lisi could see him wavering. She remembered how much her father had loved cake when he'd been alive. What did her mother always say? 'Show me a man who says he doesn't like cake, and I'll show you a liar!'

'Oh, go on!' she urged softly. 'Have some—I was only going to throw it away!'

'Now there's an offer I can't refuse!' He laughed, and he realised how alien his own laughter sounded to his ears. When had he last laughed so uninhibitedly? He couldn't remember. 'Sure,' he said, because he hadn't eaten much since yesterday. 'Why not?'

She was aware of his green eyes on her as she cut him a hefty portion and piled it onto one of the paper plates she had brought in with her. 'The last of Minnie Mouse.' She smiled, as she handed it to him. 'See? You've got her spotty skirt!'

'So I see,' he murmured. 'Aren't you a little old for Minnie Mouse?'

'Twenty-two,' she said, in answer to a question he hadn't asked, and when he frowned rather repressively she added inconsequentially, 'I *love* Disney characters—I always have!'

He took the plate from her and sat down in the chair opposite her desk, and bit into the cake. She had been right. Too sweet. Too sickly. Bloody delicious. He tried and failed to remember the last time he had eaten birthday cake. Or celebrated a birthday. Or celebrated anything. But there hadn't been a whole lot to celebrate lately, had there?

Lisi watched him, pleased to see him eating it with such obvious appetite. She thought how fined-down his face seemed, and wondered when was the last time he had eaten properly. She struggled against the instinct to offer to take him home and to have her mother cook a decent meal of meat and two veg with a vast portion of apple pie afterwards.

What was she *thinking* of? The man was a client! And a very well-heeled client, too—not the kind of man who would thank her for trying to mother him!

She licked her lips unconsciously as she looked at his long fingers breaking off another piece. Maybe mothering was the wrong word to use. There were probably a lot more satisfying things a woman would feel like doing to Philip Caprice than mothering, she realised, shocked by her wayward thoughts.

She watched him finish every crumb on his plate and decided to show him how efficient she could be. 'Right then, Mr Caprice—let me find these properties for you to have a look at—Jonathon has sorted them all out for you.'

She bent her head as she began flicking through an old-fashioned filing box, and Philip felt an uncomfortable and unwanted fluttering of awareness as he looked at the ebony sheen of her hair and the long, elegant line of her neck.

Out of necessity, he had schooled himself not to be tempted by women, and certainly not women who were such a devastating combination of the innocent and the sensual, but for once he felt his resolve waver.

'Here we are.' Lisi found the last of what she was looking for, and held them out to him.

He noticed the way that the tip of her tongue protruded from between her teeth when she was concentrating. Tiny and pink. Shiny. He swallowed. 'Thanks.' He leaned across the desk and took the sheaf of house details from her.

'Jonathon should be back any minute, unless—' she gave him her most hopeful smile '—you'd like *me* to show you round?' She would have to leave the office unattended for a while, but Jonathon would be back from lunch any minute. She saw him frown and hoped that hadn't sounded like some sort of come-on. She blushed. 'I know I'm relatively inexperienced, but I'd be more than happy to.'

She seemed sweet and uncomplicated, and he couldn't deny that he wasn't tempted, but he steeled his heart against temptation.

'Listen, Jonathon knows me pretty well. He knows the kind of thing I like.' He saw her face fall, as if he'd struck her a blow, and he felt the sweet remains of the birthday cake in his mouth and sighed. 'Maybe next time, perhaps?'

This cheered Lisi up considerably, and later, when Jonathon had come back from the viewings and Philip had gone, she began to quiz him in a very casual way.

'He seems nice,' she offered.

Jonathon was busy writing up the offer which Philip Caprice had just made on some sprawling mid-Victorian mansion. 'Nice? Huh! Ruthless would be a better description! He's just got himself a terrific property at a knock-down price—beats me how he does it!'

'Maybe he's just a good businessman?' suggested Lisi serenely.

Jonathon scowled. 'Meaning I'm not, I suppose?'

'No, of course not—that wasn't what I meant at all!' Lisi glanced over his shoulder. 'Anyway—that isn't far off the asking price, is it?'

'True.' Jonathon sighed. 'If only he hadn't managed to wheedle out of the owner that they were desperate for a quick sale we might have held out for the full price.'

'I thought we were supposed to tell the vendor to keep out of negotiations with the purchaser, wherever possible?'

'I did,' said Jonathon glumly, then added, 'Only it was a *woman*. She took one look at him and decided to give him a gushingly guided tour of the place—only unfortunately it backfired. After that, he had her eating out of his hand and she's several thousand pounds out of pocket as a result.'

So was that ruthless, or just good business-sense? Whatever it was, it wasn't really surprising—Lisi thought that he could probably have *any* woman eating out of his hand.

'What's he like?' she asked. 'As a person?'

'Who knows?' Jonathon shrugged. 'He keeps his cards very close to his chest. I've dealt with him on and off for ages and I know next to nothing about him—'

Other than the very obvious attributes of being rich and gorgeous and irresistible to women, thought Lisi and put him out of her mind.

Until next time he came in.

Jonathon had gone to do some photocopying in the back room, and Lisi looked up to see the strikingly tall figure standing in the doorway and her heart gave a queer lurch. She frowned, shocked by the deep lines of strain which were etched onto his face.

Now there, she thought, is a man who is driving himself much too hard.

Philip glanced across the room to see the Birthday Girl sitting at her desk and smiling at him, and realised that he didn't even know her name.

'Hello, Mr Caprice!' she said cheerfully.

Reluctantly he smiled back—but there was something about her which made him *want* to smile. 'I think the trade-off for your delicious cake was that we should be on first-name terms, don't you? Except that I don't know yours.'

'It's Lisi—short for Elisabeth. Lisi Vaughan.'

Pretty name, he thought, and the question seemed to come out of nowhere. 'So are you going to show me around today, Lisi Vaughan?'

Lisi gulped, her heart banging excitedly in her chest. 'Are you sure you want me to?'

'Only if you're confident you can.'

She knew that confidence was the name of the game— particularly in selling—and why on earth should her confidence desert her just because she was about to accompany the most delicious man she had ever seen? She gave him her most assured smile. 'Oh, yes. I'm confident! That's if Jonathon doesn't mind.'

'I'll make sure he doesn't,' he said easily.

Jonathon knew better than to argue with his most prestigious client. 'Sure,' he agreed. 'Let's throw her in at the deep end!'

The viewing was unsuccessful—at least from a buying point of view. Philip tore the places to pieces in his car as he drove her back to the office afterwards.

'Overpriced!' he scorned. 'I don't know how people can ask that much—not when you consider how run-down the property is! And when you look what they've done to the garden—that garage they've built is nothing short of monstrous!'

'You didn't like it, then?' asked Lisi meekly.

He swiftly turned his head and, seeing her expression, laughed. 'Oh, very perceptive,' he murmured sardonically. 'You were good, Lisi,' he added unexpectedly.

'Was I?'

'Very good.' She had diplomatically left the monstrous garage until last and drawn his attention to all the good points in the house, but not in an in-your-face kind of way. She was chatty, but not intrusive, beautiful yet not flirtatious. In other words, she was a little like a glass of water—refreshing, but without any pernicious undertaste.

He sighed. Most of the women he met these days were nurses, and then only in a grimly professional capacity. Not that he wanted to meet women, of course he didn't—not with Carla lying so...so...

He flinched and changed gear more aggressively than he had intended to.

'It's a shame there's nothing else you're interested in,' Lisi was saying. 'I'll keep an eye out for your dream house!'

He threw her a rather mocking look. 'Do you think there is such a thing?'

Lisi thought of her mother's house and gave a slow smile. 'Oh, yes,' she said in a soft voice, and smiled. 'Very, very definitely.'

He smiled back, but the smile died on his lips as he forced himself to look away from the slender outline of her legs, relieved when Langley High Street came into view and he was able to draw up outside her office.

'Thanks very much,' she said as she began to push open the door. 'I enjoyed that!'

'No, thank *you*,' he said gravely, but as soon as she had slammed the door closed behind her, he made the car pull away. He didn't want to watch her confident young stride as she walked to the office, or the way her firm young breasts pushed against her soft, clinging sweater.

Lisi saw Philip seven, maybe eight times after that—on a purely professional basis. Sometimes Jonathon would accompany him on the viewings, but mostly it was her. For some reason she grew to know his tastes better than Jonathon. Often she would mentally reject a house once she had skimmed through the details, then phone him and suggest that he might like to see it.

'Do *you* like it?' he would demand.

She hesitated.

'*Do* you, Lisi?'

'I don't think it's quite what you're looking for.'

'Then I won't waste my time coming to see it.'

Leaving her wondering why she had been so foolish! Why hadn't she said that it was the most gorgeous place she had ever set eyes on?

Because then he wouldn't trust her judgement, and the fact that a man like Philip *did* meant more to her than it should have done.

She adored him, despite his emotional distance, but she kept it hidden from everyone—from Jonathon, from Saul Miller, even from her mother. And, especially, from Philip himself. Maybe she was aware that to fall for Philip Caprice would be batting right out of her league. And besides, it would be strictly unprofessional.

But she looked forward to his visits and they became the highlight of her life. Casually, she used to scour the diary to see when he was coming next, and—although she didn't make it look *too* obvious—she always felt her best on those days. Her hair always newly washed, and a subtle touching of fragrance behind her ears and at her wrists.

And then one glorious spring afternoon Philip walked into the office without his customary, flinty expression. He had loosened his tie and he seemed *lighter* in his mood, Lisi thought, though she wouldn't have dreamed of asking him why. That was not the way their relationship worked. They talked houses. Interest rates. Business trends.

'Hello, Philip.' She smiled.

He looked into her aquamarine eyes and smiled back. Carla had moved her fingers last night. The doctors were cautious, but quietly optimistic, and for the first time since the accident Philip had slept the night without waking. This morning he had awoken without the habitual tight knot of tension in his stomach. 'Hello, Lisi.' He smiled back. 'So what have you got for me?'

'I think you'll like it,' she said demurely.

The house she had rung him about was about as perfect as it was possible for a house to be. She had never heard Philip sound quite so enthusiastic, and the offer he made was accepted immediately. A rather more generous offer than usual, she noted, and briefly wondered what had made his mood quite so expansive.

It was getting on for six o'clock by the time he drove her back into Langley, and all the way along the lanes the hedges and trees were laced with the tender green buds of spring. He sighed. Spring. The time of new beginnings. He prayed that the signs were not misleading, and that there would be a new beginning for Carla.

Lisi heard the sigh, saw where he was looking. 'It's beautiful around this time of year, isn't it?'

He glanced across at her as she put her notebook back into her bag and snapped it shut.

He liked her. She worked hard and she didn't ask any questions. With Lisi he could relax, and he tried to think back to the last time he had done that. Really relaxed. 'I feel like celebrating,' he said.

'Well, then—why don't we? A quick drink won't hurt.' Her heart missed a beat while she waited to hear what he would say.

'Okay.' He changed down a gear. 'Where shall we go?'

'There's the pub or the hotel—either are good.'

'Yeah,' he said thoughtfully. 'I'm driving on to Somerset tomorrow, so I'm staying at the hotel.' Maybe they'd better go to the pub.

'I'll just have to ring my mother and tell her I'm going to be a little late.'

He raised his eyebrows, surprised. 'You live with your mother?'

Lisi smiled at his expression. How little of her he knew! 'Yes, I do.'

'Unusual, at your age.'

'I suppose so—but we get on very well.' No need to tell him that on her salary there was no way she could afford a place of her own, even if she had wanted to.

They went to the pub and settled down with their wine, but away from the usual professional boundaries which defined their relationship, Lisi found herself gulping hers down more quickly than usual.

He saw her empty glass and one elegant eyebrow was elevated. 'Another?'

'Please.' She nodded automatically, her eyes drinking in his tall, lean frame as he went up to buy her another drink.

She told him little anecdotes about village life, and when he smiled that slow, sexy smile she felt as though she had won first prize in a competition.

'You must let me buy *you* a drink now!' she offered, wishing that the evening could just go on and on.

He shook his dark, ruffled head. 'I'm fine. Really.'

'No, honestly—I insist! Just the one.' She smiled up at him. 'Equal rights for women, and all that!'

He laughed, thinking, Why not? 'Okay, Lisi,' he said gently. 'Just the one.'

In the cosy warmth of the bar, Lisi chatted away, and Philip was thinking that maybe it was getting just a little *too* cosy. He glanced at his watch. 'I guess it's about time we made a move,' he said, when he noticed that her cheeks had gone very pink and that she kept blinking her beautiful aquamarine eyes. 'Are you okay?' he frowned.

She nodded, even though the room was beginning to blur a little. 'I'm fine,' she gulped. But with a quick a glance at her watch she realised she'd drunk in record quick time. 'I'm just a bit whoozy. I guess I'm not used to drinking.'

'Have you eaten?' he demanded.

'No.'

His mouth tightened. A great influence he was turning out to be. And now she had acquired a deathly kind of pallor. He couldn't possibly send her home to her mother if she was half-cut, could he?

'Come on,' he said decisively, standing up and holding out his hand to her. 'You need something to soak up that alcohol.'

She clutched onto his hand gratefully and allowed him to lead her out of the pub. Outside the fresh air hit her like a sledgehammer, and she swayed against him and giggled.

Philip shot her a swift, assessing look. She needed food and then he needed *out*. What he did not need was some beautiful young woman brushing the delectable curves of her body so close to his.

But by the time they reached his hotel, Lisi had gone very pale indeed and Philip realised that he was trapped. He couldn't send her home like this, but neither could he see her managing to sit through a meal in a stuffy restaurant.

'You need to lie down,' he said grimly.

It sounded like heaven. 'Oh, yes, please,' she murmured indistinctly.

'Wait here while I get my keys,' he told her shortly, relieved to see that the foyer was completely empty, apart from the receptionist. And receptionists were trained to turn a blind eye, weren't they?

Lisi followed him up the stairs and walked with exaggerated care. She wasn't drunk, she told herself. Just feeling no pain!

Grimly, he pushed open the door, wondering just how he had managed to get himself into a situation which could look to the outside world as though he were intent on *seduction*. While nothing could be further than the truth. But he averted his eyes as she flopped down onto the bed like a puppet which had just had its strings cut.

'Kick your shoes off,' he growled.

The alcohol had loosened her inhibitions, and she giggled again as she obeyed his terse command, sneaking a look at him from between her slitted eyes and thinking how utterly gorgeous he looked. She wriggled and stretched her arms above her head with a blissful sigh.

The sight of her lying with such abandon on the scarlet silk coverlet was too much to bear. 'Go to sleep now,' he told her tightly. 'I'll wake you in a couple of hours and give you some food, then send you home.'

He made her sound like an abandoned puppy! thought Lisi. But her indignation faded into the distance as delicious sleep claimed her.

Philip sat moodily at the bar, sipping at a coffee and wondering whether he should ring the hospital. Maybe later. After Lisi had gone. And he *wanted* her gone!

But his body was telling him other things. Tormenting him with tantalising reminders of making love to a woman. He shifted uncomfortably on the bar stool, and would have taken the longest and coldest shower in the world had it not been for the fact that his room was occupied by the cause of his torment.

He waited a couple of hours and then ordered a plate of steak and chips to take upstairs to her. 'And a pot of strong coffee,' he added grimly. But it was with a heavy heart and an aching body as he slowly carried them into his room, and his breath froze in the back of his throat.

Because she was naked.

Naked in his bed.

Her arms were flung above her head, and part of the scarlet silk coverlet had slipped down to reveal one pert and perfect breast—pale and luscious and centred by a tiny thrusting peak of rose. Her long legs were accentuated by the coverlet which moulded itself against them and her clothes were in an untidy heap on the floor beside the bed, with a wispy thong lying uppermost.

Sweet heaven! Philip very nearly dropped the tray.

His heart was pounding fit to deafen him and he could feel the immediate jerk of a powerful erection as he shakily put the tray down on a small table.

He strode over to the bed, trying to use his anger to dampen down the overpowering need to join with her in the most fundamental way possible.

He reached his hand down to shake her by the shoulder but something happened along the way. His fingers irresistibly reached for her breast and he was appalled to find them stroking little circles, but unable to stop himself from finding the bud of her nipple and feeling it harden beneath his touch.

'Oh!' she breathed.

Eyes closed, still in the mists of sleep, Lisi writhed with pleasure beneath the bedclothes and the unconsciously sexy action nearly made him lose his mind. The blood roared in his head, his composure utterly shattered by the sight of a naked woman, warm and responsive and waiting in his bed.

With an unbearable effort, he tore his hand away from her nipple and moved it up to the soft silk of her shoulder, intending to shake her. But instead of shaking her, again he found his fingers kneading rhythmically against her cool flesh, urged on by the clamouring demands of his body.

'Wake up,' he ordered, in a low, furious voice. 'Wake up, Lisi!'

Lisi's eyes snapped open and she stared with disbelief into the dark, angry eyes of Philip. It took a second or two to get her bearings.

A strange bed.

A hotel room.

One drink too many.

'Oh, hell!' She sat bolt upright in bed and heard him utter something agonised beneath his breath, and she realised that she was wearing nothing at all and that Philip was staring at her bare breasts with a wild kind of furious hunger in his eyes.

'Put something on!' he snapped.

She was still befuddled by sleep. 'Where are my clothes?'

'How should I know where your bloody clothes are?' he roared. 'It wasn't me who took them off!'

Lisi blushed as vague memories came back to her. Feeling too hot and tossing her clothes to the ground with abandon. She had! Acutely aware of her nakedness and of the sound of Philip's quickened breath, she leaned over the side of the bed to hunt for them, and the movement made her breasts jiggle unfettered.

Suddenly Philip lost it completely. He moved towards her, tumbling onto the bed next to her and pulling her roughly into his arms to kiss her before he had the time or the inclination to think about the wisdom of his actions.

And once he had kissed her that was the beginning of the end—his starved senses and hungry body made sure of that.

The thong fell uselessly from her hand and there was a split second of doubt in Lisi's mind but that doubt fled the moment that he kissed her.

His mouth plundered hers as if it were the richest treasure

he had ever encountered and her lips parted for him immediately, moist and sweet and tasting faintly of wine.

Lisi's heart was beating so hard she thought that it might burst. This was every wish she'd ever had, every sweet dream come true. Philip. Here. In her arms. Her hands went up to his shoulders and felt the silk of his shirt beneath her fingertips. She was wearing nothing and he was covered up with all these clothes—it wasn't fair!

He lifted his head from hers and she could see that his eyes looked almost ebony in the lamplit room. 'Do you want to undress me, Lisi?' he asked unsteadily, because he couldn't trust himself to do it with any degree of finesse. Not when her breasts were peaking towards him like that and he longed to take one into his mouth and suckle her.

'Yes,' she murmured throatily, made bold by that look of raw need on his gorgeous face. Deftly, she began to unbutton his shirt, springing open the tiny buttons to reveal a golden-skinned torso sprinkled with a smattering of dark hair. She indolently ran the flat of her hand over the soft whorls, feeling him shudder beneath her as she did so, loving the power of having this big, handsome man respond so passionately to her.

He kissed her again. And again. Until she was mindless with longing—willingly pinned to the bed by his muscular frame and praying for him to make love to her properly.

Logic and reason had vanished from his mind—obliterated by the wet lick of her tongue as it flicked against his. If he didn't have her soon, he would explode. 'Undress me,' he commanded huskily. 'Undress me *now*, Lisi!'

She slid the shirt over his shoulders, anointing the flesh which she laid bare with soft little kisses which made him moan with pleasure beneath her mouth.

His belt came off easily, but her fingers faltered slightly when she was unzipping his trousers as she felt the formidable hardness of him brush against her palm.

'Don't touch me,' he pleaded. 'Not there. Not yet.'

He couldn't wait to be free of his clothes and yet he could hardly bear to watch the erotic vision she made as she pushed the covers off and sank down on her knees astride him, easing the trousers down slowly over the long, powerful shaft of his thighs. She eased them over his knees and further still, her hands brushing against the soft swell of his ankles and lingering there.

'Hurry up,' he pleaded.

Lisi skimmed one of his socks off—immensely flattered by his eagerness and yet slightly taken aback by it. Instinctively, she had known that he would be a passionate man, but she had expected him to exercise restraint as well. And steely control. Those were the qualities which seemed to fit more with the Philip Caprice she knew.

But it seemed that she had been completely wrong. She freed his foot from the second sock.

And then at last he was naked, too.

And aroused.

Very, very aroused.

Lisi swallowed. Surely he couldn't possibly… Surely she couldn't possibly… But then she bucked beneath his fingers as he slithered his middle finger along where she was so hot and slick and hungry. 'Oh!' she moaned in ecstasy.

He smiled, but it was a smile laced with a daunting kind of promise and Lisi felt the briefest shiver of apprehension as she saw the new and urgent tension which had entered his body.

'I want you,' he whispered.

'And I want you, too.'

'Now?' he teased. 'Or shall I play with you a little first?'

His provocative words made her melt even more. She had never been turned on so quickly, nor so thoroughly. There was no need for prolonged foreplay; she was ready.

And very, very willing. She put her arms around his neck and looked up at him with open invitation in her eyes.

'Let's play together,' she whispered back.

He groaned as he moved over her. It was like a dream—the most erotic dream he had ever encountered. He moved on top of her and could feel her shudder as he pressed right up against her burning heat. He delayed it for as long as he could—probably about a second—before powerfully thrusting into her and a deep, helpless cry was torn from his throat.

Lisi gasped aloud as she felt him fill her, but she wanted him deeper still, as deep as it was possible to go. She moved without thinking, lifting her legs right up so that her ankles were locked tightly around his neck, and he raised his head in a kind of dazed wonderment as he looked down at her.

'God, Lisi,' he groaned, and then thrust into her so deeply that she gasped again.

Through the stealthy lure of approaching orgasm, Philip heard warning bells ringing in his head, and he realised what he had never before failed to remember.

'Oh, God,' he groaned. 'Protection! Lisi, I never thought—' With a monumental effort he began to pull out, but Lisi only clenched her muscles, and gripped him even tighter and he shuddered. 'D-don't,' he commanded unsteadily.

'It's o-okay,' she gasped, because she had thought that she would die if he stopped what he was doing. 'It's safe.'

'You sure?'

She nodded. Of course she was sure. 'Make me come,' she begged, astonished by her lack of inhibition, but then something about Philip was making her feel this free. Freer than she had ever been in a man's arms.

'With pleasure,' he ground out, and moved inside her. He held back his own needs while he thrust into her over and over again, his mouth suckling at her breast, while his finger flicked tantalisingly over the tight, hot little core of her. And he whispered things to her, words so erotic, they were almost shocking.

Lisi was nearly crying with the pleasure—almost overloaded with it—and then the crying became a shudder and she was calling out his name and telling him that he was the most perfect lover in the world as waves upon waves took her soaring.

He let himself go, sweat sheening his chest as it slicked against her breasts, and when it happened it was stronger and more intense than any other orgasm he had ever experienced, so that even in the midst of pleasure, he felt the first shimmerings of guilt.

She felt him shuddering inside her for so long that she thought he would never stop. She wished that he wouldn't. Just go on filling her with his seed all night long. And only when he was completely spent did she let her legs drift down to lie on either side of him. With a satiated little smile, she lifted her head to kiss him but he turned away, as if her mouth contained poison, then rolled away from her completely, so that he was right on the other side of the bed.

Lisi's heart pounded.

Perhaps he was just tired. He always seemed to *look* tired. She would let him sleep and then he would reach for her again in the night, and…

She heard the sound of movement and saw that he was getting off the bed and reaching for his clothes.

Her heart pounded again. He couldn't be *leaving*! He couldn't! She swallowed down what was surely an irrational fear. He was obviously going to the bathroom—but he didn't need to put his clothes on to do that, surely? 'Philip?'

He finished buttoning up his shirt before he turned

around and when he did his face was as cold and as expressionless as flint. He raised his eyebrows. 'What?'

'You're not going?'

He was sickened with disgust at his lack of control, and his mouth tightened. 'Yes.'

She stared at him without understanding. 'But why?' she asked, in a mystified voice. 'Why are you leaving now?'

It hurt to say it, probably more than it hurt her to hear it. 'Because I'm married,' he said, in a hard, cold voice.

He grabbed his jacket and his unopened overnight bag and walked out without a backward glance.

And Lisi didn't see him again.

CHAPTER FOUR

PHILIP spent a sleepless night, tossing and turning, his thoughts full of Lisi and the effect of seeing her again.

He hadn't thought beyond his trip to Langley. He had just found himself on the road here, driven on by a burning need to tie up the loose ends of a regrettable liaison—so that he could put it behind him, once and for all.

But he had not reckoned on how he would feel if he saw her again. Part of him had thought that she might have moved on. Or settled down. Married some upstanding local and be well on the way to producing a brood of children. To his astonishment, she was still single.

And just the sight of her had been like a touch-paper to his senses. He still wanted her—wanted her more than he felt comfortable with, and, to judge from her response to his kiss, she wasn't exactly immune to him, either.

He owed her the truth, he realised. There would be no sense of closure for either of them until he had done that. *She* might have instigated what had happened, but he had gone into it more than willingly. She needed to know why he had feasted on her body and then just left her lying there without a second glance.

He glanced at his watch, but it was still early. He showered and dressed and drank some coffee before switching on his computer to check his e-mails. But he stared blankly at the untouched messages in his inbox and turned his head instead to study the forbidding grey of the winter sky.

Just as soon as the office opened he would go and see her. And tell her.

Marian Reece glanced up as the bell on the office door

rang and in walked the tall, expensively dressed man who had been talking so intently with Lisi the day before.

She smiled. 'Good morning! Mr Caprice, isn't it?'

Philip nodded and forced an answering smile. 'That's right. Philip Caprice.' He glanced around the office. 'Is Lisi around?'

Marian shook her head. 'Oh, no! She's finished now. For the Christmas holidays. She—' She seemed to change her mind about her next words. Instead, she said, 'But I'm sure that I can help you.'

He looked at her blankly. 'Help me?'

Marian studied him in bemusement. 'Well, you *did* say that you were interested in buying a house in this area!'

He narrowed his eyes. Did he? Wasn't the truth rather more complex than that? He had been doing business in the area, and something—the dreams, perhaps?—had prompted him to call in and see if Lisi Vaughan was still around. And she was—though wasn't there a part of him which wished she weren't? That had hoped she would have been long gone and then he could consign her to bitter-sweet memory? But at least the suggestion of house-hunting would legitimise his being here. 'That's right,' he said evenly. 'If you could let me have a few details to glance through.'

'Of course.' She gave a coy smile. 'I'll need to know your price range, though.'

He mentioned a sum that made her pupils dilate and she immediately reached for a sheaf of papers which stood neatly stacked on a corner of her desk. 'I *thought* you'd be looking at the top end of the market,' she said triumphantly, and handed them to him.

Philip glanced down at them without interest.

'The most attractive property we have on our books is The Old Rectory,' said Marian, straightening up and looking at him expectantly, but his gaze remained noncommittal. 'It's a beautiful old house, with a wealth of architectural detail—although it does require considerable updating, of course—'

'Why hasn't it sold already?' he cut in.

Marian blinked. 'Sorry?'

'If it's so beautiful, then why hasn't it been snatched up?'

Marian gave a little cough and lowered her voice. 'Because it's unrealistically priced,' she admitted.

'Then get the vendors to lower it.'

'They're reluctant.' She sighed, and pulled a face. 'It's a divorce sale, you see, and they need every penny they can get. I've told them that they may not get a buyer unless they're prepared to be realistic, but you know what people are.'

He nodded and gave an impatient smile, eager to be away. 'Listen, I need to see Lisi. Can you tell me where she lives?'

Marian hesitated. 'I'm...I'm not sure that I should. She might not want me to.'

Philip met her eyes with an unwavering stare. 'Oh, I think she would,' he said pleasantly. 'But, of course, if you won't tell me—then I'll just have to find out for myself. Only it would save me a little time.' He gave her a lazy smile. 'Giving me more opportunity to look at houses.'

There was a long pause while she considered the subtext behind his words, and then she nodded. 'She lives at Cherry Tree Cottage—it's on Millbank Lane. A bright blue front door—it's easy enough to find.'

He folded up the house details and slid them into the pocket of his overcoat. 'Thanks very much.'

Marian looked at him anxiously. 'I don't know whether I should have told you.'

He gave a tight smile. 'I would have found her anyway.'

* * *

Lisi had just finished pinning the flouncy paper frill onto the birthday cake when there was a knock at the door, and she sighed. What she *didn't* need at the moment was an interruption! There were a million and one things to do before Tim's party—when the house would be invaded by five of his friends and she would have her work cut out to prevent six small boys from wrecking her little home!

She brushed some stray icing sugar from her hands and went to the front door, and there, standing on the step, was Philip, and her heart lurched with a combination of apprehension and lust.

He looked pretty close to irresistible, dressed casually in jeans which emphasised the long, muscular thrust of his thighs and a soft grey sweater which made the green eyes look even more dazzling than usual. He wore an old-fashioned flying jacket, and the sheepskin and worn leather only added to his rugged appeal.

She thought of Tim in the sitting room, watching a video, and the lurch of her heart turned into a patter of alarm.

'Hello, Philip,' she said calmly. 'This is a surprise.'

He gazed at her steadily. 'Is it? Surely you didn't think that I was going to go away without speaking to you again, Lisi?'

'I have nothing to say to you.'

'But I do,' he said implacably.

He can't make you do anything, she told herself. 'I'm afraid that it isn't convenient right now.'

He let his eyes rove slowly over her, and the answering flood of heat made him wish that he hadn't.

Her dark hair was scraped back from her face into a pony-tail and she wore cheap clothes—nothing special—a pair of baggy cotton trousers and an old sweater which clung to the soft swell of her breasts. There was a fine line of flour running down her cheek which made him think of warpaint.

And she looked like dynamite.

'Been cooking, have you?'

'*Am* cooking,' she corrected tartly. 'Busy cooking.'

'Mum-mee!'

Lisi froze as green eyes lanced through her in a disbelieving question.

'Mum-mee!' A child who was Lisi's very image appeared, and Tim came running out from the sitting room and up to the door, turning large, interested blue eyes up at the stranger on the doorstep. 'Hello!'

Lisi had always been proud of her son's bright and outgoing nature—she had brought him up to be confident—but at that moment she despaired of it. Why couldn't he have been shy and retiring, like most other boys his age? 'I really must go, Philip, you can see I'm really—'

He ignored her completely. 'Hello,' Philip said softly as he looked down at the shiny black head. 'And what's your name?'

The boy smiled. 'I'm Tim, and it's my birthday!' he said. 'Who are you?'

'I'm Philip. A friend of Mummy's.'

Tim screwed his eyes up. 'Mummy's boyfriend?'

Lisi saw the cold look of distaste which flickered across his face, and flinched.

'Does Mummy have lots of boyfriends, then?' Philip asked casually.

'*Tim*,' said Lisi, a note of desperation making her voice sound as though it was about to crack, 'why don't you go and colour in that picture that Mummy drew for you earlier?'

'But, *Mum*-mee—'

'Please, darling,' she said firmly. 'And you can have a biscuit out of the tin—only one, mind—and Mummy will come and help you in a minute, and we can organise all the games for your party. Won't that be fun? Run along now, darling.'

Thank heavens the suggestion of an unsolicited biscuit had captured his imagination! He gave Philip one last, curious look and then scampered back towards the sitting room.

Lisi tried to meet the condemnatory green stare without flinching. 'It's his birthday,' she explained. 'And I'm busy organising—'

'So *that* was why you had to ring your mother,' he observed softly.

It was not the aggressive question she had been expecting and dreading. She stared at him uncomprehendingly. *'What?'*

'The night you slept with me,' he said slowly. 'I wondered why you should bother to do that, when we were only *supposedly* going for a quick drink,' he added witheringly. 'I guess you had to arrange for your mother to babysit. Poor little soul,' he finished. 'When Mummy jumps into bed with a man whenever the opportunity presents itself.'

For a moment, Lisi couldn't work out what he was talking about, and then his words began to make sense. Tim was a tall boy, as Marian had said. He looked older than his years. And Philip didn't even suspect that the child might be his. God forgive me, she thought. But this is something I have to do. For all our sakes. He hates me. He thinks the worst of me—he's made that heartbreakingly clear. What good would it do *any* of us if he found out the truth?

'I have never neglected my son, Philip,' she said truthfully.

Did this make them quits? All the time he hadn't told her about Carla, lying desperately sick in her hospital bed— Lisi had carried an awesome secret, too. A baby at home. And who else? he wondered. 'So where's the father?' he demanded. 'Was he still on the scene when you stripped off and climbed into my bed?'

'How dare you say something like that?'

'It was a simple question.'

She jerked her head in the direction of the sitting room door. 'Just keep your voice down!' she hissed, and then met the fury in his eyes. 'Oh, what's the point of all this? You've made your feelings about me patently clear, Philip. There is nothing between us. There never was—other than a night of mad impetuosity. We both know that. End of story. And now, if you don't mind—I really do have a party to organise.'

He made to turn away. Hadn't a part of him nurtured a tiny, unrealistic hope that her behaviour that night had been a one-off—that it had been something about *him* which had made her so wild and so free in his bed? And all the time she'd had a child by another man! It was a fact of modern life and he didn't know why he should feel so bitterly disappointed. But he did.

'Goodbye, Philip.' Her overwhelming feeling was one of relief, but there was regret as well. She couldn't have him—she would never have him—not when his fundamental lack of respect for her ran so deep. But that didn't stop a tiny, foolish part of her from aching for what could never be.

He looked deep into her eyes and some sixth sense told him that all was not how it seemed. Something was not right. She was tense. Nervous. More nervous than she had any right to be, and he wondered why.

She started to close the door when he said, 'Wait!'

There was something so imperious in his command, something so darkly imperative in the glacial green gaze that Lisi stopped in her tracks. 'What?'

'You didn't say how old Tim was.'

She felt the blood freeze in her veins, but she kept her face calm. 'That's because you didn't ask.'

'I'm asking now.'

A thousand thoughts began to make a scrabbled journey through her mind. Could she carry it off? Would he see through the lie if she told him that Tim was four? It was credible—everybody said that he could easily pass for a four-year-old.

Her hesitation told him everything, as did the blanching of colour from her already pale face. He felt the slow, steady burn of disbelief. And anger. 'He's mine, isn't he?'

If she had thought that seeing him again was both nightmare and dream, then this was the nightmare sprung into worst possible life. She stared at him. 'Philip—'

'*Isn't* he?' he demanded, in a low, harsh voice which cut through her like a knife.

She leant on the door for support, and nodded mutely.

'Say it, Lisi! Go on, say it!'

'Tim is your son,' she admitted tonelessly, and then almost recoiled from the look of naked fury in his eyes.

'You bitch,' he said softly. 'You utter little bitch.'

She had played this unlikely scenario in her mind many times. Philip would magically appear and she would tell him about Tim, but she had never imagined a reaction like this—with him staring at her with a contempt so intense that she could have closed her eyes and wept.

'Go away,' she whispered. 'Please, just go away.'

'I'm not going anywhere. I want to know everything.'

'Philip.' She sucked in a ragged breath. Should she appeal to his better nature? Surely he must have one? 'I *will* talk to you, of course I will—'

'Well, thanks for nothing!' he scorned.

'But not now. I can't. Tim will come out again in a minute if I'm not back and it isn't fair—'

'*Fair?*' he echoed sardonically. 'You think that what you have done is *fair*? To deny me all knowledge of my own flesh and blood? And then to lie about it?'

'I did not lie!' she protested.

'Oh, yes, you did,' he contradicted roughly. 'It was—to use your own words, my dear Lisi—a lie by omission, wasn't it? Just now, when I asked you his age, you thought about concealing it from me.' His mouth hardened into a cruel, contemptuous line. 'But I'm afraid your hesitation gave you away.'

'Just go,' she begged. 'Don't let Tim hear this. Please.'

He hardened his heart against the appeal in her eyes. He had lived with death and loss and all the time she had brought new life into the world and had jealously kept that life to herself. As if they had stumbled across unexpected treasure together, and she had decided to claim it all for herself.

'What time does his party finish?'

She could scarcely think. 'At around s-six.'

'And what time does he go to bed?'

'He'll be tired tonight. I should be able to settle him down by seven.'

'I'll come at seven.'

She shook her head. 'Can't we leave it until tomorrow?' she pleaded.

He gave her a look of pure scorn. 'It has already been left three years too long!'

'Then one more night won't make any difference. Sleep on it, Philip—you won't feel so…so…angry about it in the morning.'

But he couldn't ever imagine being rid of the rage which was smouldering away at the pit of his stomach. 'How very naive you are, Lisi—if you think that I'll agree to that. Either I come round tonight once Tim has gone to sleep, or I march straight in there now and tell him exactly what his relationship to me is.'

'You wouldn't do that.'

'Just try me,' he said, in a voice of soft menace.

Lisi swallowed. 'Okay. I'll see you here. Tonight. Unless...' she renewed the appeal in her eyes '—unless you'd rather meet on...neutral territory? I could probably get a babysitter.'

But he shook his head resolutely. 'Thanks, but no thanks,' he said coldly. 'Maybe I might like to look in on my sleeping son, Lisi. Surely you wouldn't deny me that?'

My sleeping son. The possessive way that he said it made Lisi realise that Philip Caprice was not intending to be an absentee father. Already! How the hell was she going to cope with all the implications of *that*?

But what about Tim? prompted the voice of her conscience. What about him?

'No, I won't deny you that,' she told him quietly. 'I'll see you here tonight, around seven.'

He gave a brief, mock-courteous nod and then turned on his heel, walking away from her without a second glance, the way he had done the night his son had been conceived.

She shut the door before he was halfway down the path, and looked down to see that her hands were shaking.

She waited until her breath had stopped coming in short, anxious little breaths, but as she caught a glance at her reflection in the mirror she saw that her face was completely white, her eyes dark and frightened, like a trapped animal.

I must pull myself together, she thought. She had a son and a responsibility to him. Today was his party—his big day. She had already messed up in more ways than one. She mustn't let the complex world of adult relationships ruin it for him.

She forced a smile onto her lips and hoped that it didn't look too much like a grimace, and then she opened the door to the sitting room, where her beloved son sat with his dark head bent over his colouring, his little tongue protruding from between his teeth, just the way hers did. He's my son, too, she told herself fiercely. Not just Philip's.

'Hello, darling,' she said softly. 'Shall Mummy come and help for a bit?'

Tim looked up, his eyes narrowed in that clever way of his, and Lisi stared at him with a sudden, dawning recognition. His eyes might be blue like hers, but that expression was pure Philip. Why had she never seen it before? Because she had deliberately blinded herself to it as too painful?

'Mum-mee,' said Tim, and put his crayon down firmly on top of the paper. 'Who was that man?'

Not now, she told herself. How he must be told was going to take some working out.

'Oh, he's just a friend, darling,' she said, injecting her voice with a determined cheerfulness. 'A friend of Mummy's.'

But the words rang hollow in her ears.

CHAPTER FIVE

THE hours ticked by so slowly while Philip waited. He felt as though the whole landscape of his life had been altered irrevocably—as if someone had detonated a bomb and left a familiar place completely unrecognisable.

He went through the motions of working. He faxed the States. He replied to his e-mails. He made phone-calls to his London office, and it seemed from the responses given by his staff that he must have sounded quite normal.

But he didn't feel in the least normal. He had just discovered that he was the biological father of a child who was a complete unknown to him and he knew that he was going to have to negotiate some paternal rights.

Whether Lisi Vaughan liked it or not.

He deliberately turned his thoughts away from her. He wasn't going to think about her. Thinking about her just made his rage grow, and rage would not help either of them come to some kind of amicable agreement about access.

Amicable?

The word mocked him. How could the two of them ever come to some kind of friendly understanding after what had happened?

He went for a long walk as dusk began to fall, looking up into the heavy grey clouds and wondering if the threatened snow would ever arrive, and at seven prompt he was knocking on her door.

She didn't answer immediately and his mouth tightened. If the secretive little witch thought that she could just hide inside and he would just go away again, then she was in for an unpleasant surprise.

The door opened, and he was unprepared for the impact of seeing her all dressed up for a party. Red dress. Red shoes. Long, slim legs encased in pale stockings which had a slight sheen to them. He had never seen her in red before, but scarlet had been the backdrop to her beauty when she had lain with such abandon on his bed. Scarlet woman, he thought, and felt the blood thicken in his veins.

'You'd better come in,' said Lisi.

'With pleasure,' he answered, grimly sarcastic.

She opened the door wider to let him in, but took care to press herself back against the wall, as far away from him as possible. She was only hanging onto her self-possession by a thread, and if he came anywhere near her she would lose it completely. But he still came close enough for her to catch the faint drift of his aftershave—some sensual musky concoction which clamoured at her senses.

He followed her into the sitting room, where the debris from the party still littered the room. He wondered how many children there had been at the party. Judging by the clutter left behind it could easily have run into tens.

There were balloons everywhere, and scrunched up wrapping paper piled up in the bin. Half-eaten pieces of cake and untouched sandwiches lay scattered across the paper cloth which covered the table.

Philip frowned. 'Weren't they hungry?'

'They only ever eat the crisps.'

'I see.' He looked around the room in slight bemusement. 'They certainly know how to make a mess, don't they?'

Lisi gave a rueful smile, thinking that maybe they *could* be civil to one another. 'I should have cleared it away, but I wanted to read Tim a story from one of his new books.'

The mention of Tim's name reminded him of why he was there. 'Very commendable,' he observed sardonically.

'Can I...?' She forced herself to say it, even though his manner was now nothing short of hostile. But she had told herself over and over again that nothing good would come out of making an enemy of him, even though the look on his face told her that she was probably most of the way there. 'Can I get you a drink?'

'In a minute. Firstly, I want to see Tim.'

She steeled herself not to react to that autocratic demand. 'He's only just gone to sleep,' she said. 'What if he wakes?'

'I'll be very quiet. And anyway, what if he *does* wake?'

'Don't you know *anything* about children?' she asked, but one look at his expression made her wonder how she could have come out with something as naive and as hurtful as that.

'Actually, no.' He bit the words out precisely. 'Because up until this morning, I didn't realise that I might have to.'

'Just wait until he's in a really deep sleep,' she said, desperately changing the subject. 'He might be alarmed if he wakes up to find a strange man...' Her words tailed off embarrassedly.

He gave a bitter laugh. 'A strange man in his room?' he completed acidly. 'You mean it doesn't happen nightly, Lisi?'

It was one insult too many and on top of all the tensions of the day it was just too much. Her hand flew up to his face and she slapped him, hard. There was a dull ringing sound as her palm connected, but he didn't react at all, just stood there looking at her, his expression unreadable.

'Feel better now?'

She bit her lip in horror. She had never raised her hand to anyone in her life! 'What do you think?'

He turned away. He didn't want her looking at him all vulnerable and lost like that. He wanted to steel his heart against her pale beauty and the black hair which streamed down her back, tied back with a scarlet ribbon which matched the dress. 'You don't want to hear what I think,' he said heavily. 'I'll take that drink now.'

She went into the kitchen and took wine from the fridge and handed him the bottle, along with two glasses. 'Maybe you could just open that, and I'll clear up a little,' she said.

He sat down in one of the squashy old armchairs and began to open the wine, but his eyes followed her as she moved around the room, deftly clearing the table and bundling up all the leftover party food into the paper cloth.

He wished that she would go and put on the baggy trousers she had been wearing this morning. The sight of the shiny red material stretching over the pert swell of her bottom was making him have thoughts he would rather not have. He was here to talk about his son, not fantasise about taking her damned dress off.

She had lit the fire, and the room flickered with the shadowed reflections of the flames. On the now-cleared table he saw her place a big copper vase containing holly, whose bright berries matched the scarlet of her dress. It was, he thought, with bitter irony, a delightfully cosy little scene.

She took the glass of wine he handed her and sat in the chair facing his, her knees locked tightly together, wishing that she had had the opportunity to change from a dress which was making her uncomfortably aware of the tingling sensation in her breasts. Just what did he do to her simply by looking? She twisted the stem of her glass round and round. 'What shall we drink to?'

He studied her for a long moment. 'How about to truth?'

She took a mouthful and the warmth of the liquor started to unravel the knot of tension which had been coiled up in the pit of her stomach all day. She stared at him. 'Do you really think that *you* have a monopoly on truth? Why the hell do you think I didn't contact you and tell you when I found out I was pregnant?'

'What goes on in your mind is a complete mystery to me.'

Because you don't know me, thought Lisi sadly. And now you never will. Philip's opinion of her would always be distorted. He saw her as some kind of loose woman who would fall into bed with just about any man. Or as a selfish mother who would deliberately keep him from his own flesh and blood.

'Think about the last words you said to me,' she reminded him softly, but the memory still had the power to make her flinch. 'You told me you were married. What was I supposed to do? Turn up on your doorstep with a bulging stomach and announce that you were about to be a daddy? What if your wife had answered the door? I can't imagine that she would have been particularly overjoyed to hear that!'

He didn't respond for a moment. He had come here this morning intending to tell her about the circumstances which had led to that night. About Carla. But his discovery of Tim had driven that far into the background. There were only so many revelations they could take in one day. Wouldn't talking about his wife at this precise moment muddy the waters still further? Tim must come first.

'You could have telephoned me,' he pointed out. 'The office had my number. You could have called me any time.'

'The look on your face as you walked out that night made me think that you would be happy never to see me again. The disgust on your face told its own story.'

Self-disgust, he thought bitterly. Disgusted at his own weakness and disgusted by the intensity of the pleasure he had experienced in her arms. A relative stranger's arms.

He put the wineglass down on the table and his eyes glittered with accusation.

'The situation should never have arisen,' he ground out. 'You shouldn't have become pregnant in the first place.'

'Tell me something I don't know! I didn't exactly *choose* to get pregnant!'

'Oh, really?' The accusation in his voice didn't waver. 'You told me that it was safe.' He gave a hollow laugh. 'Safe? More fool me for believing you.'

Her fingers trembling so much that she was afraid that she might slop wine all over her dress, Lisi put her own glass down on the carpet. 'Are you saying that I lied, Philip?'

His cool, clever eyes bored into her.

'Facts are facts,' he said coldly. 'I realised that we were not using any protection. I offered to stop—' He felt his groin tensing as he remembered just when and how he had offered to stop, and a wave of desire so deep and so hot swept over him that it took his breath away. He played for time, slowly picking up his glass and lifting it to his lips until he had his feelings under control once more.

'I offered to stop,' he continued, still in that hard, cold voice. 'And you assured me that it was safe. Just how was it safe, Lisi? Were you praying that it would be—because you were so het-up you couldn't bear me to stop? Or were you relying on something as outrageously unreliable as the so-called ''safe'' period?'

'Do you really think I'd take risks like that?' she demanded.

'Who knows?'

She gave a short laugh. If she had entertained any lingering doubt that there might be some fragment of affection for her in the corner of his heart, then he had dispelled it completely with that arrogant question.

'For your information—I was on the pill at the time—'

'Just in case?' he queried hatefully.

'Actually—' But she stopped short of telling him why. She was under no obligation to explain that, although she had broken up with her steady boyfriend a year earlier, the pill had suited her and given her normal periods for the first time in her life and she had seen no reason to stop taking it. 'It's none of your business why I was taking it.'

I'll bet, he thought grimly. 'So why didn't it work?'

'Because…' She sighed. 'I guess because I had a bout of sickness earlier that week. In the heat of the moment, it slipped my mind. It was a million-to-one chance—'

'I think that the odds were rather higher than that, don't you?' He raised his eyebrows insolently. 'You surely must have known that there was a possibility that it would fail?'

Unable to take any more of the cold censure on his face, she leaned over to throw another log on the fire and it spat and hissed back at her like an angry cat. 'What do you want me to say? That I couldn't bear for you to stop?' Because that was the shameful truth. At the time she had felt as if the world would come to an abrupt and utter end if he'd stopped his delicious love-making. But she hadn't *consciously* taken a risk.

'And couldn't you, Lisi? Bear me to stop?'

She met his eyes. The truth he had wanted, so the truth he would get. 'No. I couldn't. Does that flatter your ego?'

His voice was cold. 'My ego does not need flattering. And anyway—' he topped up both their glasses '—how it happened is now irrelevant—we can't turn the clock back, can we?'

His words struck a painful chord and she knew that she had to ask him the most difficult question of all. Even if she didn't like the answer. 'And if you could?' she queried softly. '*Would* you turn the clock back?'

He stared at her in disbelief. Was she really that naive? 'Of course I would!' he said vehemently, though the way her mouth crumpled when he said it made him feel distinctly uncomfortable. 'Wouldn't you?'

She gave him a sad smile. He would never understand— not in a million years. 'Of course I wouldn't.'

'You *wouldn't*?'

'How could I?' she asked simply. 'When the encounter gave me a son.'

He noted her use of the word *encounter*. Which told him precisely how *she* regarded what had happened that night. Easy come. His mouth twisted. Easy go. She certainly had not bothered to spare his feelings, but then why should she? He had not spared hers. There was no need for loyalty between them—nothing at all between them, in fact, other than an inconvenient physical attraction.

And a son.

'He looks like you,' he observed.

'That's what everyone says,' said Lisi serenely, and saw to her amazement that a flicker of something very much like…disappointment…crossed his features. 'And it's a good thing he does, isn't it?' she asked him quietly.

'Meaning?'

'Well, I would hate him to resemble a father who wished that the whole thing never happened.'

'Lisi, you are wilfully misunderstanding me!' he snapped.

She shook her head. 'I don't think so. You would wish him unborn, if you could.'

'You can't wish someone unborn!' he remonstrated, and then his voice unexpectedly gentled. 'And if I really thought the whole situation so regrettable, then why am I here? Why didn't I just stay away when I found out, as you so clearly wanted me to?'

She shrugged. 'I don't know.'

'Then I'll tell you.' He leaned forward in the chair. 'Obviously the circumstances of his conception are not what I would have chosen—'

'What a delightful way to phrase it,' put in Lisi drily.

'But Tim is here now. He exists! He is half mine—'

'You can't cut him up in portions as you would a cake!' she protested.

'Half mine in terms of genetic make-up,' he continued inexorably.

'Now you're making him sound like Frankenstein,' observed Lisi, slightly hysterically.

'Don't be silly! I want to watch him grow,' said Philip, and his voice grew almost dreamy. 'To see him develop into a man. To influence him. To teach him. To be a father to him.'

Lisi swallowed. This didn't sound like the occasional contact visit to her. But she had denied him access for three whole years, wouldn't it sound unspeakably mean to object to that curiously possessive tone which had deepened his voice to sweetest honey?

And besides, what was she worrying about? He lived in London, for heaven's sake—and, although Langley was commutable from the capital, she imagined that he would soon get tired of travelling up and down the country to see Tim.

She knew how fickle men could be. She thought of Dave, her best friend Rachel's husband, who had deserted Rachel just over a year ago. They had a son of Tim's age and Dave's visits to see him had dwindled to almost nothing. And that was from a man who had fallen in love with and married the mother of his child. Who had seen that child grow from squalling infant to chubby toddler. If *he* had lost interest—then how long would she give Philip before he tired of fatherhood?

'I'd like to see him now, please.'

This time there was no reason not to agree to his request, but Lisi felt almost stricken by a reluctance to do so. Something was going to end right here and now, she realised. For so long it had been just her and Tim—a unit which went together as perfectly as peaches and cream. No one else had been able to lay claim on him and, since her mother had died, she had considered herself to be his only living relation. He was hers. All hers—and now she was going to have to relinquish part of him to his father.

A lump rose in the back of her throat and she swallowed it down.

Philip was staring at her from between narrowed eyes. Did her eyes glitter with the promise of tears? 'Are you okay?'

'Of course I'm okay,' she answered unconvincingly. 'Why shouldn't I be?'

'Because you've gone so pale.'

'I *am* pale, Philip—you know that.' He had told her so that night in his arms. 'Pale as the moon,' he had whispered, as his lips had burned fire along her flesh. 'Come with me,' she said slowly.

The two of them walked with exaggerated care towards the closed door with its hand-painted sign saying, 'Tim's Room'.

Lisi pushed the door open quietly and tiptoed over to the bed, where a little hump lay tucked beneath a Mickey-Mouse duvet, and Philip was surprised by the clamour of a far-distant memory. So she still had a thing about Disney, did she?

He went to stand beside her, and looked down, unprepared for the kick of some primitive emotion deep inside him. The sleeping child looked almost unbearably peaceful, with only one small lock of dark hair obscuring the pure lines of a flawless cheek. His lashes were long, he realised—as long as Lisi's—and his mouth was half open as he took in slow, steady breaths.

'So innocent,' he said, very softly. 'So very innocent.'

It was such a loaded word, and Lisi felt a strange, useless yearning. He thought *her* the very antithesis of innocence, didn't he? If only it could be different. But she knew in her heart that it never could. She nodded, gazing down with pride at the shiny-clean hair of her son. Their son. He looked scrubbed-clean and contented. Good enough to eat.

She stole a glance at Philip, who was studying Tim so intently that she might as well not have existed. Strange now how *his* profile should remind her of Tim's. Had that been because he had not been around to make any comparisons? How much else of Tim was Philip? she wondered. What untapped genetic secrets lay dormant in that sweet, sleeping form?

Philip turned his head and their eyes made contact in a moment of strange, unspoken empathy. She read real sadness in *his* eyes. And regret—and wondered what he saw in hers.

He probably didn't care.

She put her finger onto her lips and beckoned him back out. She did *not* want Tim to wake and to demand to know what this man was doing here. Again. She shut the door behind them and went back into the sitting room, where Philip stood with his back to the fire, looking to all intents and purposes as if he were the master of the house.

But he never would be. She must remember that. In fact, it was almost laughable to try to imagine Philip Caprice living in this little house with her and Tim. The ceiling seemed almost too low to accommodate him, he was so tall. She tried to picture them all cramming into the tiny bathroom in the mornings and winced.

'Would you like some more wine?' she asked.

He shook his head. 'No, thanks. Coffee would be good, though.'

She was glad of the opportunity to escape to the kitchen and busy herself with the cafetière. She carried it back in with a plate of biscuits to find him standing where she had left him, only now he was staring deep into the heart of the fire with unseeing eyes.

He took the cup from her and gave a small smile of appreciation. 'Real coffee,' he murmured.

At that moment she really, really hated him. Did he have any idea just how *patronising* that sounded? 'What did you expect?' she asked acidly. 'The cheapest brand of instant on the market?'

He shook his head, still dazed by the emotional impact of seeing his son. 'You're right—if anything was cheap it was my remark.'

And what about the others? she wanted to cry out. The intimation that she had deliberately got pregnant. Wasn't that the cheapest remark a man could ever make to a woman? He wasn't taking *those* back, was he?

'So who else knows?' he demanded.

Lisi blinked. 'Knows what?'

'About Tim,' he said impatiently. 'How many others are privy to the secret I was excluded from?

She shook her head. 'No one. No one knows.'

'No-one at all?' he queried disbelievingly.

'No. Why should they? As far as anyone knew—we simply had a professional relationship. Even Jonathon thought that—and nobody was aware that I went up to your room at the hotel that night.' She shuddered, thinking how sordid that sounded. She bit her lip. 'The only person I told was my mother, just before she died.'

'You told her the whole story?' he demanded incredulously.

Again, she shook her head. 'I edited it more than a bit.'

'Was she shocked?'

Lisi shrugged. 'A little, but I made it sound…' She hesitated. She had made it sound as though she had been in love with him, and that bit she had found surprisingly easy. 'I made it sound rather more than it had been.' And her mother had pleaded with her to contact him. But then the bit she had omitted to tell her mother had been that Philip had already been married.

He looked at her and gave a heavy smile. 'My parents will want to meet him,' he said, wondering just how he was going to tell his elderly parents that he, too, was a parent.

'Your p-parents?'

His eyes were steady. 'But of course. What did you expect?'

What *had* she expected? Well, for one thing—she had expected to live the rest of her life without ever seeing Philip again. 'I don't know,' she admitted. 'I haven't really thought it through.'

'He's in my life now, too, Lisi,' he said simply. 'And I don't come in a neat little box marked "Philip Caprice"— to be opened up at will and shut again when it suits you. I have family who will want to get to know him. And friends, too.'

And girlfriends? she wondered. Maybe even one particular girlfriend who was very special to him? Maybe even… She raised troubled aquamarine eyes to his. 'Have you married, again, Philip?' she asked quietly.

'No.'

She felt the fierce, triumphant leap of her heart and despaired at herself. Fool, she thought. Fool! 'So where do we go from here?'

He despised himself for the part of him which wanted to say, Let's go to bed—because even though the distance between them was so vast that he doubted whether it could ever be mended, that didn't stop him from being turned on by her. He shifted uncomfortably in the chair. Very turned on indeed. He met her questioning gaze with a look of challenge. 'You tell Tim about me as soon as possible.'

Her mouth fell open. '*Tell* him?'

'Of course you tell him!' he exploded softly. 'I'm back, Lisi—and I'm staking my claim.'

It sounded so territorial. So loveless. 'Oh, I see,' she said slowly.

He narrowed his eyes. 'Just how were you planning to explain to him about his father? If I hadn't turned up.'

'I honestly don't know. It's not something I ever gave much thought to. He's so young, and whenever he asked I just said that Mummy and Daddy broke up before he was born and that I hadn't seen you since.' It had seemed easier to bury her head in the sand than to confront such a painful issue. 'Maybe one day I might have told him who his real father was.'

'When?' he demanded. 'When he was five? Six? Sixteen?'

'When the time was right.'

'And maybe the time never *would* have been right, hmm, Lisi? Did you think you could get away with keeping me anonymous for the rest of his life, so that the poor kid would never know he had a father?'

She met the burning accusation in his eyes and couldn't pretend. Not about this. 'I don't know,' she whispered.

He rose to his feet. 'Well, just make sure you do it. And soon. I don't care how you do it—just tell him!'

She nodded. She wanted him gone now—with as long a space until his next visit as possible. 'And when will we see you again? Some time after Christmas?'

He heard the hopeful tinge to her question and gave a short laugh. 'Hard luck, Lisi,' he said grimly. 'I'm afraid that I'm not going to just conveniently disappear from your life again. I'm intending to be around quite a bit. Just call it making up for lost time, if it makes you feel better. And it's Christmas very soon.'

'Christmas?' she echoed, in a horrified whisper.

'Sure.' His mouth hardened into an implacable line. 'I was tempted to buy him a birthday present today, but I didn't want to confuse him. However, there's only a week to go until Christmas and some time between now and then he needs to know who I am.' His eyes glittered. 'Because you can rest assured that I will be spending part of the holiday with him.'

She wanted to cry out and beg him not to disrupt the relatively calm order of her life, but as she looked into Philip's strong, cold face she knew that she would be wasting her breath. He wasn't going to go away, she recognised, and if she tried to stop him then he would simply bring in the best lawyers that money could buy in order to win contact with his child. She didn't need to be told to know that.

'Understood?' he asked softly.

'Do I have any choice?'

'I think you know the answer to that. Don't worry about seeing me to the door. I'll let myself out.'

As if in a dream she watched him go and shut the front door quietly behind him, and only when she had heard the last of his footsteps echoing down the path did she allow herself to sink back down onto the chair and to bury her head in her hands and take all that was left to her.

The comfort of tears.

CHAPTER SIX

LISI was woken by the sound of the telephone ringing, and as she picked it up she was aware that something was not as it should be.

'Hello?'

'Lisi, it's Marian.'

Sleepily, Lisi wondered what her boss was doing ringing her this early in the morning... She sat bolt upright in bed. That was it! That was what was not right! She had over-slept—she could tell that much by the light which was fil-tering through the curtains. 'What time is it?' she asked urgently.

'Nine-thirty, why—?'

'Wait there!' swallowed Lisi, and left the receiver on the bed while she rushed into Tim's bedroom. What was the matter with him? Why hadn't he woken at his usual un-earthly hour? Had Philip Caprice climbed in through one of the windows in the middle of the night and kidnapped his son?

But to her relief her son was sitting on his bed, engrossed in playing with some of his new birthday toys. He looked up as Lisi flew into the room, and smiled.

'Lo, Mum-mee,' he said happily. 'Me playing with trac-tor!'

'So I see! And a lovely tractor it is too, darling,' said Lisi, charging across the room to drop a kiss on top of his head. 'Mummy's just talking to Marian on the telephone and then we'll have a great big breakfast together!'

But Tim's head was bent over his toy again and he was busy making what he imagined to be tractor noises.

On the way back to speak to Marian, Lisi reflected how different things felt this morning. She no longer felt weak or intimidated by Philip. He had decided that he wanted contact and there was nothing she could do about it—but he could do all the legwork. She would just be polite. Icily polite.

Because during the middle of her largely sleepless night she had come to her senses and a great sense of indignation had made her softly curse his name.

He had been so busy attacking her that she hadn't really had time to consider that he had shown no remorse about betraying his wife. Nor any shame for his part in what had happened. Philip obviously wanted to make her the scapegoat—well, tough! He should look to himself first!

She picked the phone back up. 'Hello, Marian—are you still there?'

'Just about,' came the dry reply. 'Where did you go—Scotland?'

'Very funny.'

'You sound more cheerful today,' observed Marian.

'I am,' said Lisi. '*Much* happier!'

There was a short pause. 'I don't know if you're going to be after what I'm about to tell you.'

A sudden sense of foreboding filled Lisi with dread. This was something to do with Philip. 'What is it?'

'It's Philip Caprice.'

Exasperation and impatience made Lisi feel like screaming—until she reminded herself that the worst had already been exposed. There was nothing he could do to hurt and upset her now. 'What now?' she asked.

'He wants you to show him round a property later this morning.'

'He has to be kidding! Did you tell him that I'm off now until after Christmas?'

'I told him that yesterday. Lisi, has something happened between you two?'

'Apart from the very obvious?' she asked tartly.

'You know what I mean.'

Yes, she knew what Marian meant and she guessed that it was pointless keeping it from her boss—especially as she had already guessed that Philip was Tim's father.

'I told him,' she said flatly.

'You *told* him?'

'He guessed,' Lisi amended.

'And?'

Lisi sighed. She had planned to get onto the phone first thing and tell Rachel all about it, but just then she badly needed to confide in somebody, and Marian was older and wiser. Lisi suspected that she had known straight away that a man as discerning as Philip would be bound to guess eventually.

'He wants to be involved.'

'With you?'

'Oh, no,' said Lisi with a hollow laugh. 'Definitely not with me. With Tim.'

'I see.' Marian's voice sounded rather strained. 'That explains it, then.'

That sense of foreboding hit her again. 'Explains what?' she asked, her voice rising with a kind of nameless fear.

'He really *does* want to buy somewhere here. In Langley.'

Lisi's mouth thinned. 'I see.'

'And that's not the worst of it.'

'What do you mean?'

'He wants *you* to show him around a property—'

'But I'm on *holiday*, Marian!'

'I already told him that.'

'And even if I weren't—I don't *want* to show him around a property!'

'He's...well, he's insisted, dear.'

'He can't insist,' whispered Lisi. 'Can he?'

Another pause. 'He *is* the customer,' said Marian apologetically, and suddenly Lisi understood. Marian was a businesswoman—and business was business was business. Philip Caprice was a wealthy and influential man and if he said jump, then presumably they would all have to leap through hoops for him.

She thought of all the times when Marian had let her have the morning, or even a couple of days, off work. When Tim had been ill. Or when she had taken him to have his inoculations. She was an understanding and kind employer, and Lisi owed her.

'Okay,' she sighed. 'I can probably arrange for Rachel to look after Tim. When does he want to look round?'

'Later on this morning. Think you can manage it? You can even leave Tim in here with us, if it's difficult.'

'I'm sure Rachel will be able to have him.'

'Good!' Marian's voice grew slightly more strained. 'There's just one more thing, Lisi.'

Lisi tried to inject a note of gallows humour into her voice. 'Go on, hit me with it!'

'The property in question...it's...it's The Old Rectory.'

The world spun. It was a cruel trick. A cruel twist of fate. Was he planning to hurt her even more than he already had done? Lisi heard herself speaking with a note of cracked desperation. 'Is this some kind of joke, Marian?'

'I wish it was, dear.'

Lisi didn't remember putting the phone down, she just found herself sitting on the bed staring blankly at it. He couldn't, she thought fiercely. He couldn't do this to her!

The Old Rectory.

The house she had grown up in. The house her mother had struggled to keep on, even after the death of her father, when everyone had told her to downsize and to move into something more suitable for a mother and her daughter on their own.

But neither of them had wanted to. A house could creep into your heart and your soul, and Lisi and her mother had preferred to put on an extra sweater or two in winter. It had kept the heating bills down at a time when every penny had counted.

After her mother had died, Lisi had reluctantly sold the house, but by then she had needed to. Really needed to, because she'd had a baby to support. She had bought Cherry Tree Cottage and invested the rest of the proceeds of the sale, giving just enough for her and Tim to live on. To fall back on.

And now Philip Caprice was going to rub her nose in it by buying the property for himself!

Over my dead body! she thought.

She gave Tim his breakfast.

'I want birthday cake,' he had announced solemnly.

'Sure,' said Lisi absently, and began to cut him a large slice.

'*Can* I, Mum-mee?' asked Tim, in surprise.

She glanced down at the sickly confection and remembered feeding Philip birthday cake all those years back and her heart clenched. She looked into Tim's hopeful face and relented. Oh, what the heck—it wouldn't hurt for once, would it?

While Tim was chomping his way through the cake, she phoned Rachel, who agreed to look after him without question.

'Bless you!' said Lisi impulsively.

'Is everything okay?'

She heard the doubt in Rachel's voice and wondered if she sounded as mixed-up and disturbed as she felt. Probably. 'I'll tell you all about it later,' she said grimly.

'Can't wait!'

Lisi went through the mechanics of getting ready. She ran herself a bath and left the door open and Tim trotted happily in and out. She wondered whether Philip was prepared for the lack of privacy which caring for a young child inevitably brought. And then she imagined him lording it in her old family home and she could have screamed aloud with fury, but for Tim's sake—and her own—she won the inner battle to stay calm.

She supposed that she ought to dress as if for work and picked out her most buttoned-up suit from the wardrobe. Navy-blue and pinstriped, it had a straight skirt which came to just below the knee and a long-line jacket. With a crisp, white blouse and her hair scraped back into a chignon, she thought that she looked professional. And prim.

Good!

The scarlet dress had been a big mistake last night. He might not like or respect her, but it was obvious that he still felt physically attracted to her. She had seen the way he'd watched her last night, while trying to appear as if he hadn't been. And she had seen the tension which had stiffened his elegant frame, had him shifting uncomfortably in his chair. It had been unmistakably a sexual tension, and Lisi wasn't fooling herself into thinking that it hadn't been mutual.

Later that morning, after she had deposited Tim and some of the leftover party food at Rachel's house, Lisi walked into the agency to find Philip waiting for her.

His face was unsmiling and his eyes looked very green as he nodded at her coolly. 'Hello, Lisi,' he said, speaking as politely and noncommittally—as if this were the first time he had ever met her.

Marian was sitting at her desk looking a little flustered. 'Here are the keys,' she said. 'The owners are away.'

Her heart sinking slightly, Lisi took them. She had hoped that one of the divorcing couple would be in. At least the presence of a third party might have defused the atmosphere. She could not think of a more unpalatable situation than being alone in that big, beautiful house with Philip.

Unpalatable? she asked herself. Or simply dangerous?

'We can walk there,' she told him outside. 'It's just up the lane.'

'Sure.'

But once away from Marian's view, she no longer had to play the professional. 'So you're going through with your threat to buy a house in the village,' she said, in a low, furious voice.

'I think it makes sense, under the circumstances,' he said evenly. 'Don't you?'

Nothing seemed to make sense any more—not least the fact that even in the midst of her anger towards him—her body was crying out for more of his touch.

Was that conditioning? Nature's way of ensuring stability? That a woman should find the father of her child overwhelmingly attractive? No. It couldn't be. Rachel had completely gone off Dave—she told Lisi that the thought of him touching her now made her flesh creep. But then Dave *had* run off with one of Rachel's other supposed 'friends'.

Lisi reminded herself that Philip was not whiter-than-white, either. *He* had been the one who had been attached—more than attached. He had actually been married, and yet his anger all seemed to be directed at her. His poor wife! It was, Lisi decided, time to start giving as good as she got.

Her rage was almost palpable, thought Philip as he looked at the stiff set of her shoulders beneath the starchy-looking suit she wore. He suspected that she had dressed in a way to make herself seem unapproachable and unattractive to him, but if that *had* been the case, then she had failed completely.

'This is in the same direction as *your* house,' he observed as she took him down the very route he had used last night.

She stopped dead in her tracks and gave him a coolly questioning stare. 'You didn't know?'

'I've only seen the details.'

'It's just down the bloody *road* from me!'

'Handy,' he murmured.

She didn't want him making jokey little asides. That kind of comment could lull you into false hopes. She preferred him hostile, she decided.

Her breath caught in her throat as they walked past her cottage to the end of the lane, where, beside the old grey Norman church, stood the beautiful old rectory. And her heart stood still with shock.

The place was practically falling down!

The yew hedge which her mother had always lovingly clipped had been allowed to overgrow, and the lawn was badly in need of a cut.

'Not very well presented,' Philip observed.

'They're getting divorced,' explained Lisi icily. 'I don't think that house-maintenance is uppermost in their minds at the moment.'

He turned away. People sometimes said to him that death must be easier to bear than divorce. When a couple divorced they knowingly ripped apart the whole fabric of their lives. Only anger was left, and bitterness and resentment.

'At least Carla died knowing that you loved her, and she loved you,' his mother had said to him softly after the funeral and then, like now, he had turned away, his face a mask of pain. What would his mother say if she knew how he had betrayed that love?

And the woman who had tempted him stood beside him now, mocking him and tempting him still in her prissy-looking worksuit. He would be tied to Lisi for ever, he realised—because children made a bond between two people which could never be broken.

'Philip?' Her voice had softened, but that was instinctive rather than intentional for she had seen the look of anguish which had darkened the carved beauty of his features. 'Shall we go inside, or did you want to look round the garden first?'

He shook his head. 'Inside,' he said shortly.

Lisi had not been inside since the day when all the packing crates had made the faded old home resemble a warehouse. She had perched on one waiting for the removals van to arrive, her heart aching as she'd said goodbye to her past. Tim had lain asleep in his Moses basket by her feet— less than six months at the time—gloriously unaware of the huge changes which had been taking place in his young life.

Unbelievable to think that this was the first time she had been back, but Marian had understood her reluctance to accompany clients around her former home. Until Philip Caprice had swanned into the office and made his autocratic demand Lisi hadn't set foot inside the door.

Until today.

Lisi had to stifle a gasp.

When she had lived here with her mother there had been very little money, but a whole lot of love. Surfaces had been dusted, the floorboards bright and shiny, and there had always been a large vase of foliage or the flowers which had bloomed in such abundance in the large gardens at the back.

But now the house had an air of neglect, as if no one had bothered to pay any attention in caring for it. A woman's tee shirt lay crumpled on one corner of the hall floor and a half-empty coffee cup was making a sticky mark on the window-ledge. Lisi shuddered as she caught the drift of old cooking: onions or cabbage—something which lingered unpleasantly in the unaired atmosphere.

She knew from statistics that most people decided to buy

a house within the first few seconds of walking into it. At least Philip was unlikely to be lured by this dusty old shell of a place. She thought of the least attractive way to view it, and she, above all others, knew the place's imperfections.

'The kitchen is along here,' she said calmly, and proceeded to take him there, praying that the divorcing couple had not had the funds to give the room the modernisation it had been crying out for.

She led the way in and let out an almost inaudible sigh of relief. Not only was the kitchen untouched, but it had clearly been left during some kind of marital dispute—for a smashed plate lay right in the centre of the floor. Pots and pans, some still containing food, lay on the surface of the hob, and there was a distinctly nasty smell emanating from the direction of the fridge.

He waited for her to make some kind of fumbling apology for the state of the place, but there was none, she just continued to regard him with that oddly frozen expression on her face.

'Like it?' she asked flippantly.

He narrowed his eyes. 'Hardly. Where's the dining room?'

'I'm afraid that it's some way from the kitchen,' she said, mock-apologetically. 'It isn't a terribly well-designed property—certainly not by modern standards.'

'You really don't want me to buy this house, do you, Lisi?'

'I don't want you to buy any house in Langley, if you must know.' And especially not this one. She put on her professional face once more. 'Would you like to see the dining room?'

'I can't wait,' he answered sardonically.

The dining room looked as though it had never had a meal eaten in it; instead there was a pile of legal-looking papers heaped up on the table, as if someone had been using it for a office. Philip looked around the room slowly, but said nothing.

'Where next?' asked Lisi brightly.

'To the next enchanting room,' he murmured.

Perversely, his criticism stung her, making her realise that she was still more attached to the place than she was sure she should be. How she wished he could have seen it when *she* had lived here, particularly at this time of the year. At Christmas it had come into its own. The hall used to be festooned with fresh laurel from the garden and stacks and stacks of holly and great sprigs of mistletoe had been bunched everywhere.

The choir would come from the church next door on Christmas Eve, and drink sherry and eat mince pies and the big, wide corridors would echo with the sound of excited chatter, while in the sitting room a log fire had blazed out its warmth.

Fortunately—or unfortunately in Lisi's case—no neglect could mar the beauty of the sitting room. The high ceiling and the carved marble fireplace drew the attention away from the fact that the curtains could have done with a good clean.

Philip nodded and walked slowly around the room, his eyes narrowing with pleasure as he looked out of the long window down into the garden beyond.

A winter-bare garden but beautiful nevertheless, he thought, with mature trees and bushes which were silhouetted against the curved shapes of the flower beds.

Lisi wandered over to the window and stood beside him, past and present becoming fused for one brief, poignant moment.

'You should see it in springtime,' she observed fondly.

He heard the dreamy quality of her voice which was so at odds with her attitude of earlier. 'Oh?'

'There are bulbs out everywhere—daffodils and tulips and narcissi—and over there…' she pointed to where a lone tree stood in the centre of the overgrown lawn '…underneath that cherry, the first snowdrops come out and the lawn is sprinkled with white, almost as if it had been snowing.'

The sense of something not being as it should be pricked at his senses. Instincts, Khalim had taught him. Always trust your instincts.

'You seem to know this house very well for someone who only works part-time in the estate agency,' he observed softly.

She turned to face him. What was the point of hiding it from him? 'You're very astute, Philip.'

'Just observant.' His dark brows winged upwards in arrogant query. 'So?'

'I used to live here.' No, that remark didn't seem to do the place justice. 'It was my childhood home,' she explained.

There she was, doing it again—that vulnerable little tremble of her mouth which made him want to kiss all her hurt away.

'What happened?' he asked abruptly.

'After my father died, it was just my mother and me—'

He sounded incredulous. 'In this great barn of a place?'

'We loved it,' she said simply.

He let his eyes roam once more over the high ceilings. 'Yes, I can see that you would,' he said slowly.

'We couldn't bear to leave it. When my mother died, I had to sell up, of course—because there was Tim to think about by then.'

'So you sold this and bought the cottage?' he guessed. 'And presumably banked the rest?'

She nodded.

He thought of her, all alone, struggling along with a little baby, and he felt the sharp pang of conscience. 'Lisi, why in God's name didn't you contact me? Even if I hadn't been able to offer you any kind of future—don't you think that I would have paid towards my son's upkeep?'

She gave him a look of icy pride. 'I wasn't going to come begging to you, cap in hand! I had to think of what was best for everyone, and I came to the conclusion that the best thing would be to cut all ties.'

'And did you enjoy playing God with people's lives?'

She heard his bitterness. 'I thought it would only complicate things if I tried to involve you—for you, for me, for Tim. And for your wife, of course,' she finished. 'Because if it had been me, and my husband had done what you did to her—it would have broken my heart.' She looked at him and her eyes felt hot with unshed tears for the dead woman she had unknowingly deceived. But not Philip—his betrayal had been cold-bloodedly executed. 'Did she know, Philip? Did your wife ever find out?'

'No,' he said flatly. 'Carla never knew anything about it.'

'Are you sure? They say that wives always know—only sometimes they pretend not to.' She stared at him as if she were seeing him for the first time. 'How could you do it? How could you do that to her and live with yourself afterwards?'

Her condemnation of him was so strong that he felt he could almost reach out and touch it, but he knew he couldn't let her stumble along this wrong track any longer, no matter how painful the cost of telling her.

'She didn't know,' he ground out, 'because she wasn't aware. Not of me, or you, or what happened. Not aware of anything.'

She blinked at him in confusion. 'What are you talking about?'

'The night I made love to you—my wife hadn't spoken to me for eighteen months.'

Foolish hope flared in her heart, putting an entirely different perspective on events. 'You mean...you mean that you were *separated*?'

He gave a bitter laugh at the unwitting irony of her words. 'In a sense, yes—we had been separated for a long time. You see, the car crash happened *before* I met you, Lisi, not after. It left her in a deep coma from which she never recovered. She didn't die for several months after...after...'

'After what?' she whispered.

His eyes grew even bleaker. 'After I made love to you. You must have been about six months pregnant when she died.'

CHAPTER SEVEN

THE sitting-room of her childhood retreated into a hazy blur and then came back into focus again and Lisi stared at Philip, noting the tension which had scored deep lines down the side of his mouth.

'I don't understand,' she said.

'Don't you?' He gave a short laugh. 'My wife—'

His wife. His *wife*. 'What was her name?'

He hesitated, then frowned. What was it to her? 'Carla,' he said, grudgingly.

Carla. A person who was referred to as a 'wife' was a nebulous figure of no real substance, but Carla—Carla existed. Philip's wife. Carla. It hurt more than it had any right to hurt. 'Tell me,' she urged softly.

He wasn't looking for her sympathy, or her understanding—he would give her facts if she wanted to hear them, but he wanted nothing in return.

'It happened early one autumn morning,' he began, and a tale he had not had to recount for such a long time became painfully alive in his mind as he relived it. 'Carla was driving to work. She worked out of London,' he added, as if that somehow mattered. 'And visibility was poor. There were all the usual warnings on the radio for people to take it easy, but cars were driving faster than they should have done. A lorry ran into the back of her.' He paused, swallowing down the residual rage that people were always in a hurry and stupid enough to ignore the kind of conditions which led to accidents.

'When the paramedics arrived on the scene, they didn't think she'd make it. She had suffered massive head injuries.

They took her to hospital, and for a while it was touch and go.'

Lisi winced. What words could she say that would not sound meaningless and redundant? He must have heard the same faltering platitudes over and over again. She nodded and said nothing.

'Her body was unscathed,' he said haltingly. 'And so was her face—that was the amazing thing.' But it had been a cruel paradox that while she had lain looking so perfect in the stark hospital bed—the Carla he had known and loved had no longer existed. Smashed away by man's disregard for safety.

'I used to visit her every day—twice a day when I wasn't out of London.' Sitting there for hours, playing her favourite music, stroking the cold, unmoving hand and praying for some kind of response, some kind of recognition he was never to see again. Other than one slight movement of her fingers which had given everyone false hope. 'But she was so badly injured. She couldn't speak or eat, or even breathe for herself.'

'How terrible,' breathed Lisi, and in that moment her heart went out to him.

'The doctors weren't even sure whether she could hear me, but I talked to her anyway. Just in case.'

He met a bright kind of understanding in her eyes and he hardened his heart against it. 'I was living in a kind of vacuum,' he said heavily. 'And work became my salvation, in a way.' At work he had been forced to put on hold the human tragedy which had been playing non-stop in his life. He gave her a hard, candid look. 'Women came onto me all the time, but I was never...'

She sensed what was coming. 'Never what, Philip?'

'Never tempted,' he snarled. 'Never.' His mouth hardened. 'Until you.'

So she *was* the scapegoat, was she? Was that why he

had seemed so *angry* when he had walked back into her life? 'You make me sound like some kind of *femme fatale*,' she said drily.

He shook his head. That had been his big mistake. A complete misjudgement. Uncharacteristic, but understandable under the circumstances. 'On the contrary,' he countered. 'You seemed the very opposite of a *femme fatale*. I thought that you were sweet, and safe. Innocent. Uncomplicated.'

Achingly, she noted his use of the past tense.

'Until that night. When we had that celebratory drink.' He walked back over to the window and stared out unseeingly. 'I'd only had one drink myself—so I couldn't even blame the alcohol.'

Blame. He needed someone to blame—and she guessed that someone was her. 'So I was responsible for your momentary weakness, was I, Philip?'

He turned around and his face was a blaze of anger. 'Do you make a habit of getting half-cut and borrowing men's hotel rooms to sleep it off?' he ground out, because this had been on his mind for longer than he cared to remember. 'Do you often take off all your clothes and lie there, just waiting, like every man's fantasy about to happen?'

'Is that what you think?' she asked quietly, even though her heart was crashing against her ribcage.

'I'm not going to flatter myself that I was the first,' he said coldly. 'Why should I? You didn't act like it was a once-in-a-lifetime experience.'

His words wounded her—but what defence did she have? If she told him that it had *felt* like that, for her, then she would come over at best naive, and at worst—a complete and utter liar.

'I'll take that as a compliment,' she said, and regretted it immediately. 'I'm sorry,' she amended. 'I shouldn't be flippant when you're telling me all this.'

Oddly enough, her glib remark did not offend him. 'It was a long time ago,' he said heavily. 'I don't want to be wrapped up in cotton wool for the rest of my life.'

'Won't you tell me the rest?' she asked slowly, because she recognised that he was not just going to go away. And if he *was* around in her life—then how could they possibly form any kind of relationship to accommodate their son, unless she knew all the facts? However painful they might be.

He nodded. 'That night I left you I went straight to the hospital. The day before Carla had moved her fingers slightly and it seemed as if there might be hope.'

She remembered that his mood that day had been almost high. So that had been why. His wife had appeared to be on the road to recovery and he had celebrated life in the oldest way known to man. With her.

'But Carla lay as still as ever, hooked up to all the hospital paraphernalia of tubes and drips and monitors,' he continued.

He had sat beside her and been eaten up with guilt and blame and regret as he'd looked down at her beautiful but waxy lips which had breathed only with the aid of a machine. Carla hadn't recognised him, or had any idea of what he had done, and yet it had smitten him to the hilt that he had just betrayed his wife in the most fundamental way possible.

His mouth twisted. To love and to cherish. In sickness and in health. Vows he had made and vows he had broken.

He had always considered himself strong, and reasoned and controlled—and the weakness which Lisi had exposed in his character had come as an unwelcome shock to which had made him despise himself.

And a little bit of him had despised her, too.

'She died a few months later,' he finished, because what else was there to say? He saw her stricken expression and

guessed what had caused it. 'Oh, it wasn't as a result of
what you and I did, Lisi, if that's what you're thinking.'

'The thought had crossed my mind,' she admitted slowly.
'Even though I know it's irrational.'

Hadn't he thought the same thing himself? As though
Carla could have somehow known what he had done.

'What did you do?' she questioned softly.

There was silence in the big room before he spoke again.

'I went to pieces, I guess.' He saw the look of surprise
in her eyes. 'Oh, I functioned as before—I worked and I
ate and I slept—but it was almost as if it was happening
to another person. I think I was slowly going crazy. And
then Khalim came.'

'Khalim?' she asked hesitantly.

'Prince Khalim.' He watched as the surprise became
astonishment, and he shrugged. 'At the time he was heir to
a Middle-Eastern country named Maraban—though of
course he's ruler now.'

'How do you know him?' asked Lisi faintly.

'We were at Cambridge together—and he heard what
had happened and he came and took me off to Maraban
with him.'

'To live in luxury?'

He smiled at *this* memory as he shook his head. 'The
very opposite. He told me that the only way to live through
pain and survive it was to embrace it. So for two months
we lived in a tiny hut in the Maraban mountains. Just us.
No servants. Nothing. Just a couple of discreet bodyguards
lurking within assassination distance of him.'

Her eyes grew wide with fascination. 'And what did you
do?'

'We foraged for food. We walked for hours and sometimes rode horses through the mountains. At night we
would read by the light of the fire. And he taught me to
fight,' he finished.

'To *fight*?'

He nodded. 'Bare-knuckled. We used to beat hell out of each other!'

'And didn't he...*mind*?'

Philip shook his head. 'Out there, in the mountains—we were equals.' Indeed, he suspected that Khalim had learned as much from the experience as he had—for certainly the two men who had emerged from their self-imposed exile had been changed men.

She had wondered what had brought about the new, lean, hard Philip. Why he had looked so different—all the edges chiselled away. She swallowed. 'And then?'

'Then he offered me a job, working as his emissary. It took me all over the world.'

'And did you enjoy it?'

'I loved it.'

'But you left?'

He nodded.

'Why?'

'The time had come. Everything has its time of closure. Khalim fell in love with an English woman. Rose.'

His mouth curved into a warm and affectionate smile and Lisi felt the dagger of jealousy ripping through her.

'Khalim and I had developed the closeness of brothers—in so much as his position allowed. It was only right that Rose should have him all to herself once they were married.'

In all the time she had been listening to his story, Lisi had been entranced, but as he drew to the end of it reality reared its head once more.

She gave a little cough. 'Would you like to see upstairs now?'

'No, thanks—I've seen enough.'

Thank God! She nodded understandingly. 'Well, I'm sure

we'll be getting a lot more properties on the market—especially after Christmas.'

He gave a slow smile as he realised what she was thinking. 'You may have misunderstood me, Lisi,' he said silkily. 'I want this house and I want you to put an offer in.'

'But it's overpriced! You know it is!' she declared desperately. 'Ridiculously overpriced!'

He wondered whether she tried to put *other* buyers off in quite such an obvious way, but somehow doubted it. 'So Marian Reece told me.'

'And they've stated *unequivocally* that they can't possibly accept anything other than the full asking price.'

'Then offer it to them,' he said flatly.

She could not believe her ears. This was Philip Caprice speaking—the man famed for driving the hardest bargain in the property market! 'Are you serious?' she breathed.

He saw the way her lips parted in disbelief and he felt a wild urge to kiss them, to imprison her in his arms and to take the clips from her hair and have it tumble down over that masculine-looking jacket. His eyes slid down past the pencil skirt to the creamy tights which covered her long legs and that same wildness made him wonder what she would do if he began to make love to her.

Should he try? See if she would respond with passion and let him slide his hand all the way up her legs and touch her until she was begging him for more. He struggled to dampen down his desire.

'I've never been more serious in my life,' he said, and then his voice became clipped. 'Tell the vendors that my only condition is that I want *in* and I want them out. So let's tie up the deal as quickly as possible, shall we?'

If she could have had a wish at that moment, it would have been to have been given a huge sum of money—enough to buy back her own home herself instead of letting it go to Philip Caprice. Couldn't he guess how much she loved the place? Wasn't he perceptive enough to realise how heartbreaking she was going to find it, with *him* living here.

Or maybe he just didn't care.

He was walking around the room now, touching the walls with a proprietorial air she found utterly abhorrent. She gritted her teeth behind a forced smile. 'Very well. I'll get that up and running straight away.' There was a question in her eyes. 'Though it's going to need a lot of work to get it up to the kind of specifications I imagine you'll be looking for.'

His answering smile was bland. 'Just so.'

'You certainly couldn't expect to be in before Christmas. Probably not until springtime at the earliest,' she added hopefully.

Her wishes were beautifully transparent, but, unfortunately for her, they were not going to come true. 'Not Christmas, certainly,' he agreed, and saw her visibly relax. 'But I think spring is a rather pessimistic projection.'

'All the builders and decorators around here are booked up for *months* in advance!' she told him, trying to keep the note of triumph from her voice.

'Then I shall just have to bring people down from London, won't I?'

She glared at him. 'As you wish,' she said tightly. 'And now, if there's nothing further, I'll call into the office and then I really must get back—'

'To Tim?' he interjected softly.

How she wished he wouldn't use that distinctly possessive tone! He might be Tim's father—but the two had barely exchanged a few words. He couldn't just walk back into their lives unannounced and expect to be an equal partner!

'Yes, to Tim,' she said coldly, and began to walk towards

the hall, her high heels clip-clopping over the polished floorboards.

'Oh, Lisi?'

She stopped, something in his tone warning her that she was not going to like his *next* words, either. She turned round, wishing that he were ugly, and that he didn't have those piercing green eyes which could turn her knees to jelly. 'Yes?'

'We haven't discussed Christmas yet, have we?'

'Christmas?' she echoed stupidly. 'What about it?'

'I want to spend it with Tim.'

She fought down the urge to tell him that he could take a running jump, but she knew that open opposition would get her nowhere. Softly, softly it must be.

She put on her most reasonable smile. 'I'm afraid you can't. I'm really sorry.'

Yeah, she sounded *really* sorry. He kept his face impassive. 'Oh? And why's that?'

'Because we've already made arrangements for Christmas.'

'Then unmake them,' he said flatly. 'Or include me.'

She drew in a deep breath. 'We've arranged to have lunch with my friend Rachel and her son, Blaine—he's Tim's best friend. I couldn't possibly take you along with us!'

He thought about it. 'I'm supposed to be having lunch with my parents,' he reflected. 'But I'll drive down here afterwards. We can all have tea and Christmas cake together, can't we, Lisi?'

'*No!*'

'Why not?'

'Because…because he doesn't know who you are!'

He narrowed his eyes, but not before she had seen the flash of temper in them. 'You mean you haven't told him yet?'

'When?' she demanded angrily. 'In the hour I had this morning between waking up and being summoned into the office at your bidding?'

The accusation washed over him. 'I thought that it was important for you to see where I was buying.'

'Why?'

'Because eventually Tim will come to stay with me. Naturally.'

Feeling as though her world were splintering all around her, Lisi prayed that it didn't show. Keep calm, she told herself. He may be powerful and rich, but he can't just ride roughshod over your wishes. He can't.

She drew a deep breath.

'Listen, Philip—I can understand that you want to build a relationship with Tim—'

'How very good of you,' he put in sarcastically.

'But he doesn't know you properly, and until he does then I'm afraid that I cannot permit him to stay with you. In fact, he probably won't want to come up to the house without me.'

The expression on his face grew intent. 'I want bathtimes and bedtimes and all the normal things which fathers do, and if you think I'm cracking my skull on the ceiling of your cottage every time I stand up, then you've got another think coming!'

She opened her mouth to object and then shut it again, because she could see from his unshakable stance that to argue would be pointless. 'I can't see that happening for a long time,' she said coldly.

'We'll see.' He gave a bland smile. 'And in the meantime, I'll be around on Christmas afternoon. Shall we say around five?'

She couldn't bring herself to answer him, and so she nodded instead.

CHAPTER EIGHT

'TIM, darling—*please* don't eat any more—you'll be sick!'

'*One* more, Mum-mee!'

Lisi lunged towards him, but he had crammed another chocolate in his mouth before she could stop him. She took the stocking away from him firmly. 'That's enough chocolate!' she said sternly. 'We've got tea to get through next.' And her face fell.

Rachel leaned across the table, holding a bottle of port. 'Have a glass?' she suggested. 'You haven't got far to go, and it *is* Christmas Day!'

'You don't need to remind me,' said Lisi gloomily. She looked down at her son, who was busy licking chocolate off the inside of the wrapper. 'Put that down, darling, and go away and play with Blaine until it's time to go!'

To her relief, Tim went scampering off, and, after a swift glance at her wrist-watch, Lisi curled her feet up underneath her. Another hour until the avenging Caprice appeared on her doorstep. 'I could just go to sleep.' She yawned.

'On Christmas Day? Show me the mother of a child under ten who couldn't, and I'll show you a liar!' chortled Rachel, and then a look of concern criss-crossed her brow as she glanced across at her friend. 'You okay?'

Lisi shrugged. 'As okay as anyone can be when they're having their arm twisted.' She had told Rachel everything. She had seen no cause not to. There was no longer any point in keeping anything back. People would know—or guess—soon enough when she and Tim started traipsing down the lane for cosy afternoons and evenings with him!

'I still can't believe he's bought The Old Rectory,' said

Lisi crossly. 'And what is even more unbelievable is that he railroaded his lawyers into rushing through the deal. They complete in the New Year,' she finished. 'What a wonderful way to start the year—Philip Caprice firmly ensconced in my old family home.'

'I think it's rather romantic,' sighed Rachel.

'*Romantic?*' squeaked Lisi.

'Mmm. I can't imagine Dave doing something like that—even if he could afford to.'

'But you wouldn't want him to, would you?' asked Lisi, raising her eyebrows in surprise. 'I thought you said that if you never saw him again, it would be much too soon?'

Rachel shrugged and swirled her port around in the glass, so that it looked like a claret-coloured whirlpool. 'I suppose not. It's just that sometimes I get lonely—well, often, actually—and Christmas is the worst. Even if Dave wasn't the most wonderful husband in the world, at least he was *there*. I guess I miss having a man around the place.'

And that was the difference between them, thought Lisi—she had been content enough with her single status. Not that she had been anti-men, or anything like that—she just hadn't particularly missed having a partner. Until she reminded herself that she had never actually *had* a partner.

'I'd better think about making a move,' she said reluctantly, thinking how warm and cosy it was by Rachel's fireside.

Rachel nodded. 'You'll need to change.'

'Will I hell? There's nothing wrong with this dress!'

'Except that Tim has smeared chocolate all over it,' commented Rachel, with a smile.

Lisi looked down at her dress to see several brown, sticky thumbprints! She smiled at her friend. 'We've had a wonderful time today,' she said softly.

'Me, too.'

'Sure you won't come over for a drink later on?'

Rachel pulled a face and giggled. 'And face the daunting Philip Caprice after what you've told me about him? Er, I'll take a rain check, thanks, Lisi!'

Lisi packed up their presents in a carrier bag and wrapped Tim up warmly in his little duffle-coat and the brand-new bobble hat and matching scarf which Santa had brought him. She kissed Rachel and Blaine goodbye and they set off home in the crisp air.

Although it was only just past four, it was already pitch-black and there was a curious silence which had descended over the whole village. But then it *was* Christmas Day. Everyone was inside, making merry with their families—falling asleep after their big lunches, or playing games or watching weepie films on television.

She let them in and thought how cold the house was. Better light a fire. She drew the curtains and knelt in front of the brand-new toy railway track and began to push one of the trucks around it with her finger. 'Choo-choo,' she chanted. 'Choo-choo!'

'*Me*, Mum-mee! Me play with the train!'

She smiled. 'Go on, then, and I'll light the fire.'

She efficiently dealt with the logs and paper until the blaze was spitting and glowing. She put the big fire-guard in front of it, and went into her bedroom to change.

She had just stripped off her dress and was standing in her bra and pants when there was a knock at the front door and she glanced at her watch in horror. He couldn't be here! Not yet. But who else would it be on Christmas afternoon?

Saying a few choice words underneath her breath, she dragged on her dressing gown and opened the front door to find his tall figure dominating her view, blotting out the moon completely. He was carrying presents, but she barely gave them a second glance. Not only had he demanded this visit—he didn't even have the courtesy to be on time!

'You're early!' she accused.

He thought that no woman had the right to look as sexy as that—not when she was wearing an old flannelette dressing gown which had clearly seen better days—but Lisi did. Maybe it was something to do with the fact that he knew only too well what fabulous curves lay beneath its rather shapeless covering. Or because, for once, she had let her hair fall free and unfettered, spilling in abundant ebony streams to her waist. He had only ever seen it loose once before and he felt the blood begin to sing in his veins as he remembered just when.

'And a very happy Christmas to you, too,' he replied sardonically. 'I left my parents slightly ahead of schedule because they predicted snow—'

'Where?' asked Lisi, theatrically peering at the sky and then at the ground. 'I don't see any snow!'

He tried to take into consideration the fact that she had obviously been changing. 'My apologies,' he murmured. 'And now, do you think I can come inside? It's getting pretty chilly standing here.'

She held the door open ungraciously, but as she closed it on the bitter night she reminded herself that she had vowed there would be no unpleasantness. Not in front of Tim. And especially not today, of all days.

Philip lowered his voice. 'Have you told him?'

She bit her lip. 'Not yet.'

He looked at her in disbelief. 'Hell, Lisi—it's been a week!'

She shook her head. 'I just couldn't work out how to do it—it's not something you can come out with very easily and explain to a child of three. "By the way, darling—you know that strange man who turned up on the doorstep on your birthday? Well, he's your daddy!"'

'There's no need to make it sound so—'

'So like the truth?'

He sighed. 'So when *are* you going to tell him?'

'Not *me*, Philip. Us. You, mainly.'

'Me?'

'Yes, you! I'll leave you to do the talking—I'm sure you'll put it in the most diplomatic way possible.' Hot tears stung at her eyes and she turned away before he could see them. 'I just haven't got a clue what to say. *Tim!*' she called. 'Tim!'

'Is it Faver Chrissmas 'gain?' squeaked a little voice and Tim came pelting out and almost collided with the tall figure in the hall. He looked up at him with huge aquamarine eyes.

So like Lisi's eyes, thought Philip. 'Hello,' he said.

'You're Mum-mee's friend!' announced Tim triumphantly.

'That's right! And I've come to have tea with you both— if that's okay with you?'

'Did Faver Chrissmas bring you lots of presents?'

'Not lots,' said Philip gravely. 'Some.'

'I got lots!'

Philip smiled. 'Do you want to show me?'

Tim nodded excitedly and eyed the brightly wrapped parcels in Philip's arms with interest. 'Who are *those* presents for?' he asked coyly.

Philip laughed. 'They're for you. We'll open them when Mummy has changed out of her dressing gown.' He shot Lisi a questioning look and she realised that she had been standing there just gawping.

'I'll go and get changed.' She nodded, wondering just how he had always had the knack of seeming to be in charge!

She shut the bedroom door behind her, her heart thundering just with the knowledge that *he* was here, such a short distance away, and that she was standing in her underwear and looking at it critically in the mirror.

A functional peach-coloured bra and knickers which

didn't even match—but who cared? She certainly wasn't planning for him to get a glimpse of them.

But you would like him to, wouldn't you? taunted a mischievous voice in her head, and she shook her head at her reflection in the mirror.

She still wanted him, yes—but things were complicated enough as they were. Resuming a physical relationship with him would only add to those. She gave a wry smile as she pulled on a pair of old blue jeans and an ice-blue sweater. Who was she kidding? As if a few short hours in someone's arm could be defined as a relationship.

She raked the brush through her hair, tempted to tie it back—but decided that she couldn't leave him sitting out there waiting for her for much longer, so she left it loose.

She walked back into the sitting room to find that he was playing trains with Tim, and when he looked up his eyes were quietly smouldering.

'Is—everything okay?' she asked.

He steeled himself against the impact of her beauty, and jerked his head towards the roaring fire instead. He stood up and came to stand beside her, lowering his voice into an undertone so that only she could hear. 'Do you usually leave Tim here on his own, while you titillate yourself in the next room?'

For a moment she didn't quite get his drift, and when she did her mouth set itself into a mulish line. So he thought he could walk back into their lives and start criticising her skills as a mother, did he?

'I was hardly titillating,' she answered icily, gesturing to her casual clothes with an angry, jerking motion. 'Just getting changed out of a dress which Tim had liberally smeared with chocolate.'

'Lisi, he was alone in the room with a fire—for heaven's sake! Do you really think that's safe for a three-year-old?'

The injustice of it stung her. 'I'll go and put the kettle

on,' she said, between gritted teeth, and marched out to the kitchen.

He followed her, as she had known he would, but remained standing in the doorway so that he could keep an eye on the toddler who was still engrossed in his new train-set.

He saw the fury in the stiff set of her shoulders. 'Listen, I wasn't meaning to be judgemental,' he said softly.

She clicked the kettle on and turned round, her eyes spitting pale blue fire. 'Like hell you weren't!'

'I was only just pointing out—'

'Well, don't!' she said, in a low, shaking voice. 'Do you think I've brought him up in a house which has a fire and not taught him that he is never to go near it?'

'Listen—'

'No, *you* listen! What do you think it's like as a single parent living with a little boy? Have you ever stopped to think about it?'

'Actually, no—but then it wasn't number one on my list of priorities. Until now.'

She met the quizzical green stare fearlessly. 'Even taking a bath has to be planned with all the attention you would give to a military campaign!' she declared. 'As for going to the bathroom—well, you don't want to know!'

He glanced back towards Tim and then at her again. It had never occurred to him. Why should it? People rarely considered the practical problems of child-rearing unless they were contemplating taking the plunge themselves. He sighed. 'You're right. I had no right—'

'No, you didn't!' she agreed furiously. 'You have only to take a look at him to realise that he is a happy, contented little boy. The world is full of dangers, Philip—and I have had to teach him about them all. Never to talk to strangers. Never to approach a dog that might bite him. The fact that the roads aren't safe—' She saw him flinch, and wished she hadn't chosen an example which would remind him of Carla. 'I'm sorry.'

He shook his head. 'The cotton-wool remark still holds true. I shouldn't have said what I did.'

'No, you shouldn't!' She pointed to the kitchen cupboards with an air of frustration. 'I've had all these cupboards child-proofed so that he can't get into them. I don't leave bottles of bleach lying around the place for him to find—and there's a stair-gate at the foot of the stairs! Please credit me with a little more sense and caring, Philip! He has had it drummed into him from the word go that fires are dangerous and must be treated with respect and caution—and that Mummy is the only person who touches the fire.'

He watched her warm the pot and then make the tea. He had been lucky in a way, he guessed. She could have been the kind of mother who didn't care—who saw Tim as a mistake who had taken away her youth and her freedom. But she had created a home for him, a warm and loving home, he realised.

She was right. You had only to look at the child to see that he was happy and contented and well cared for. Stimulated, too—to judge from his conversation.

'Can I do anything?' he asked.

She couldn't resist it. 'Better go back in and keep your eye on Tim,' she said sweetly. 'I can manage here.'

He nodded, and his gaze swept over her, beguiling her and capturing her in its intense green light. 'And we'll tell him?'

Lisi swallowed. She couldn't keep putting it off. *They* couldn't keep putting it off. 'I have no choice, do I?' she asked quietly, but noticed that he didn't bother answering that—he didn't need to—just turned away and walked back into the sitting room.

She carried the tea-tray through and brought in Christmas cake and mince pies and slices of Stollen.

Philip looked up as she began to unload it all onto the table and gave a rueful smile. 'Not sure if I can eat again—at least until the New Year.'

She forced herself to be conversational. They were shortly to drop the biggest bombshell into Tim's life—let him see that his mother and his father didn't actually hate one another.

'Did your mother feed you up?'

He nodded. 'It's my first Christmas here for years—in Maraban they don't celebrate it.'

Tim looked up. 'Where's Malaban?' he chirped.

'Maraban,' corrected Philip, and his eyes softened as he looked down at the interested face of his son. 'It's a country in the Middle East. A beautiful land with a great big desert—do you know what a desert is, Tim?'

He shook his dark head, mesmerised.

'It's made of sand—lots of sand—and only the very toughest of plants can grow there.'

'What telse?' asked Tim. 'In Malaban?'

Philip smiled. 'Oh, there are fig trees and wild walnut trees, and the mountain slopes are covered in forests of juniper and pistachio trees—'

'What's st-stachio tree?' piped up Tim. 'Like an apple tree?'

Philip shook his head. 'Not really. A pistachio is a nut,' he explained. 'A delicious pale green nut in a little shell—'

'He's too young for nuts!' put in Lisi immediately.

He guessed that he deserved that, and nodded. 'Oh, and there are lots of animals there, too,' he said. 'Jackals and wild boar and rare, pink deer.'

Tim's eyes were like saucers, thought Lisi. He probably thought that Philip was concocting a wonderful fairy-tale

land, and, come to think of it, that was exactly what it
sounded like.

'Do you live there?' asked Tim.

'I did. But not any more.'

'Why?'

'Because it was time for me to come back to England.'

'Why?'

'Tim—' began Lisi, but Philip shook his head.

'I used to work for a prince.'

Lisi looked at Tim—now he really *did* think that this
was a story!

'A *real* prince?'

'Uh-huh. Prince Khalim. Only the prince got married and
so it was time for me to move on.'

Tim nodded solemnly. 'Will you play trains with me?'

He met her eyes across the room. *Now*, they urged her,
and Lisi knew that she must begin this particular story. She
took time pouring tea, and gave Tim a beaker of juice, and
then she went to sit down on the floor next to both of them
and cleared her throat.

'Tim, darling?'

A train was chugged along the track by a small, chubby
finger.

'Tim? Look at Mummy, darling.'

His long-lashed eyes locked on hers and she felt the almost painfully overwhelming love of motherhood. She
steadied her breathing. 'Do you remember that once you
asked me why you hadn't got a daddy?'

Philip stilled as Tim nodded.

'And I told you that he had gone away a long time ago
and that I wasn't sure if he was ever coming back?'

Again Tim nodded, but this time Philip flinched.

'Well…' She hesitated, but in her heart she knew that
there was no way to say this other than using clear and

truthful words which a three-year-old would understand. 'Well, he did come back, darling and…'

Tim was staring up at Philip. 'Are *you* my daddy?'

He felt the prick of tears at the back of his eyes as he nodded. 'Yes, Tim,' he answered, his voice thickening. 'I am.'

Tim nodded, and bent his head to push the train around the track once more.

'Tim?' questioned Lisi tentatively, because she couldn't see the expression on his face, and when he lifted it it was unusually calm and accepting, as if he were told things like this every day of the week.

'An' are you going 'way again? To Malaban?' he asked casually, as if it didn't really matter, but Lisi could tell from that oddly fierce look of concentration on his little face that it did.

Philip shook his head, unable to speak for a moment. 'No, Tim,' he said eventually. 'I'm not going anywhere. I'm going to buy a house in the village and see you as many weekends as your mummy will let me.'

He met her gaze with a question in his eyes.

So if I don't let him, then I'm the big, bad witch, she thought bitterly.

'An' are you and Mummy getting married?'

The silence which greeted this remark made Lisi as uncomfortable as she had ever felt in her life. She shook her head. 'Oh, no, darling—nothing like that!'

'Why?'

Oh, *why* had she brought him up to be so alert and questioning? To pursue every subject until he was satisfied with the answers?

'Because not all mummies and daddies live together, now, do they?' she asked gently. 'Blaine's daddy doesn't live with Blaine's mummy any more, does he?'

'That's 'cos he's livin' with a witch!'

'A *witch*?' squeaked Lisi in confusion.

'That's what Blaine heard his Mum-mee say!'

Philip bit back a smile. He suspected that the word had been 'bitch'. 'I would like to get to know you a little better, if that's okay with you, Tim. And Mummy and I will be great friends, won't we, Lisi?'

'Oh, yes,' she agreed, but her eyes flashed him a different message entirely. 'Definitely.'

'So what have you got to say to all that?' asked Philip, and, unable to resist it for any longer, reached out his hand to ruffle the silky blackness of the little head.

Tim put his train down and looked up at her. 'Can I have more chocolate, Mum-mee?' he asked.

The question shattered the tension in the atmosphere, and Philip and Lisi both burst out laughing, their eyes colliding in a brief expression of shared joy that made her heart thunder beneath her breast. It's just relief, she told herself fiercely—nothing to do with her. Tim has accepted him, and he's got what he wanted.

Though she wouldn't have been human if she hadn't half hoped that he wouldn't.

She put more logs on the fire and then watched while Philip wholeheartedly entered into playing with Tim. For a man with little or no experience of children, she was forced to the conclusion that he was very good with them. If Tim's reaction was anything to go by.

He stared wide-eyed while Philip made a horse out of some balloons and then blew up some others and let the air whizz out of them in a sound which had Tim collapsing in peals of giggles.

She had taken all the remains of the tea back out to the kitchen, and when she returned it was to find them playing rough and tumble on the rug and she realised that there were some things that fathers could do, which mothers never could.

They both looked up as she walked in, both flushed with pleasure but tinged with a kind of guilt—identical expressions on their faces. How could I ever have thought that they weren't alike? thought Lisi with a touch of despair. The colouring might be hers, but Marian was right: he *did* have bits of Philip—lots of Philip—in him. Of course he did.

Gently, Philip lowered Tim back down onto the carpet, from where he had been sitting on his shoulders, and stood up.

'Am I interrupting your routine, Lisi?'

So I am the bringer of routine and order, and he provides the fun, does he? thought Lisi. Or was she being unfair?

Philip saw the look of discomfort which had pleated her brow and understood exactly what had caused it. She had agreed to let him get to know Tim, but she had probably not anticipated what a success it would be.

Neither had he.

A different child might have refused to answer him. Or spoken in sulky monosyllables. Not chatted so openly and with such obvious interest. And much of that must be down to her.

'It's your bathtime, Tim,' she said, with a quick glance at her watch, and then forced herself to meet Philip's gaze. 'Unless you'd like to?'

He would like to. He wanted to bath his son more than he had wanted anything in a long time, but he recognised that Lisi might now be feeling the outsider. He shook his head. 'No, you do it. He's used to you.'

'Philip do it!' demanded Tim, unwilling to lose sight of his new friend.

Philip shook his head. 'I have to make a few phone calls,' he said.

She carried Tim to the bathroom and wondered who he was phoning on Christmas Day. Obviously somebody very close to him. He had told her that he wasn't married—but that didn't preclude a girlfriend, did it?

But he kissed you, a voice reminded her. He kissed you passionately and told you that he still wanted you—would he betray a second woman if he got the opportunity?

He isn't going to *get* the opportunity, she told herself as she squirted bubble bath into the running water and watched it become big, foamy clouds. No matter how much *she* wanted to—it wasn't right. There was too much bitter history behind them and only potential heartache lay ahead if she was crazy enough to give in.

She let Tim splash around in the bath for ages, wondering whether Philip would stick around. He might just get the message and go. But he was still there, talking in a low voice into his mobile phone as she carried a sleepy, pyjama-clad Tim past the sitting room to his bedroom and tenderly put him into bed.

'Have you had a lovely Christmas, darling?' she asked him softly.

'Yes, Mum-mee.' His eyes opened wide. 'Is Philip coming tomorrow?'

She sincerely hoped not, but she made herself smile a placating smile. 'We'll see. Okay?'

He nodded against the pillow, letting his eyelids drift down, and then automatically stuck his thumb in his mouth.

He was almost asleep, but story-telling was sacrosanct and Lisi put her hand out and pulled out the nearest book, which just happened to be *Cinderella*. How very appropriate, she thought wryly, and began to read.

She waited until she was certain that he was sound asleep, then reluctantly made her way back to where Philip lay sprawled on the floor in front of the fire, his phone-call finished. He had, she noted with surprise, put all the toys neatly away, so that the room for once didn't look as though a bomb had hit it. She had never had anyone do that for her before.

She hovered in the doorway, unsure of what to say or do. She could hardly ask him to leave. 'Can I get you a drink of something?'

He heard the lack of enthusiasm in her voice. 'One for the road?' he suggested sardonically.

She shrugged. 'If you like.'

He shook his head, got to his feet and went over to where she stood. 'No, thanks. You must be tired.'

Again she had the sense of him dominating the room, of his raw masculinity exuding from every pore of that spectacular body. In an effort to distract herself, she said, rather awkwardly, 'It went well, I think, didn't it?'

'Yes.' He was aching to touch her, but he realised that he owed her something. 'Thank you, Lisi,' he said simply. 'For letting me.'

She wasn't going to read anything into what he said. This was a purely practical arrangement, solely for the welfare of Tim. 'I had no choice, did I?' she questioned tartly. 'I imagine that if I'd refused you would have sought some kind of legal redress.'

Her brittle words extinguished the warmth he had been feeling, but did absolutely nothing to put out the fire in his groin. He knew he shouldn't do this, but something drove him on—a need to see that cold, frozen look wiped clean off her beautiful face.

He reached his hand out to cup her chin, his thumb and his forefinger stroking along its outline almost reflectively.

Lisi shivered. Where he touched her, he set her on fire. She knew that she should move away but something was stopping her and she wasn't sure what. 'Please don't,' she whispered.

Her lacklustre words belied the shining darkness in her

eyes and the need to kiss her overpowered him. 'You want me to,' he whispered back.

'No—'

But he kissed the word away with his mouth, feeling its unresisting softness become as hard and as urgent as his.

She rocked against him—all the cold and the hunger and frustration she had experienced letting itself go as his mouth explored hers with a thoroughness guaranteed to set her on the path to inevitable seduction. She felt the prickling sensation as her breasts grew heavy and aroused, and a long-forgotten molten sweetness began to build up at the very core of her.

Her mind was spinning. She wanted to burrow her hands up beneath his sweater and to feel the warm bare silk of his skin once more, but she had been a mother for too long to let her own wishes be paramount. For one split-second she imagined what could—*would*—happen next, if she didn't put a stop to it.

They couldn't possibly let things progress naturally and make love in front of the fire—Tim might walk in at any second. Which left going to her bedroom and the embarrassment of silently getting undressed, of having to keep their voices—and moans—low, just in case they woke Tim.

She tore herself away.

What was she *thinking* of? She didn't want to make love to him!

He had never been so frustrated in his life. 'Lisi—'

'No!' She shook her head vehemently. 'I am *not* going to have sex with you, Philip. The first time was bad enough—'

'I beg to differ,' he murmured, thinking how magnificent she looked when she was angry.

She carried on as if he hadn't interrupted. 'When I discovered you were married I felt like hell—but at least I thought that you had been so overcome with desire that you had been unable to stop yourself. Desire for *me*,' she finished deliberately.

His eyes narrowed as he tried to work out exactly what she was getting at. 'I'm not sure that I understand you, Lisi.'

'It didn't even have to be me, did it? I was just a vessel for your more basic needs!' she carried on wildly. 'Anyone would have done! Your wife was sick and you were frustrated—that's what really happened, isn't it, Philip?'

He went rigid. 'My God,' he said, in disgust. 'You really know how to twist the knife, don't you?' He picked up his overcoat and walked to the front door and opened it without another word.

She wanted to call after him, to take back the hateful words which had seemed to come pouring out of her mouth like poison, but one look at the icy expression on his face as he turned round made her realise that it would be a futile gesture.

He gave a cold, hard smile. 'If your idea was to insult me so much that I would go away and never come back again, then you have just very nearly succeeded,' he said.

And, bizarrely, the thought that her hurt pride and resentment might have cost Tim a relationship with his father wounded her far more than anything else. 'Philip—'

He shook his head. 'Please don't say any more—I don't think I could take it. I'd better just tell you that this particular campaign won't work. You see, Tim is far more important to me than the obvious loathing you feel for me. I'm here, Lisi—and I'm here for the duration. Better get used to it.'

And without another word, he was gone.

CHAPTER NINE

MARIAN Reece pursed her lips together in a silent whistle. 'Good heavens—just how much do you think he's spending on that property?'

Lisi looked up from her computer, and, lo and behold—another upmarket van was cruising past the office towards The Old Rectory. What was it this time? Lisi peered out of the window and read from the gold lettering on the side of the van. 'Tricia Brady; Superior Interiors'. 'He's obviously having the place decorated now,' she said, with a sigh.

Marian's eyes goggled. 'And how!' she exclaimed. 'I've heard of her—she must have come all the way down from London. This early in the New Year, too—I'm surprised she wasn't fully booked.'

'She probably was,' said Lisi gloomily. 'She's probably got long blonde hair and legs up to her armpits and Philip probably just outrageously batted those beautiful eyes at her and she probably cancelled every engagement in her diary!'

Marian gave her a shrewd look. 'Do I detect a sign of the green-eyed monster?' she asked.

Lisi replaced the gloomy look with a fairly good impression of devil-may-care. 'Not at all,' she said airily. 'I expect that's exactly what happened. Either that or he's paying well over the odds.'

'He must be,' said Marian. 'It's only the middle of January—and already he's transformed the place! I've never known builders be quite so willing, or so efficient!'

'No,' said Lisi tonelessly.

Marian shot her a glance. 'How's it going between you two?'

'It's not between *us* two,' replied Lisi carefully. 'The only relationship I have with Philip is that we happen to share a child.'

'Only?' spluttered Marian, then sighed. 'And is it…amicable?'

Lisi sighed. She had vowed to keep it that way, but ever since her outburst on Christmas night he had been keeping his distance from her. He had been round three times to see Tim, and the atmosphere had been awkward, to say the least.

For a start, the house always seemed so much smaller when he was in it, and the unspoken tension between them was so strong that Lisi was surprised that Tim wasn't made uncomfortable by it.

But no. Tim didn't seem to notice anything or anyone—he was so enraptured by the man he had almost immediately taken to calling 'Daddy'.

The first time he'd done it, Lisi had spoken to him gently at bedtime that night. 'You don't have to say Daddy if you don't want to,' she suggested gently. 'Philip won't mind being called just Philip, I'm sure.'

He didn't answer and she wasn't even sure if he had registered her words or not, but he obviously had, because at the end of Saturday's visit Philip paused on his way out of the front door, his eyes spitting with undisguised rage.

'Did you tell Tim not to call me Daddy?' he demanded.

She sighed. 'That's not what I said at all.'

'That's what he told me!'

She kept her voice low, tried to stay calm, though heaven only knew—it wasn't easy. 'I merely suggested that he might find it easier to call you Philip. For the time being—'

'Until *you* decided that the time was right, I suppose?'

he questioned witheringly. 'And when would that be, Lisi? Some time? Never?'

She stuck to her guns. She was not going to let his hostility get to her. *She was not.* 'I just didn't want him to feel that he was being railroaded into anything—'

'By me?'

'Not by anyone!' she retorted, her voice rising. 'It's just such a huge thing to suddenly start calling you Daddy!'

He had moved a little closer, his body language just short of menacing—so how come she didn't feel in the least bit intimidated by it? How come she wanted to tell him to forget their stupid rows and to kiss her like he had done on Christmas night?

'Or is it just that *you* feel threatened by it, Lisi?'

'Threatened? Me?'

'Yes, you! Unwilling to share him, are you? Do you want all his love for yourself, is that it?'

'Oh, don't talk such rubbish!' she snapped. 'I was thinking of *Tim*!'

'So you claim. When it would clearly suit you far more to have me as far away from you as possible! Well, just don't use him as a pawn in our little disagreement—do you understand, Lisi!'

Little disagreement? If this was his idea of a little disagreement, then she'd hate to enter into all-out warfare with him!

Marian was still staring at her with a question in her eyes, and Lisi shook her head.

'No,' she said slowly, in answer to her boss's question. 'It isn't exactly what I'd call amicable—even though that's what we both wanted originally.'

'You should talk to him about it!' urged Marian.

But there didn't seem anything left to say, thought Lisi as she picked up the telephone which had just begun to ring. 'Good afternoon, Homefinders Agency.'

'Lisi? It's Philip.'

Of course it was Philip—no one else had a voice that rich, that deep, that dark. 'Hello, Philip,' she said, cursing her body's reaction as she felt the inevitable prickle of excitement. 'What can I do for you?'

Silently, he cursed. How shocked she would be if he answered that question truthfully.

'I'm up at the house,' he said.

'*Here?*' she questioned stupidly, her heart racing. 'In the village?'

'Yeah. I drove up early this morning.'

He was here, just down the road and he hadn't even bothered to tell her he was coming. Just why that should hurt so much she didn't know, but it did.

'I'm having the house decorated,' he was saying. 'Someone is over here now with some sample fabrics.'

She certainly wasn't going to pander to his ego by telling him that she had seen the plush van driving by. 'Really?' she asked pleasantly.

'Really,' he echoed, mocking her insincere tone. 'And I wondered whether you were free for half an hour?'

Her pulse began to race. 'Why?'

She could be so damned abrupt, he thought. 'I didn't know if you wanted to choose some colours for Tim's room.'

Time stopped. He seemed to be speaking in some strange, terrible language. 'T-Tim's room?' she croaked.

Something in the way she said it made him want to offer reassurance, until he remembered her monstrous accusation on Christmas night, and he hardened his heart against the tremor in her voice. Did she think that *he* didn't have feelings, too?

'That's right. He will *need* his own room, Lisi—surely you realise that?'

The only thing she realised was that she was fighting to

control her breath. 'I have to discuss this with you, and we can't do it on the phone,' she said.

'Then come up to the house.'

'I'm working.'

'Doesn't Marian owe you a few hours? For your un-scheduled work when I demanded that you show me around the rectory?'

'I'll ask her,' she said, in a low voice. 'I can't promise anything.'

His voice sounded noncommittal. 'Suit yourself. It's up to you, Lisi—you're the one who wants to talk.'

She put the phone down, feeling close to tears, and saw Marian looking at her with concern.

'Philip?' she asked.

'How did you guess?'

'Normal clients don't usually leave the agent looking as though the bottom has just fallen out of their world.'

Maybe it just had. Lisi cleared her throat. 'Marian—would it be possible to take an hour off? I need to talk to Philip and he's up at the rectory.'

'Of course it would.' Marian hesitated. 'Listen, my dear—have you thought about consulting a lawyer?'

Lisi shook her head. 'There's no point—it would achieve precisely nothing. He isn't being unreasonable. Tim adores him. He's his father—by law he is *allowed* contact. It's just me who has the problem with it.'

Marian nodded. 'Take as long as you need.'

Lisi gathered up her coat and wrapped herself up in it, but once outside it seemed to offer little protection against the bitter wind, although maybe it was the bitter heartache which was making her teeth chatter.

She trudged up the lane to The Old Rectory, and for a moment she stood stock-still with amazement, for she had seen the comings and goings of various vans and contrac-tors, but had deliberately stayed away from the place, telling herself that it would be too traumatic to see her former home being completely changed.

But her amazement was tinged with admiration, because, whatever Philip was doing inside the house, on the outside, at least—his taste could not be faulted.

The exterior had been painted a cool, pale grey and all the mildew had been removed. Window frames were gleaming, as was the newly painted front door, and the garden had obviously been lovingly attacked by experts.

The front door was slightly ajar, and when she received no reply to her knock she pushed it open and walked into the hall where another shock awaited her. The walls were a deep, vibrant scarlet—red as holly berries—and the floor-boards gleaming, with an exquisite long, silk runner in shades of deepest cobalt and scarlet and jade.

It looked utterly beautiful, she thought, and a lump rose in her throat as she called.

'Hello?'

'Hello, Lisi,' came a voice from upstairs. 'Come on up—we're up here.'

We? And then she remembered the interior design van.

With reluctant feet she made her way slowly upstairs in the direction of the voices she could hear speaking and laughing, and she felt a wave of objection that he should feel happy enough to laugh while her world seemed to be caving in.

To her horror, the voices were coming from the direction of a room she knew only too well—her old childhood bed-room—and her heart sank even further. Had he known, or guessed, she wondered, or was it simply coincidence which had made Philip select that particular room for Tim?

Drawing a deep breath, she walked straight in, and then stopped.

Two heads were bent close over a swatch of fabrics—one dark and nut-brown, the other blonde, and Lisi almost gave a hollow laugh. She had imagined Tricia Brady to be blonde with legs up to her armpits, and in that she had been uncannily accurate—but she had imagined the blonde hair to have come out of a bottle and for an aging face to be caked in heavy make-up.

But this woman fulfilled none of those criteria.

Her shiny blonde hair was fair and pale and completely natural, and when she lifted her head at the sound of Lisi's footsteps she didn't appear to be wearing any make-up at all. But then she didn't need to—skin that flawless and china-blue eyes that saucer-like did not need any help from nature to enhance them.

She was dressed practically and yet stunningly—in a pair of butter-soft suede trousers which must have cost what Lisi earned in a month. A cream silk shirt and a sheepskin-lined waistcoat completed the look and Lisi shuddered to think what her off-the-peg department store workaday suit must look like in comparison.

Philip smiled, but the expression on his face was as cool as it had been since Christmas. 'Lisi, hi,' he said. 'This is Tricia Brady—she's helping me with decor for the house.'

She's helping me. It didn't sound like a strictly working relationship, did it? thought Lisi indignantly. He could have said, Tricia is the designer, or, Tricia is working for me.

'Hello,' she said, thinking how wooden her voice sounded. 'I'm pleased to meet you.'

'Me, too.' Tricia grinned. 'I would shake hands, but my fingers are freezing—I keep telling Philip to turn the heating up, but he won't listen!'

'That's because people tend to go to sleep if it's too warm. Not good—but especially not good for people who are working,' he responded drily, but flashed her an answering smile.

Lisi felt sick, but she guessed that this was something she was going to have to get used to. If it wasn't Tricia it would be someone else. Some beautiful, expensively dressed woman who would temporarily or permanently share Philip's life one day.

And become a surrogate mother to Tim while he was here, she reminded herself, gritting her teeth behind a smile which pride forced her to make.

'Lisi is the mother of my son,' explained Philip. 'And so I thought she could give us some input on colours and fabrics.'

It was the coldest and most distancing description he could have given her—and yet, when she thought about it, how else could he have put it? She wasn't his girlfriend—current *or past*.

Pulling herself together, she walked over and looked down at the swatch of fabrics which Tricia was still holding. 'May I?' she asked pleasantly, and Tricia handed it to her.

She pretended to lose herself in them, though her mind was only half on the task—but she had spotted immediately the one which Tim would like the most.

'This one,' and she jabbed at the brightly coloured piece of material which depicted Mickey Mouse dancing all over it.

'Lisi likes Disney,' Philip explained with a smile, thinking how jerky and unnatural her movements were. 'She always has done, haven't you, Lisi?'

He was remembering her birthday cake, and so was she. That innocent start to a supposed friendship which had brought so much heartache in its wake. She nodded. 'Wh-what colour are you planning to do the walls?'

Tricia peered down at the fabric and pointed a perfect fingernail at several of the colours. 'We could pick out one of these shades,' she suggested and turned her head. 'What do you think, Phil?'

Phil?

Phil?

Lisi wanted to scream and to demand what right she had to call him by a nickname that *she* had never heard used before, but there was absolutely no point at all. Tricia could call him anything she liked, and probably did—in bed at night when he was making mad, passionate love to her.

'I like the...I like the yellow.' She swallowed.

'Mmm!' Tricia smiled. 'Perfect! Sunny and positive—and with all that glorious light flooding in—' She waved an expansive arm at the window. 'The room will look irresistible!' She shot a look at Philip, and her eyes glimmered. 'We could do it in the same colour as your London dining room, in fact—or would you rather something different down here?'

'Something a touch brighter, perhaps?' he murmured as Lisi turned abruptly away.

So Tricia had decorated his other home, too, had she? That was a pretty big compliment to pay a woman, no matter that she was being paid for her skills. To be selected to choose paints and fabrics for a man as discerning as Philip must mean that he rated her very highly indeed.

Lisi walked over to the window and looked out, the way she had done countless times before, as a child. She used to sit on the ledge for hours and watch the change as each new season came upon the garden, though she could never remember a scene so bare and unforgiving as the one which lay outside today.

'Shall we tackle the main bedroom today?' Tricia was asking.

Philip was watching Lisi and saw the way that her body had stiffened and some pernicious devil made him want to take Tricia up on her offer, but he decided against it.

'Not today, thanks, Trish,' he said casually. 'I have a few things I need to discuss with Lisi.'

'Oh. Okay. Well, call me later, if you like, and we'll sort out what needs doing. Nice to have met you, Lisi!'

Lisi turned around, wishing that her features would stop feeling as if they were made out of stone. 'Nice to have met you, too,' she managed.

There was silence in the room while Tricia gathered up her samples and put them all in a soft leather case, then she stood on tiptoe and kissed first Philip's right cheek, and then his left.

'See ya!' She smiled. 'I'll let myself out.'

'I'll call you,' he promised.

Lisi studied the floorboards with intense interest and not a word was spoken as they heard Tricia running down the stairs and the front door slamming behind her.

'Lisi?' he questioned softly.

She lifted her eyes to find herself imprisoned in a cool green gaze and her cheeks flooded with heat as she gave into the unwelcome but inevitable.

I want him, she thought suddenly, and the tip of her tongue flicked out to lick at the sudden unbearable dryness of her lips. I always have and I always will—and I can't bear the thought of anyone else having him. If he still wants me—*if*—then who on earth am I benefitting by turning him down? He is tied to me through Tim, she told herself with a fierce, primitive feeling of possession—and he will always be tied to me.

Now what was she playing at? he wondered. Why was she giving him that flushed and glittering look as though she wanted him to go and take her in his arms—especially as she had made so clear on Christmas night that physical closeness was the very last thing on her mind. Damn her! he thought, feeling his body immediately reacting to what looked like an unmistakable invitation in her eyes.

She didn't break the stare, just carried on looking at him, feeling her body begin to flower with need as his eyes darkened and then narrowed in a slowly dawning comprehension.

'Lisi?' he said again, only now his voice had thickened to honey. 'What the hell do you think you're doing?'

She wasn't going to play games; there was no time for games, and even if there were—wouldn't games be totally inappropriate between a couple who had been through what they had been through?

She moistened her lips again and saw the dull flush of awareness arrow up the carved cheekbones. 'Is Tricia *just* your designer?' she asked.

Her question told him everything. She was jealous. *Jealous!* He felt the heady flood of triumph as he realised that now he had her exactly where he wanted her.

'And if she is?'

The instant denial she had been preying for had not materialised, but his ambiguous question did nothing but fuel the fire which was slowly building inside her.

'Yes, or no?'

'What's it to you, Lisi? Don't you like me having women friends?'

'No!' The word shot out all by itself before she could stop it.

He could see the tension building in her—he would build it and build it until it all came rushing out and she would be unable to stop it. His question was silky. 'Why not?'

Damn him! Was he going to make her beg? She wanted him, yes, but she would never, ever beg. Her breathing was so shallow and erratic that she could barely get the words out. 'You know why not.'

Oh, yes, he knew. He could tell just by looking at her. She shouldn't be able to appear so damned sexy—not in that dull, chain-store suit with her hair scraped right back off her face. Some men might have been turned on by Tricia's blonde, pampered perfection—but he wanted this complex, beguiling woman who could not disguise the hunger in her eyes.

'Come here,' he ordered softly.

Pride forgotten, she went to him, staring up at him with wide eyes, praying for him to take the next step and to pull her into his arms. But he did not touch her. Not straight away. His eyes were mocking her and enchanting her, his lips curved into a predatory smile.

'What do you want, Lisi? Tell me.'

Peace of mind, that was what she wanted—and she suspected that she would never get it with Philip Caprice in her life, in whatever capacity. She tipped her head to one side and wondered whether she could break *him*.

'Don't you know?' she responded shakily.

Something snapped inside him as he realised that he had wasted enough time. Tease her too much and she might just turn on her high heels and walk right out of here and he might never get another opportunity to discover whether she was as dynamic as he remembered, or whether time had distorted the memory and made it into something it wasn't.

He reached to her hair and removed the restraining clip and her hair tumbled free. 'Beautiful,' he murmured unsteadily as he pulled her into his arms and bent his head and she could feel his hot breath on her face.

'Are you jealous, Lisi?' he taunted. 'Jealous of Tricia?'

Jealous of every woman who might end up in his arms, like this. 'Yes,' she whispered.

His laugh was a low sound of victory as he bent his mouth to hers, teasing it open with the elusive flicker of his tongue, and Lisi closed her eyes and gave into it, snaking her hands up to the broad shoulders as he levered her up close to him.

He could feel her breasts pushing against him—their fullness growing by the second—and something primal exploded inside him in a ferment of desire so blisteringly hot that he shuddered in its power, scarcely aware of his actions as he began to feverishly unbutton her suit jacket.

She knew exactly what he was doing, and that she ought to stop him, that they shouldn't be doing this now, here, but the moment his hand cupped at her breast Lisi knew she was lost.

'Philip,' she cried.

Through the mists of wanting, her broken little cry penetrated. 'What?'

She shook her head. 'Philip, Philip, Philip,' she said, over and over again, and his name tasted as delicious as the warm lips which were plundering hers so expertly, so that she felt as if she were drowning in sheer forbidden pleasure.

He pushed the jacket from her shoulders and it fell to the floor, and then he unbuttoned her white blouse and sucked in a shivering breath as he looked down at her breasts. Rich, ripe breasts, covered by some washed-out looking bra which had clearly seen better days. But none of that mattered, not when each tight little bud was so clearly defined.

With a small moan he reached his hand round her back and unclipped the bra in a fluid gesture until it dropped redundantly to join the jacket, and her breasts were free.

She jerked her head back with a moan as she felt the first hot lick of his tongue teasing each nipple into near-painful awareness. He was unbuttoning her skirt now and sliding the zip down and she wanted him to, couldn't wait for him to touch her where she so squirmingly needed to be touched. The room was cool, but all she could feel was the heat of his hands and his mouth as they trailed paths of delight over the skin he was swiftly uncovering.

She was down to her panties and tights now, and Philip pulled impatiently at his belt, silently groaning at the nec-

essary delay of getting free from this damned clothing. Her
fingers were scrabbling at his sweater and he momentarily
moved away from her so that he could haul it over his head,
and pulled her back again so that her breasts nudged so
enchantingly against his bare chest.

She was clumsily jerking at the zip now and he shook
his head, stilling her hand and moving it away while he
dealt with it, because he was so aroused that it needed a
man's hand to protect his straining hardness.

Shoes and socks and boxers were kicked and pulled off
and he unceremoniously hoicked her tights and panties off
before tossing them disdainfully into the corner. 'I'm going
to buy you stockings,' he promised unsteadily. 'From now
on you will wear nothing but stockings!'

She neither knew nor cared what he was intending to do,
apart from what lay in the immediate future.

'Are you still on the pill?' he was demanding.

She shook her head. 'Not any more.'

He grabbed his trousers and pulled a pack of condoms
out, thanking some merciful hand which had guided him to
buy some. 'I'd like you to slide this on for me, Lisi,' he
whispered as he ripped open the foil. 'Come on. Put it on
for me.'

She glanced down, and swallowed. She couldn't, not this
first time—it was too daunting, too intimate. 'You do it,'
she whispered back.

She felt him sliding the condom on, then heard him
swear softly, and when she opened her eyes to see what
was the matter he was glowering down at the bare floorboards with a look of disgust on his face.

'There's no bloody bed in the house yet!' he groaned,
and swiftly picked her up to carry her to the other side of
the room, out of view of the window.

'Wh-what are you doing?' She gasped as he leaned her

back against the wall and lifted her up, positioning her legs around his naked waist.

'What do you think I'm doing?' he ground out. His fingers moved down to find her slick and ready and he uttered silent thanks because he felt as if he would go insane unless he…he…

'Oh, Philip,' she sobbed as his great strength thrust into her, and she thought that nothing could ever feel this good, or this right. 'Philip,' she said again, on a long-drawn-out shudder.

Her pleasure only intensified his. He had never had to fight to maintain control quite so much as he moved inside her, watching her face as it bloomed, feeling her hot tightness encasing him in a moist, exquisite sheath.

He sought to distract himself with words rather than sensation. 'Tell me how it feels,' he urged throatily.

How to describe paradise in a sentence? she despaired with another helpless moan as he cupped her buttocks and thrust into her even deeper.

'Tell me!' he commanded.

'It's…it's…'

'It's what, Lisi?' he prompted, his voice a silken caress.

It's Philip, the father of my child, she thought as the unbelievable waves of orgasm crept unexpectedly upon her, sweeping her up in their swell, rocking her until she was left shuddering and weak, her tears spilling down like rain onto his shoulder.

Her tears confused him, acted as a temporary deterrent to his own fulfilment. For a second he almost wanted to lift her head and dry her tears away, demand that she tell him what had made her cry like that, but his own orgasm was too strong to be denied. Even as he began to frame the question he felt himself caught in its inexorable path, and he drove into her, pulled her closer still until his seed spilled out, and he was rocked with the force of it all.

Seconds—minutes?—later, he kissed the top of her head and felt her shiver.

'You're cold,' he observed. 'Better get dressed.'

So that was it. Wild and passionate sex up against the wall and all he could talk about was the temperature of the room.

Reminding herself that she had wanted it as much—if not more—than him, Lisi nodded and snuggled against his chest for one last precious moment of physical closeness, listening to the muffled thunder of his heart as it began to slow.

He could have stayed like this all day. Still inside her, with her naked body locked so indulgently around his and her hair spilling all over him—making everything black where it touched. He felt himself begin to stir again and knew that, if one of them did not begin to make an effort to get dressed, he would grow inside her to fill her again, and want to make love with the same sweet abandon as before.

'You acted like you really needed that,' he observed in a whisper.

She lifted her eyes to his and suddenly thought—tell him. Why not? 'It's…it's been a long time,' she admitted.

'How long?' he demanded, though his body tensed as it prepared itself for the stab of jealousy.

'Since that night with you,' she answered slowly and heard him suck in a disbelieving breath.

His eyes narrowed. 'Honestly?'

'There's no reason for me to lie, Philip.'

'I'm flattered,' he murmured.

Ridiculously disappointed by his reaction, she let her feet slide slowly to the ground. 'I have to get back to work,' she said.

He thought how matter-of-fact she sounded—still, if that was the way she wanted to play it, it was fine by him. At least there were to be no hypocritical words of love and affection, which neither of them would mean. 'There's hot water,' he offered. 'If you want to take a shower?'

Lisi blushed. She hadn't thought that she would have to go back all sticky and redolent of the scent of their sex—but she wouldn't, not really. Unlike last time, he had used a condom.

'Use the bathroom off the main bedroom,' he suggested. 'It's—'

'I know where it is, thank you, Philip,' she said impatiently, shaking her head. 'I used to live here, remember?' And then *she* remembered just which room they were in.

He felt her tense. 'What's the matter?'

She bit her lip as she reached for her underwear. 'This used to be *my* room,' she moaned. 'And soon it will be Tim's, and we've just…just…'

'Just had sex in it?'

Lisi turned away before he could see her face. He could not have termed it in a more insulting way. 'Yes,' she said tonelessly, and suddenly the desire and the passion which had made her want him so very badly—seemed like the worst idea she had ever had in her life.

'Lisi?'

Despairing at the hope which leapt up inside her, she turned around again. 'What?'

'Here!' He threw over her blouse and noted that she caught it like an athlete. 'There's nothing wrong with what we just did,' he said softly. 'It's as natural and as old as time. So what if it *is* going to be Tim's room—how can what we just did in here possibly harm him? It's how he got here in the first place, after all!'

'I don't need you to give me a basic lesson in sex education,' she said crossly, pulling her skirt up over her hips and zipping it up.

No, she certainly didn't. He had never met a woman so

free and generous in her love-making before. Still slightly reeling from learning that there had been no other lover, he came over and began to button up her blouse for her, tempted to lay the flat of his hands over the magnificent thrust of her breasts, but her unsmiling face told him not to bother trying.

'What's the matter?' he asked quietly. 'Are you regretting what just happened?'

There was no reason to be anything other than truthful—not now. Too much water had passed underneath the bridge for coyness or prevarication.

'A little. Aren't you?'

He shrugged as he slipped his shoes on. 'There's no point in feeling regret—you know it was inevitable.'

'I don't understand.'

'I think you do.' His eyes pierced her with their green light. 'Don't you think we *needed* that? To get rid of some of the tension between us?'

'You make it sound so…so…'

'So what, Lisi?''

'So *functional*.' She shuddered.

'Sometimes sex is. We were always going to have trouble creating the candlelight and roses scene, weren't we—what with Tim being around and your obvious low opinion of me?' He picked up his jacket. 'So what happened to make you change your mind about hating me? Was it purely jealousy—because you thought that I had something going with Tricia?'

'And do you?' she asked boldly. 'You never did answer that.'

The question angered him. 'You really think I would have just had sex with you, if I was involved with Tricia?'

She wanted to say that he had done once before, except that now she was beginning to look at that night differently. Could a man who was married to a woman who lay in a deep coma be considered married in the true sense of the word? She looked at him and shook her head, some bone-deep certainty giving her an answer she had not expected. 'No,' she said quietly. 'I don't.'

He expelled a long, pent-up sigh. 'Well, thanks for that, at least.'

'I have to go.' She straightened her jacket and at that moment felt almost close to him, though maybe that was just nature's way of justifying what they had just been do-ing. But she plucked up the courage to ask another ques-tion, one which had been praying on her mind for much longer. 'Philip?'

He narrowed his eyes. 'What?'

'What made you make love to me?' She saw the gleam in his eyes and hastily shook her head. 'No, not this time— last time. When you didn't really…know me…nor I you. Was it just lust? Me being in the wrong place at the wrong time?'

For a long time he had thought that it was simply lust— but if that were the case, then why hadn't he followed up one of the countless other invitations which had come his way? He remembered what Khalim had said, but then Khalim was a born romantic. He shook his head, knowing that he owed her his honesty. 'That's just it, Lisi—I don't know.'

It was not the answer she had wanted—but it was better than nothing.

'Listen,' he said, and she prayed for some sweetener, something to tell her that she wasn't just Lisi-the-body, but Lisi a woman who was entitled to a modicum of respect.

'What?'

'Can I come to the nursery with you later, when you collect Tim?'

It would be his first 'outing' as Tim's father and she knew that she could not refuse him—but he hadn't needed to make love to her first to ensure that she said yes. She nodded. The only way forward was with truth and honesty and no game-playing. She wasn't going to regret what she had been unable to resist, and neither was she going to use Tim as a pawn to try to make her feel better about her mixed-up emotions.

She smiled. 'Of course you can,' she said simply, but the smile cost her almost as much as the words to make.

CHAPTER TEN

MARIAN glanced across the office. 'Telephone, Lisi.' She smiled. 'For you. It's Philip.'

Lisi reached out for the phone. As if she needed to be told! Marian's gooey expression said it all, because her boss seemed to be labouring under the illusion that all was hunky-dory between the two of them.

She sighed. Maybe that was what it looked like to the outside world. He visited Langley nearly every weekend and he took the three of them to the zoo and to parks. Dragged them on long walks around the beautiful countryside. Tim liked it that way and so, stupidly, did she.

Philip had even started teaching Tim to play football and she had watched the bond between them grow and grow, happy for her son that it should be so, convincing herself that it did not mean that she was in any way marginalised.

But he had made no further attempt to make love to her again, and, while she didn't know why, she couldn't bring herself to ask him. She feared that once had been enough for him. He had got all the hunger out of his system and now he could move on. What choice did she have, other than to respect and accept that, even though in the long, restless nights her body ached for him?

She still wanted him like crazy, and she guessed that she always would—certainly no man had ever captured her quite so completely, neither before nor since. But sex complicated things and sex with Philip sent her whole world spinning into a vortex of confusion.

Sex with Philip made you long for the impossible—the

impossible in this case being his love. And in her heart she knew she would never have that.

'Hello?'

'Hi. How are things?'

'Good.' He only ever rang her at the office, and part of her wondered whether this was because this guaranteed her polite courtesy towards him. Perhaps he thought that she would not be nearly so compliant if she didn't have Marian half listening in on the conversation. And if he thought that, then he was a fool—because all the fight and hostility had left her. Sex could complicate things, yes—but it could also help define what was most important, and Lisi knew, rightly or wrongly, that she loved him with a fervour which made her ache for him.

'How's life in the big metropolis?' she asked.

'How long have you got?' he asked, with a short laugh, thinking that the quiet village life of Langley was the one true oasis in his high-powered life these days. 'It's busy, crowded, pressured, competitive. Want more?'

Lots more. More than he would ever give her. She laughed back. 'I think I get the picture.' She waited. Was today's request going to be the one she most dreaded? That he would ask if Tim could spend the night at The Old Rectory with him alone, and the separation of their lives as joint parents would begin? She had been astonished that he hadn't asked already, when the bright yellow room with its Mickey Mouse curtains had been ready for occupation since mid-January, and they were now well into April.

'I was wondering whether you were free on Saturday?' he asked.

'Saturday? Of course I am—why?'

He thought that most women might have pretended to think about it. 'There's a ball I have to attend up here— it's usually pretty good fun. I know it's short notice, but I wondered whether you'd like to come?'

'As your guest?' she asked stupidly.

'I wasn't planning on asking you to be my chauffeur!' Had he been instrumental in heightening her insecurity? His voice softened. 'Of course as my guest!'

'I don't know whether I can get a babysitter for Tim, not this late. And anyway, I don't know if I'd want to leave him while I went up to London,' she added doubtfully.

'You wouldn't have to. I want you to bring him—an old friend of mine has offered to babysit. It's all arranged, if you're agreed?'

Her heart was pounding with excitement. Oh, for goodness' sake—calm down, Lisi! she told herself. Somebody else has probably let him down at the last minute.

'Well?'

She swallowed. 'Okay,' she replied, as casually as she could. 'I'd love to.'

'Good.' There was a pause. 'And I'd like to buy you something to wear.'

Lisi froze, and her fingers tightened around the receiver. 'I'm not sure that I understand what you mean,' she said icily.

'Something nice—a pretty dress. Whatever you like,' he amended hastily.

So he was ashamed of his country bumpkin, was he? 'What's the matter, Philip?' she asked sarcastically. 'Afraid that I'll turn up in something completely inappropriate and let you down?'

He sighed. Hadn't he anticipated just this response? She could be so damned *proud* about some things. Like her dogged insistence on paying her share whenever the three of them went out. Time after time she had infuriated him by letting him pay for Tim, but not her, and he worried about how much their outings were eating into her limited budget.

'That wasn't what I meant!' he protested.

'Well, that's what it sounded like!'

'Let's call it a Christmas present, then,' he said placatingly. 'Since I didn't buy you one.'

They had scarcely been able to be civil to one another at the time, so that was hardly surprising, but Lisi felt the slow pulse of anger ticking away inside her. Anything more designed to make her feel like a kept woman, she could not imagine!

'Thanks, but no thanks,' she said shortly. 'I'm sure that I can dig *something* suitable out!'

Philip sighed, recognising a stubbornness which would not be shifted, no matter how he played it. 'Okay, Lisi. Have it your own way. I'll arrange to have a car pick you and Tim up on Saturday afternoon—let's say about three. Does that suit you?'

'I can get the train!'

'Yes, you can—but you aren't going to,' he argued grimly. 'It'll take you for ever, and I'm sure that Tim would enjoy travelling in a big, shiny car.'

Yes, he would absolutely love it—of course he would. Philip could give Tim all kinds of expensive toys which she would never be able to. Perhaps that was why he always rang her at work—so that she would not be able to point out little home truths like that one.

'Shall we say three?' he persisted.

'Yes, Philip. We'll be ready. Goodbye,' and she put the phone down to find Marian watching her.

'What's happened?' she asked quickly.

'He's invited the two of us up to London. He's sending a car, he's arranged a babysitter for Tim and he's taking me to a ball.'

'Oh, for heaven's sake, Lisi!' exclaimed Marian. 'I thought he'd given you bad news! Why on earth are you sitting there with such a long face? What woman wouldn't give the earth for an invitation like that?'

Lisi forced a smile. If only it were as simple as Marian seemed to think it was. 'I'm sure it will be very enjoyable,' she agreed evenly and saw Marian shake her head in disbelief.

She told an excited Tim, and that night, after she had tucked him up in bed and read him his story, she went into her bedroom to survey the contents of her wardrobe.

Ballgowns were long and she had precisely two long dresses—one she had worn during her pregnancy and which now looked like a tent, while the other was flower-sprigged and hopelessly outdated. She zipped it up. And cheap.

Had she been out of her mind to refuse Philip his offer of a dress?

She pulled a grim face at the milk-maid image reflected back at her from the mirror.

No. She would not be in any way beholden to him. By hook or by crook she would make a transformation as total as Cinderella's had been.

She just wasn't sure how!

The next morning she left Tim with Rachel and Blaine while she went to the nearby town of Bilchester to investigate its ballgown possibilities, but after two hours spent solidly trudging from shop to shop she was approaching a state close to despair.

The kind of dress which an evening with Philip would require would create an impossibly huge hole in her tight budget.

'Why don't you hire?' suggested an assistant at her very last port of call.

Lisi shrugged, her naturally parsimonious streak baulking at paying out good money for a dress she would only get to wear once. 'I want something to show for my money,' she admitted.

The assistant grinned. 'Makes a nice change to get someone in here who isn't completely rolling in it!' She lowered her voice as the manageress drifted past in a heavy cloud of cloying perfume. 'Have you tried the thrift shops?' she questioned.

'Thrift shops?'

'Charity shops,' the assistant amended. 'There are two here in Bilchester, and it's such a rich area that you never know what you'll pick up. I shop there myself,' she confided. 'I get staff discount in here, but the stuff is way too expensive.'

'What a brilliant idea!' said Lisi, with a grateful smile. 'Thanks!'

In the second charity shop she could scarcely believe her luck, because she looked in the window and found her dream dress staring her right in the face.

It looked old—but fashionably old—as if someone had bought this dress many years ago and looked after it with loving care. It had a tight, strapless silk bodice from which the many-layered tulle skirt flared out like a black cloud. It was a fairy-tale dress.

An elderly woman behind the till saw her looking at it.

'Beautiful, isn't it?' She smiled.

'Exquisite.'

'Only came in this morning—must have cost someone a fortune.'

'Can I...can I try it on, please?' asked Lisi breathlessly.

The woman wrinkled her nose. 'We're not really supposed to take it out of the window for a month.'

'Oh, please,' begged Lisi. '*Please.*' And the next moment she found herself telling the woman all about Philip— well, not *all*, but the bit about going to the fancy ball and refusing his offer of a dress.

'How can I refuse after a story like that? I'll get it out of the window. But don't get your hopes up too much—it might not fit. The waist is absolutely tiny.'

But it did. Just. Lisi breathed in and knew a moment's anxiety as the assistant struggled slightly with the zip, but once up, it fitted as though it had been designed for her.

'I won't be able to eat a thing!' she groaned.

'You won't want to, I shouldn't think. Looking like that I doubt whether you'll leave the dance-floor all night!'

It was the most beautiful thing she had ever worn. Tiny sequins were dotted here and there over the skirt, so that they glittered and caught the light as she moved. 'I'll take it,' she said instantly. 'Provided that I can afford it!'

'I'll make sure you can!' The woman gave a dreamy smile. 'It's such a romantic story!'

If only she knew! Still, she was not going to dwell on what she hadn't got—she was going to enjoy what she had—and a ball with Philip sounded pretty near perfect.

The car arrived on Saturday at three o'clock on the dot— an outrageously luxurious vehicle, complete with a uniformed chauffeur, and Tim squealed in excitement, and chatted incessantly for the whole journey.

'Calm down, poppet,' murmured Lisi, thinking that if he carried on at this rate they would never get him settled for the night.

But when the car drew up outside a house situated in a quiet, leafy lane in Hampstead, Lisi very nearly asked the chauffeur to take them straight back home again.

She swallowed. She had known that Philip was rich, of course she had—but not *this* rich, because the house she glimpsed as the car purred its way up the drive was more the size of a small castle! And land in London was unbelievably expensive—so just how wealthy *was* he to be able to afford a plot this size?

'*Big* house, Mummy!' squealed Tim excitedly.

Why hadn't he told her? Prepared her? She twisted the strap of her handbag nervously. But what could he have said that wouldn't have sounded like boasting? And Philip was not a boastful man, she realised. He carried his obvious success with an air of cool understatement.

Nevertheless, her heart was still beating like a piston when he opened the door before she had a chance to knock and the sight of him on his home territory quite took her breath away, and drove all thoughts of his intimidating wealth away.

He was wearing black jeans and a soft blue cashmere sweater and his dark hair was ruffled and his eyes very green, if a little wary.

'I wasn't sure if you'd pull out at the last minute,' he admitted.

'At least I'm not wholly predictable!'

Predictable? Never, ever. He still hadn't got over that highly erotic scene in her old bedroom. He felt his heart accelerate and he silently cursed himself for breaking his self-imposed promise not to dwell on that. For once, with Lisi—he was going to make his head dictate events, and not his body.

'Hello, Tim,' he said softly and crouched down to smile on a level with the boy. 'Come on in.'

Tim was strangely silent, but he slid his little hand into Philip's proffered one and went inside.

Lisi was too excited and nervous to take much in except for the feeling of light and space and exquisite decor.

'Shall we have tea in the sitting room first?' Philip asked. 'You can have the guided tour later.'

Tea was all laid out on a table by a roaring log fire—a proper, old-fashioned tea with sandwiches and scones and cake and biscuits. Tim gave a little whimper of delight, which turned into a whoop when he spotted the wooden train-set which had been laid out beneath the window, and he dashed over to it immediately. It was just like the one he had at home, Lisi noted. Only bigger.

Wondering just how she would be able to bring him—

and her—back down to earth after an experience like this, Lisi gestured nervously towards the teapot.

'Shall I be mother?' she asked brightly.

'You *are* mother,' Philip responded softly. 'Aren't you?'

She sat down and busied herself with pouring the tea. She had gone so long without mixing with men that she was in danger of misinterpreting everything this particular one said.

She glanced up to find him watching her, the beautiful green eyes narrowed thoughtfully. 'Who's babysitting to-night?' she asked.

'It's a surprise.'

'I don't know that I really like surprises—and I think I ought to know, so that I can prepare Tim.'

Philip hesitated. Was he about to break an unwritten law of betraying an official confidence? But it *was* to Lisi, and Lisi he could trust.

He looked over at Tim, but Tim was oblivious to every-thing, save his exciting new train-set.

'Choo!' he crooned. 'Choo!'

Philip lowered his voice. 'It's Khalim,' he explained.

'Sorry?'

'Khalim,' he repeated.

'P-Prince Khalim?' Lisi gulped in disbelief.

'That's right. And his wife. Rose.'

Who just happened to be a princess! Lisi put the teapot down with a shaking hand. Her son was about to be looked after by the leading members of Maraban's royal family! 'Surely they're not *that* strapped for cash!' she joked, her voice rising with a very faint note of hysteria.

Philip gave her a rueful smile. 'It does tend to have that effect on people,' he admitted. 'Everyone was a bit taken aback when they first knew he was joining us at Cambridge—but only for a time. When you are young, these things seem to matter less. *Some* people liked him for all the wrong reasons, of course—but Khalim is adept at picking out falsehood. He is a consummate judge of character, despite the isolation his position inevitably brings.'

'What will I say to them?' moaned Lisi.

Philip smiled. 'Say what you would say to anyone. Just be yourself.'

Lisi handed him his tea and gave him a puzzled look. 'I can't understand why they want to spend their Saturday evening babysitting for someone else?'

Philip took the tea and gave her a noncommittal smile. There were some confidences which were not in his gift to break. 'Normality is what they crave above all else,' he said blandly. 'Somewhere where they can relax, and be themselves.'

After tea he showed Tim his room. It had obviously been decorated especially in his honour. There were bright walls and framed posters of cartoons and more toys.

'You're spoiling him,' protested Lisi weakly.

He shrugged. 'I have a lot of time to make up for.'

She walked quickly over to the window, his remark reminding her that he would never forget the secret she had kept from him all those years. But would he ever forgive her?

'Come on,' he said. 'I'll show you where you're sleeping. Next door to Tim—of course.'

It was surprisingly small and cosy, with a fire burning brightly in the grate.

'I know how much you like fires.' He smiled. 'And this is the only bedroom in house which has a fire, apart from mine, of course.'

Her heart gave a skip of disappointment. Of course he wasn't going to move her into *his* bedroom—why on earth should he, when the physical attraction between them had obviously died? For him, at least. But, oh, she knew one mad, wild moment of longing as she pictured herself in his arms, and in his bed.

'Shall I start to get dressed now?' she asked, with a glance at her watch. 'What time are they getting here?'

'Seven-thirty,' he said.

'I'll make sure I'm ready on time.' She smiled. 'Don't worry, Philip—I won't keep them waiting.'

He smiled back. Very astute of her to realise that, despite the fact that Khalim and Rose were as close to him as they were to anyone outside their family—the fact remained that they *were* different. Only a fool would keep them waiting and Lisi was no fool. 'I'll leave you to it.'

She showered, made her face up, blow-dried her hair and pinned it back with tiny, diamanté clips, but she couldn't do the damned zip of her dress up!

She sighed, knowing there was nothing else for it but to ask Philip—and there was absolutely no reason to be shy when he knew her body more intimately than any other man.

Nevertheless, she could feel her cheeks pinkening as she called along the corridor.

'Philip! Can you zip me up?'

Philip paused in the act of clipping on his cuff-links and grimaced. Yes, he *could* zip her up, but was there any worse torture for a man who had vowed not to lay another finger on her until the time was right?

'Philip?'

'Coming,' he replied, silently cursing himself for his poor choice of word.

She stood outside the door of her room, and shrugged her shoulders apologetically, trying desperately to distract herself from the magnificent sight he made in formal dinner clothes which set off his lean physique to perfection. 'I'm afraid that I have to be almost shoe-horned into it!' she babbled.

Shoe-horned? All he could think of was how stunning she looked in black, the stark colour setting off the paleness of her skin to perfection and reflecting the deep ebony of her hair.

She turned around so that her bare back was facing him, and he sucked in a raw breath to see that she was not wearing a bra, and that her magnificent breasts were to be held in place only by the clinging folds of heavy silk.

He caught hold of the zip as gingerly as if it had been a poisonous snake. He could feel the warmth radiating off her skin, and the drift of some sweet, subtle perfume invaded his senses.

The temptation not to close her dress up, but instead to lay his fingertips against the silky surface of her skin was so powerful that he felt the unwanted jerk of arousal. He wanted to lead her by the hand to his bedroom, and to slowly undress her and make love to her all night long, but he knew that he could not. And not just because Tim was up and awake.

Time seemed to have stood still, and Lisi felt the waves of longing as they washed heatedly over her skin. She could hear the very definite sound of his breathing and she wondered whether he was actually going to get round to doing her dress up, even while her body craved for him not to, but to turn her round and kiss her instead.

'How's that?' he ground out, using every atom of self-restraint he possessed as he jerked the zip up.

'Fine! Thanks,' she gulped and fled back into the sanctuary of her room, hating herself for wanting him so badly, but hating him even more for not wanting *her*. What could have happened to kill all his desire for her?

Her impulsive response might have turned him off. That eager and frantic bout of love-making might have prompted him into thinking that it was inappropriate behaviour for the mother of his child to act in such a free and easy way.

When she eventually emerged from her room, she found him waiting for her and thought that she heard a distant barking. 'Do you have a dog?' she asked in surprise.

He shook his head, pleased to be able to focus his mind on something other than how utterly irresistible she looked. 'That'll be Khalim's people.'

'People?'

'Bodyguards,' he explained. 'They'll have dogs patrolling the grounds, as well as a couple of people stationed out front and out back.'

Lisi nodded thoughtfully. 'It must be strange to live your life like that—always being monitored and never alone.'

'They have each other,' said Philip simply. 'Their love makes everything bearable.'

Lucky Rose, thought Lisi, with a painful leap of her heart. What wouldn't she give to have that kind of closeness with Philip?

'Let's take Tim downstairs and feed him, before they arrive,' he suggested, then added, almost as an afterthought, 'You look beautiful, by the way.'

'Thank you.' She gave a weak smile, wishing that he had said it as though he really meant it, rather than just subjecting her to the kind of cool, green gaze as if he had been admiring a particularly expensive piece of furniture.

They gave Tim boiled eggs and toast and then settled him down in one of the big armchairs, happily drinking a glass of milk and watching one of many videos which Philip must have bought specially. Lisi looked at them with interest. He had certainly gone out of his way to make sure that Tim felt at home here. She might hope in vain that he would be openly demonstrative to *her*, but there was no doubting the love and pride he felt for his son.

Khalim and Rose arrived at the appointed hour, and Lisi stood nervously at Philip's side while he introduced them.

'Should I bow or should I curtsy?' she had asked him moments earlier.

'Either will do.'

In the end she managed an odd mixture of the two, but she was more than slightly awestruck by the sight of the black-eyed prince and his exquisite, blonde-haired princess.

'So you are Lisi.' Rose smiled. 'And this must be Tim.'

On cue, Tim jumped excitedly to his feet, not seeming at all phased by his high-born child-minders. He gave a little bow just as Philip had taught him to, and Khalim and Rose both laughed in delight.

'Sweet,' murmured Rose, and a dreamy look came over her face.

'He has your profile, Philip,' said Khalim suddenly, and subjected Lisi to a blinding smile. 'And his mother's magnificent colouring.'

'He has many of his mother's qualities—and not too many of mine, hopefully,' responded Philip.

Lisi found Rose's eyes on her. 'Khalim?'

He turned to his wife immediately. 'Dearest?'

'Bring me some sweet mint tea, would you, my love? And take Philip with you, and Tim. Show them how domesticated you have become!'

The prince gave a rueful smile, looking a little like a tiger who had just been offered a saucer of milk. 'You see how she orders me around, Philip? That much at least has not changed!'

'Indeed,' came Philip's murmured response as he followed Khalim out of the room. It never failed to amuse him—the autocratic leader of Maraban's ruling family capitulating to his English wife's every whim!

Once they had left, Rose beckoned towards the sofa. 'Come and sit by me.'

Lisi waited until Rose was seated and then sat down next to her.

'Philip has told us much about you,' observed Rose softly.

Lisi bit her lip. 'Oh? May I ask what he said?'

'That you were an exemplary mother. And that you were very beautiful.'

Lisi hesitated.

'Do not be afraid to speak,' commanded Rose softly. 'We are not on ceremony here.'

'Did he tell you about…about…'

Rose shook her head. 'He told *me* nothing that you would not wish us to hear, I think—though he is naturally closer to Khalim. Just that the circumstances surrounding Tim's conception were not ideal.'

Which Lisi supposed was a fairly diplomatic way of putting it.

'But my romance with Khalim was not a simple, straight road either,' mused Rose. 'We encountered many rocky paths along the way. This is often the way of love, you know.'

Love, thought Lisi. And although her heart ached with longing, she knew that she could not confide in the princess and tell her that Philip did not love her, nor ever would. To the outside world their relationship might look close, and it was not her place to make the reality known to his friends.

Rose leaned back against one of the cushions and gave another dreamy smile. 'Now, tell me, Lisi,' she said softly. 'Is childbirth really as bad as they say it is?'

Lisi narrowed her eyes, but did not ask the obvious question. 'It's different for everyone,' she said slowly. 'Some women find it easier than others.'

'And you? Was it easy for you?'

Lisi stared into the princess's clear blue eyes. 'It was different for me,' she answered candidly. 'I was all on my own. There was no partner to hold my hand or massage my back, or just to tell me that everything was going to be all right.'

'I will be on my own, too,' sighed Rose and nodded in answer to the silent query in Lisi's eyes. 'Yes, I carry the prince's child. But Khalim will not be permitted to enter the birthing chamber—it is not the Maraban custom for fathers to be present. I will be attended to by his sisters and my ladies-in-waiting, and with that I must be content.'

'I would buy every available book on the subject if I were you,' advised Lisi. 'And practise breathing techniques and relaxation—that can really help.'

Rose nodded, and then she laid her slim hand on Lisi's hand. 'You know that Philip can be very hard on himself, don't you?'

Lisi opened her mouth to ask her what she meant, but the moment was lost when Philip, Khalim and Tim reappeared, carrying the tray of mint tea.

A car arrived to pick them up, and it wasn't until they were speeding towards Hyde Park that Lisi turned towards Philip's shadowed profile.

'Rose is pregnant,' she said. 'Did you know?'

The profile shifted so that he was facing her. 'She told you that?'

Lisi nodded. 'Yes. You sound surprised.'

'I am. I would not normally expect such a personal admission from her, not on such a short acquaintanceship.'

'Actually, I'd kind of guessed.' She saw his eyes narrow. 'It's a woman thing—you can usually tell if another woman is pregnant.'

'Khalim is over the moon,' he observed softly, looking at the soft line of her lips and knowing that later he intended to kiss them. 'They both are.'

Lisi stared out of the window without really seeing anything. If only she could have had Philip's baby within the context of a warm and loving relationship like Rose and Khalim's.

'Why did you invite me tonight, Philip?' she asked suddenly. 'Did somebody let you down at the last minute?'

He swore softly beneath his breath. 'If any question was designed to remind me that you continue to think the worst of me, then that one was. I asked you, Lisi, because I thought it would be a treat for you.'

'The country girl let loose in the Big City?'

He ignored her sarcastic tone. He didn't want to fight. Not tonight. 'I can assure you that tonight you look like the most sophisticated city slicker I've ever seen!'

'Shall I take that as a compliment?'

'You could try. Now stop frowning—you'll grow old before your time. Try smiling—we're here.'

The ball was lavishly spectacular and filled with beautiful people, yet Lisi did not feel out of place—though that probably had something to do with the fact that Philip did not leave her side all night.

He danced with her and introduced her to countless people. He fetched her food and idly fed her titbits with his fingers, and because she didn't want to make a scene she didn't stop him. Didn't want to stop him, if the truth be known.

Just after midnight, the party was still in full fling, and they had just finished dancing a very slow dance in the candlelit ballroom. Lisi was reluctant to move from his arms, and he seemed in no hurry to make her. She sighed, wanting to rest her cheek against his shoulder once more, to breathe in the heady masculine scent of him and to pretend for a while that they were real lovers as well as parents.

'Lisi?'

'Mmm?'

'Look at me—I want to ask you something.'

She glanced up, something in his voice telling her that this was not a perfunctory question about whether she would like another drink. 'Yes, Philip?'

His face was as emotionless as if he were asking her the time. 'Will you share my bed tonight?'

CHAPTER ELEVEN

'MUCH as I adore Khalim and Rose, I thought they'd never go,' whispered Philip as he drew her into his arms, and quietly closed the door of his bedroom behind them.

Part of Lisi had not wanted them to go. All during the drive back from the ball she had been a bag of nerves, sitting bolt upright in the seat and wondering if she had dreamt up his provocative question and her breathless agreement to sleep with him. But this was what she had wanted for much too long, wasn't it?

He had glanced at her set features on the journey home. He certainly hadn't been going to start making love to her there, with the interested eyes of the driver looking on. Not that he'd trusted himself. If he'd started, he couldn't imagine ever wanting or being able to stop, and tonight he wanted to do it properly—with a lazy and unhurried dressing and the comfort of his big bed awaiting them.

'Lisi,' he said softly now. 'Have you changed your mind?'

She shook her head.

'Scared, then?'

She nodded. 'A little apprehensive.'

'Well, don't be. There's nothing to be apprehensive about. Here.' He lifted her fingers to his mouth and slowly kissed them, one by one, and he felt a little of the tension melt away from her. Then he pulled the diamanté clips from her hair and it fell down around her pale shoulders in streams of dark satin.

With wide eyes Lisi stared up at him, and he thought that she looked like a trapped and cornered animal. 'Lisi,' he sighed. 'We don't have to do this, you know. I thought that you wanted it as much as I do.'

Her voice trembled. 'And I do. You know I do. It's just...'

'What?'

'You haven't come near me for weeks, nor shown the slightest inclination to. I thought that you didn't want me, not in that way.' She swallowed. 'So what's happened to change your mind?'

He gazed down at her with a mixture of dismay and disbelief. Not want her? He had never stopped wanting her! Was he really so difficult to read, or just a master at keeping his feelings disguised?

'I've always wanted you, Lisi,' he said quietly. 'But our passion always seems to spring up on us unawares. I didn't want to try to make love to you at your cottage, afraid that Tim might hear because he's next door.'

'He's next door now,' she pointed out.

'And the walls here are decidedly thicker,' he commented drily.

She wasn't going to get offended by that. He was merely stating a fact, not making a comparison between the basic structure of her little cottage and the luxurious proportions of his.

'I want to make love to you properly,' he whispered and began to trace the outline of her trembling mouth with the featherlight brush of his fingertip.

The glitter from his eyes made her glow from within. 'I always quite enjoyed it when you made love to me improperly,' she joked, and he leaned forward and dropped a kiss on her lips.

'That's better,' he murmured approvingly, and her arms went up around his neck and the kiss became extended. '*Much* better. Isn't it?''

'Mmm!' She swayed against him, her doubts banished

by the warmth of his mouth and the expert caress of his tongue.

'Shall I undress you, sweetheart?'

The term of endearment made her shakier than the kiss had, and she nodded, her heart beginning to pound as he slid her zip down and laid bare her breasts.

He bent his head to take each sweet nipple in turn, inciting them into instant life with the lazy flicker of his tongue as he slid the dress down over her hips and it fell with a sigh to the floor.

He looked down at her and sucked in a ragged breath. 'Stockings,' he said thickly. 'You're wearing stockings.'

Yes, she was. 'Y-you said that you liked them,' she said, almost shyly. And tights would have seemed all wrong beneath such a fairy tale of a dress.

He wanted to beg her to keep them on, to make love to him with those silken thighs pressed hard into his back, but he knew that there would be another time for that. Right now he wanted—no, needed—her to be completely naked, there to be nothing between the two of them except skin.

'Shall I take them off for you?' he questioned unsteadily.

'Yes, please.'

His hand was shaking as he unclipped the suspender and then took a deliberately long time sliding the gauzy silk down over every delicious centimetre of her legs, his face moving tantalisingly close to the dark, triangular blur of hair which concealed her most precious gift. He longed to bury his mouth in her most secret place, but resisted, fearing that he would only end up taking her on the floor.

He unhooked the suspender belt and it joined all the other garments on the carpet and then he lifted her up and carried her over to the bed, covering her up with a duvet, so that only her cute nose and those huge aquamarine eyes were showing, and the shiny fan of black hair lay all over his pillow.

He began to unbutton his shirt, never taking his eyes from her face. 'Want me to undress for you?'

Beneath the concealment of the duvet she felt herself melt. 'Y-yes.'

The shirt fluttered from his fingers and he began to undo his trousers. It was hard to reconcile this sweetly shy Lisi with the wild lover who had gripped his shoulders so ecstatically, her fingernails making tiny little nips into his skin, her back pressed up against the wall as he'd driven into her over and over again. He stifled a groan.

Her eyes growing wider by the second, Lisi wondered what had made him briefly close his eyes like that, or why suddenly he seemed to be having more than a little difficulty sliding his zip down.

Arrogantly, he kicked off the trousers and the silk boxers followed and he stood in front of her for a moment, wanting her to see what she did to him. How she could turn him on to this pitch without having laid a finger on him.

He pulled back the duvet and climbed in next to her, and pulled her into his arms, kissing the top of her head and enjoying its meadow-sweet scent. He would just hold her for a while, stop her trembling and make her feel safe.

But the trembling only seemed to get worse, and he pulled away from her, noting the look of acute distress which had creased her brow into a deep frown.

'What's the matter, sweetheart?' And then he saw that her eyes were almost black, they were so dilated. And her breathing was shallow and rapid, and he moved his hand down between her legs to feel her slick, inviting heat. He groaned. He had been planning to make this one last and last—but what the hell? They had all night.

But he had something he needed to tell her, something she deserved to know. 'You remember the last time we did this, that morning at the rectory?' he asked, in a low voice.

'I'm not likely to forget in a hurry.'

'And you told me that there had been no other lover since me?'

She nodded. Had she been mad to expose such obvious vulnerability?

He gazed down into her watchful eyes. 'Well, it was the same for me, Lisi. There had been no one else. No one.'

There was a short, breathless silence and she could have wept with the pleasure of discovering that. 'Oh, Philip,' she murmured, and held him very close.

Lisi lost count of the number of orgasms she had that night; her last reality check was drifting into sleep sometime in the early hours, when dawn was already beginning to bring a pale, clear light to the sky.

He woke her at six and made love to her again, and she knew that she really ought to get up and get out of there before Tim got up, when there was a little rap on the door, and Tim's voice calling.

'Daddy?'

Locked in each other's arms, they both froze and looked at one another, but Lisi knew immediately that there was no way around this without the whole situation being turned into some kind of farce.

She nodded at him and he understood immediately.

'In here,' he called back. 'Come in, Tim.'

Lisi held her breath, expecting shock or outrage or even—perhaps—a touch of early masculine jealousy from the male who had been in her life the longest, but Tim displayed none of these.

Instead, he ran over to the bed, carrying his night-time bunny, glanced over at the two of them and said happily, 'Oh, *good*! Now you're just like *Simon's* mummy and daddy!'

And Lisi didn't know whether to laugh or cry.

'Why don't you go downstairs and do me a drawing?' suggested Philip. 'And I'll come down in a minute and get you some juice while I'm making Mummy her morning coffee.'

'But Mummy has *tea* in the morning.' Tim pouted.

Philip nodded. 'Then I'll make her tea,' he said gravely. 'Okay!'

They heard him scampering down the stairs and their eyes met.

'That was easier than I had anticipated,' admitted Philip.

'You were expecting him to find us in bed, then, were you?'

He shrugged. 'Well, it had to happen some time, didn't it?'

How *sure* of himself he was—and how sure of *her*. But she wasn't going to be a hypocrite and feel badly about the most wonderful night of her life.

He gave her a quick kiss, and yawned. 'At least this makes things easier.'

Lisi stilled. 'How do you mean?'

'Well.' He paused and lifted her chin so that she could not escape the cool scrutiny of his eyes. 'How would it sound if I told you that I was moving to Langley?'

The words did not seem to make any sense. 'I don't understand.'

'I love the rectory,' he said softly. 'And I find myself increasingly frustrated at commuting down there every damned weekend, when I'd happily see Tim every day.'

Tim. Not her. Just Tim. 'Go on,' she said painfully.

'So I've decided to base myself in the village.'

'But what about your business?'

He smoothed a lock of hair away from her cheek, noticing that she shut her eyes very quickly. 'Technology has given people in my kind of work the freedom to work from anywhere.' He hesitated, drawing back from telling her the one really *big* bit of news.

She opened her eyes, sensing that something else was coming. 'What?' she questioned.

'I'm in the process of buying Marian Reece out.'

'You're *what*?'

'Don't look like that, Lisi.' He put his hand on her shoulder, but she shook it away and sat up in bed, her hair tumbling down to her waist, and he had to stifle the urge to start making love to her again. Tim was downstairs, he reminded himself, though he could see from the angry look on her face that an attempt at love-making *now* would not be particularly well received.

'You just didn't bother telling *me* that you're about to become my new boss?' she accused crossly. 'And neither, for that matter, did Marian!'

'It was tricky for her. She was undecided about whether or not she wanted to stay or go—she'd been thinking of it for some time, apparently.'

'But presumably you made her an offer she couldn't refuse?' she asked sarcastically.

'I gave her a good price, yes, but then I wanted—no, I *needed* a property base in Langley.'

'Perhaps you'll be pushing the existing staff out, and bringing in new people altogether!' she said, her voice rising on a note of hysteria. 'Or maybe I'll just hand my notice in—that might be best all round! Have you thought what it would be like if we were working together?'

He had thought of little else. 'I'm not going to make you do anything you don't want to, Lisi,' he said placatingly. 'I wasn't planning to be hands-on—particularly as I hoped we might be spending a lot more time together anyway.'

She stared at him uncomprehendingly. 'Because you'll be seeing more of Tim if you're living in the village, you mean?'

'Well, not just Tim. You, as well—that's if you agree to my next proposal.'

Proposal? Her hands had gone suddenly clammy. 'Your proposal being what, exactly?'

The words had gone round and round in his head countless times, but there was no guaranteed way of making sure that she would not take them the wrong way.

'I thought that you and Tim could come and live with me. At the rectory.'

Her heart stood still. *'What?'*

'It seems crazy for us to live in two houses on the same road, when the three of us seem to have forged a pretty good relationship.'

Pretty good relationship. How tepid and passionless that sounded!

'And last night proved something, didn't it?'

'What?' she asked shakily.

'That you and I are compatible in many, many ways.'

He meant, of course, that they were good in bed together. She guessed that it was intended as a compliment, so why did it make her feel distinctly uncomfortable?

Because sex without love was only ever second-best, that was why.

She wondered whether last night's magnificent seduction had all been part of his grand plan. Have her begging in his arms for more and she would not be able to deny him anything.

Least of all his son.

She supposed that she could toss her head back in a gesture of pride and thank him for his charming 'proposal', but tell him that she preferred what she already had.

But it would be a lie.

She had already decided that she couldn't bear for anyone else to have him and that she would settle for whatever he was offering. Hearts and flowers it was not, but perhaps it was the best she could hope for.

'What do you say, Lisi?' he asked softly. 'Will you and Tim come and live with me?'

She tried telling herself that for Tim's sake she could not refuse, but that would not be the whole picture. For her sake too, there was only one answer she could possibly give.

'Yes, Philip,' she answered quietly. 'We'll come and live with you.'

CHAPTER TWELVE

'NO, MUMMY!'

'But, darling, you *need* a new pair of shoes—you know you do—and we're going to meet Philip's parents at the weekend. They have to see you looking your best, don't they?'

'Granny and Grandpa,' said Tim happily.

Lisi suppressed a sigh. Everything seemed to have happened so quickly. It seemed bizarre that a few short months ago it had been just her and Tim, and yet now he talked all the time about Daddy, and his grandparents and the uncle and aunt he was soon to meet.

One great big extended family—for him, at least—although Lisi still sometimes felt as though she was standing looking in from the sidelines. But her role was as Tim's mother and Philip's mistress, and she must never forget that.

The move from Cherry Tree Cottage to The Old Rectory had been seamless—practically, if not emotionally. She had been apprehensive about it at first, but her fears had been groundless and it had turned out to be nothing short of a delight to move into her old home, with all its happy childhood memories.

To the outside world they probably looked just like any other family—and, indeed, that was just how it felt most of the time. In every sense of the word.

After years of abstinence, Philip certainly wasn't holding back. He made love to her at every opportunity he got, and Lisi wasn't complaining. He took her to heaven and back

172

every time, even if the words of love she longed for never materialised.

He was warm and tender when she lay in his arms, but he didn't let his defences down—nor she hers. He never told her whether he regretted that circumstances had forced them into this quasi-marriage, and she didn't dare ask. And he, like her, seemed happy enough to go along with the status quo. Either that, or he was a consummate actor.

He had persuaded Marian to stay on in a consultant capacity. She now worked mornings only, two new staff had been taken on, business was booming—and Lisi had been promoted to office manageress in the afternoons.

'Philip, I can't!' she had protested, when he had first mooted the idea. 'Everyone will say it's nepotism!'

'Then everyone will be wrong,' he had replied patiently. 'You've worked here for years, and you've worked damned hard. You're good—you know you are! You deserve it, Lisi—so enjoy it!'

And she did—especially so on the all-too-infrequent occasions when Philip himself was in the office. He had not exaggerated when he had told her that he did not plan to be too hands-on. He continued to travel around the countryside and, as often as not, chose to work from the beautiful study he had created at The Old Rectory, where he said the view made his heart sing, and Lisi had never thought she could be so jealous of a view!

Thank heavens she was essentially a practical person, determinedly enjoying what she had and not wishing for the impossible.

But the trip to meet his parents loomed. She wanted to make a good impression, and that meant a brand-new outfit as well as shoes for Tim.

'Let's leave Daddy a note, shall we?' she suggested. 'You can do him a little drawing while I load up the dishwasher before we go. Here.' She scribbled a few words

down, resisting the desire to add hundreds of kisses. 'Have
taken Tim to Bilchester to buy shoes and a dress for me—
back in time for work. Love, Lisi.'

Tim grizzled from the moment she put him in the car,
and Lisi wondered whether he was coming down with a
cold.

'Don't *want* to go!' he screamed, and she looked at him.

Which was more important—a happy son, or a miserable
son? His trainers weren't *that* bad—and surely Philip's parents would be more interested in seeing their grandson, than
in analysing her choice of footwear for him! She glanced
at the heavy clouds in the sky, and the thought of being
caught in rain with an out-of-sorts Tim made her mind up
for her.

'Tell you what,' she said as the car Philip had insisted
on buying her bumped its way down the drive. 'We'll call
in to see if Rachel's there. If she is and if she isn't too
busy, we'll see if you can stay with her and Blaine, while
Mummy goes to Bilchester on her own. How does that
sound?'

'Hurrah!' cheered Tim.

Rachel seemed all too pleased to have him. 'That'll keep
Blaine from under my feet.' She grinned. 'I have four tons
of laundry to sort out, and all he wants to do is play!'

Bilchester was quiet, but Lisi suspected that the drizzle
which had now turned into a torrential downpour had something to do with the lack of shoppers.

She managed to buy a flame-coloured dress and a sexy
pair of suede shoes, but her umbrella did little to withstand
the gathering gale, and by the time she got back in the car
she was shivering.

Her progress back was slow and she found herself looking at her watch more than once, and she was just starting
to get anxious when she felt the car pulling out of control,

and she managed to steer it over to the side-verge before switching off the engine.

With the rain pouring down, she got out to investigate and her worst fears were confirmed when she looked down to see that her tyre was completely flat. To drive it would be madness, but how the hell did she get home?

She looked up and down the narrow lane, as if expecting a recovery vehicle to come roaring up to her aid, but the road was completely empty and she was miles from anywhere.

So did she sit in the car and wait, and hope to flag down a passing motorist who might just turn out to be a homicidal maniac?

Or should she start walking home—or at least to the nearest phone-box? Philip would be home and he could drive out and pick her up.

Her raincoat already almost soaked through, she took her bags and set off as icy mud spattered up the sides of her legs and the heavens continued to unleash their downpour.

It took for ever to find a phone-box, and by then she felt that there was not one part of her body which wasn't cold and wet.

With chattering teeth she inserted a coin and dialled home, but the phone rang and rang and she remembered with a sinking heart that she had not put the answering machine on before she had left.

She replaced the receiver with a sigh of resignation. Nothing else for it but to carry on walking.

Never had a journey seemed quite so long or so arduous. Two cars passed her, but she let them drive on by—she was nearly into Langley now. A little way more wouldn't kill her.

It was almost two o'clock when she trudged past the duck pond and down the lane towards The Old Rectory. With frozen fingers she was fumbling around in her bag for her doorkey when the door flew open and there stood Philip, his face so white and furious that she hardly recognised him.

'Where the hell have you been?' he exploded, although the frantic racing of his heart abated slightly.

She was taken aback by the dark fury in his eyes. 'Well, that's a nice way to greet someone,' she managed, but her teeth were chattering so much that her words sounded like gobbledygook.

'I've been worried sick! Worried out of my head! You left a note saying that you'd gone out with Tim and I thought...I thought...' he heaved in a shuddering breath '...I thought that something had happened to you!'

Lisi pushed past him into the hall, suddenly understanding his distress. He was out of his mind with worry, but it had been Tim who had been the cause of his concern, not her. Of course it had.

'Why do you have to be so damned stubborn?' he demanded. 'Why wouldn't you let me buy you a mobile phone?'

'Because I don't need one! I've never had one before now, and I'm not going to start now just because I have the good fortune to be living with a rich man!'

'How charmingly you put it!' he snarled.

'Well, it's the truth!' She had never seen Philip quite so het-up before. Never. She glared at him. 'Why haven't you even bothered to ask me where Tim is, as you're so worried about him?'

'I know where he is!' he snapped. 'He's at nursery! I've just taken him there. Rachel rang here to find out where you were because you hadn't collected him, and I told her that I didn't know. You didn't ring—'

'Yes, I did! There was no reply—'

'I was out collecting Tim, that's why. Did you bother to put the answering machine on this morning?'

'Did *you*?' she countered. 'Anyway, there's nothing to worry about now, is there? Tim's safe, and that's all that matters!'

'All that *matters*?' he said incredulously.

'Yes!' she snapped.

He went very still, and his face took on an implacable look she had never seen there before. 'Take that coat off,' he said suddenly. 'You're soaking.'

She attempted to undo her coat, but her fingers were shaking so much that they slipped ineffectually at the buttons and Philip reached across to help her. She tried to swat him away. 'G-go away!'

He ignored her. 'Now go and get changed,' he ordered. 'And then come down to my study. I've lit a fire.'

She had had enough. Too tired and cold and shaken to care about what she said, she shot him a look of defiance. 'Stop sounding like a bloody headmaster!'

'Then stop behaving like a naughty schoolgirl!'

His rage was both intimidating and yet oddly exciting. 'And if I don't come down?'

He gave a grim smile as he slipped the sopping coat from her shoulders. 'Don't stretch my patience, Lisi—I've taken just about as much as I can stand from you this morning.'

There was something about his stance and his attitude which made all the rebellion die on her lips. Of course he had been worried—wouldn't she have been out of her mind herself in the same situation?

She changed into jeans and a big, thick sweater and towel-dried her hair, and when she walked into his study, not only did he have a glorious fire blazing, but he had also made tea, and a large bowl of soup sat steaming on the tray.

He handed her the soup. 'Eat that,' he commanded.

There was something so unimpeachable about the expression on his face that Lisi took the bowl from him obediently and began to drink it, while he stood over her making sure she did.

When she had finished the soup and drunk some tea, and the colour was beginning to seep back into her pale cheeks, he sat down in the chair opposite hers beside the fire.

Lisi pouted. The least he could have done was to have taken her upstairs and to have brought complete warmth back into her body by making love to her.

Philip saw the way her eyes darkened and the way her lips had softened. He knew what she wanted, but she was damned well going to have to wait! For too long now, he realised, he had allowed the intimacy of the bedroom to help shield him from confronting *real* intimacy.

'Did you really think that it was only Tim I was concerned about?' he demanded. 'Didn't it enter your pretty little head that I might be worried sick about *you*?'

She met the accusatory green glitter of his eyes. So he wanted the truth, did he? Then the truth he would have. 'Not really, no.'

'Lisi.' His voice was incredulous. 'Why on earth do you think that you're here, living with me the way we have been? Why do you think I asked you to move in?'

'Because that way you can have Tim full-time, and a sex life into the bargain!'

He stared at her. 'You honestly think that?'

'What else am I to think? You've never told me anything apart from the fact that I'm a great mother and a great lover. Oh, and a great cook.'

'And that isn't enough?'

She wasn't going to ask him for anything he couldn't offer freely. 'It's obviously enough for you.'

There was a moment of fraught silence. 'Oh, but it isn't,' he said softly. 'Not nearly enough.' This kind of thing didn't come easy to him, but he was going to have to try.

'You see, what I want more than anything else is your love, Lisi.'

She stared at him. 'Why?'

She needed to ask him *why*? He shook his head impatiently. Didn't she *know*? 'Because I'm finding that I can't hold back my love for you. Not for much longer. I love you, Lisi—hadn't you begun to even guess?'

She didn't respond for a moment. When you had spent so long wishing that something would happen, you didn't believe the sound of your own ears when it seemed as though something just had. 'You don't have to say things like that to make me feel better.'

'I'm not,' he said patiently. 'But what if saying them makes *me* feel better? What if I told you that I don't know when I started loving you, but I do, and not just because you're mother and lover and cook, but because you make me laugh and you make me mad, and I can't imagine the world without you. And the only unknown factor in this equation is that I don't know how you feel about me.'

She felt hope—delirious, impossible hope—begin to beat out a rapid thunder in her heart. 'You must do,' she said weakly.

'Why must I? You never tell me what's going on inside your head, do you, Lisi? At night you never whisper anything more tender than the fact that I'm a bit of a stud in the bedroom.'

'And what about you?' she countered. 'You're the master of disguising your feelings! If, as you say, you love me— then why didn't you tell me before? Why didn't you make that a part of asking me to move in here with you, instead of leaving me feeling like a mistress-cum-mother?'

'Is that what I made you feel like?'

She nodded.

He sighed. 'Because I didn't know how much I loved you until you became a part of my life,' he admitted. 'It kind of crept up on me slowly, like a sunny day at the end of winter.'

Curled up in her chair, Lisi felt some of the tension begin to leave her. 'Something still stopped you, though, even when you realised?'

'I was scared,' he said simply.

'Scared?' Lisi smiled. 'Oh, no! That really *would* be stretching credibility too far—I can't imagine you being scared of *anything*, Philip.'

'Scared that it would all sound too pat. That you wouldn't believe me—and why should you? I thought you would begin to see for yourself, only...'

'Only what?' she prompted, her heart in her mouth.

He shook his head as he read the doubts and fears in her eyes. 'It was like you had erected a barrier between us, and sometimes you would lower it down, but only so far—so I didn't have a clue whether you knew how I felt. Or how you felt about me,' he finished, a question in his eyes.

He had been about as honest as it was possible to be, and she knew that, to Philip, such admissions did not come easily. It was time to make her own.

'I was scared, too,' she whispered. 'Only my fear was that the love I felt for you might frighten you away. Falling in love wasn't supposed to be part of the deal, even if that's what I wanted more than anything.'

A slow smile began to transform his face into the most carefree Philip she had ever seen. 'Come here,' he whispered.

She didn't need asking twice, just went and sat on his lap, and he wrapped his arms tightly around her waist while her head fell onto his shoulder and she fought to keep the stupid and irrational tears away.

'Don't cry, Lisi,' he soothed as he felt her tremble. 'There's nothing to cry about. Not any more.'

She thought about how far she had come to reach this

moment, and, despite his words, the tears spilled over onto his sweater and soaked right through it.

He didn't say another word, just held her very, very tight until a last little sniff told him that she was all cried out, and he lifted her head and gave her the kind of tender smile she had always dreamed of. 'Better?'

'Mmm.'

'Need a hanky?'

She bit her lip and actually giggled. 'I used your sweater, thanks.'

He smiled as he brushed a last stray tear away. 'You once asked me whether that first night had just been lust,' he said softly. 'And I said that I didn't know.' He paused. 'That wasn't quite true.'

She stilled. 'What do you mean?'

It was time at last to make sense of all his vague suspicions. 'I talked to Khalim about it—I told him the whole story, and he said that such uncharacteristic behaviour on my part meant far more than I perhaps realised.' He smiled as he touched her lips, just for the hell of it. 'I told you that Khalim was a romantic, but he would prefer to describe himself as a realist. He said that I was being too hard on myself and that my subconscious was telling me that you were—or could be—very important to me. How right he was.' He kissed her tenderly. 'How right he was!'

'Oh, Philip!' She snuggled even closer to him.

'And one more thing.' He kissed her again. 'I'm sick of not letting the world know how I feel about you. I want to marry you, Lisi—just as soon as you like, *if* you like.'

'Mmm! I can't think of anything I'd like better!' She kissed him back. But not for a while. She wanted to enjoy what she had never had with Philip—a loving courtship with no pressures.

'But let's take it step by step,' she whispered. 'Better get your parents used to having a grandson before we announce that you're getting married!'

His mouth trailed a lazy line down her cheek and he felt her shiver. 'Nervous about meeting them?' he questioned.

'A little.' She pressed herself closer, revelling in the knowledge that there were no secrets or taboo between them now. Love, she realised, was a very liberating emotion. 'We've done everything the wrong way round, Philip.' She sighed. 'Haven't we?'

'It certainly hasn't been a text-book love-affair,' he agreed. 'And I need to take you to bed,' he added softly.

She felt the raw need and tension in his body, but there was one other thing she needed to say to him. 'You must never forget Carla,' she whispered. 'I don't want you to. Let all the guilt go now and remember all good times—she would want that for you, having loved you. I would.'

There was a moment of silence. 'That's about the sweetest thing you could have said,' he said shakily, and right then he needed her as he had never needed her before. He gave a slow smile. 'We'll have to go and collect Tim in an hour, you know.'

'I know. And?'

A finger was grazed carelessly around the outline of her lips. 'Any idea how you'd best like to fill the time?'

She felt the invasive tug of desire and gave him a bewitching smile, loving the predatory and possessive darkening of his eyes. 'One or two,' she said demurely.

'Me, too. Let's say we swop notes. Upstairs,' he purred, lifting her up into his arms and slanting a provocative smile down at her.

She opened her eyes very wide. 'You're going to *carry* me to bed?'

'That depends.'

'On what?'

'On whether we make it to the bedroom!'

EPILOGUE

SOMEONE was banging a spoon against an empty wineglass and the excited chatter of the guests began to die away.

It had been the most wonderful wedding imaginable. Lisi stole a glance at her new husband and let out a small sigh of contentment. She almost didn't want it to end, except that the night ahead beckoned her with such erotic promise.

Philip slowly turned his head, as though he had known she was watching him, and mouthed 'I love you' with an expression on his face which made her heart feel like spilling over with happiness.

'May I just say a few words?' The banger of the spoon was Philip's father, who was now rising to his feet.

Charles Caprice was a poppet, thought Lisi fondly. Tall and distinguished, his hair brushed with silver, he had given her a very pleasing insight into how her darling Philip would look when he was older.

Philip's mother had been equally welcoming—embracing her as if she were the daughter she had never had, and both of them were absolutely besotted by their grandson. In fact, Tim was going to stay with them while they were away in Maraban for their honeymoon.

She looked around the room. Langley had never seen a wedding like it—but maybe that wasn't so surprising. When a small English village was invaded by the leading members of the Maraban royal family and their entourage, then excitement was pretty much guaranteed!

Prince Khalim had stood as Philip's best man, and an ecstatic Rose had proudly carried the infant Prince Aziz, who had lain contentedly in her arms throughout the ceremony.

'I do not know why Rose has brought along a nanny,' Khalim had remarked drily to Philip. 'She guards him so jealously—like a tiger!'

'And would you have it any other way?' Philip had smiled.

'Never!'

Philip looked down at the jet-dark hair of the baby Aziz, and ruffled it. He had never seen his own son as a baby, and Lisi had cried and cried about denying him that right on more than one occasion, but he had urged her to let it go, as he now had. 'There'll be more babies,' he had whispered.

'Wh-when?' she had questioned shakily.

'Whenever you like. I think Tim would like a brother or a sister, don't you?'

And she had nodded and then kissed him, too full of emotion to speak for a moment or two.

Philip's father was now clearing his throat. 'I know that it isn't conventional for the *groom's* father to speak,' he began, and then sent Lisi a gentle smile across the table. 'But Lisi has become like a daughter to my wife and I—actually, she *is* our daughter, as well as my son's wife. And that's really what I want to say to you all.' His voice faltered a little. 'I would like you all to raise your glasses in a toast. To Lisi, beautiful, sweet Lisi—who has put a smile on my son's face again, and for which I will always be grateful.'

Champagne glasses were lifted and waved in the direction of the top table, but Lisi was so choked that she didn't dare look up for fear that everyone would see her eyes brimming over with tears.

'To Lisi!' they all echoed.

Beneath the table, Philip squeezed her hand. 'Look at me, my darling,' he urged softly.

She lifted her face to his, seeing the corresponding glitter of his own eyes and immediately understanding why. His father's emotional words had reinforced that a bright, new future lay ahead and that the past was now behind them. And in a way, Philip had been saying goodbye to Carla, she guessed, and squeezed his hand back, very tightly.

'It's okay to cry at weddings, you know, sweetheart,' he whispered.

She wobbled him a smile. 'But my mascara will run!'

He laughed. She was everything to him—his passion and his soul mate—the woman who had brought the light back into his life. 'I love you very much, Mrs Caprice,' he told her simply, because he did.

NATHAN'S CHILD

by

Anne McAllister

RITA® Award-winner **Anne McAllister** was born in California and spent formative summer holidays on the beach near her home and on her grandparents' small ranch in Colorado and visiting relatives in Montana. Studying the cowboys, the surfers and the beach volleyball players, she spent long hours developing her concept of "the perfect hero." (Have you noticed a lack of hard-driving Type A businessmen among them? Well, she promises to do one soon, just for a change!)

One thing she did do, early on, was develop a weakness for lean, dark-haired, handsome lone-wolf type guys. When she finally found one, he was in the university library where she was working. She knew a good man when she saw one. They've now been sharing "happily ever afters" for over thirty years. They have four grown children, and a steadily increasing number of grandchildren. They also have three dogs who keep her fit by taking her on long walks every day.

Before she started writing romances, Anne taught Spanish, capped deodorant bottles, copy-edited textbooks, got a master's degree in theology, and ghost-wrote sermons. Strange and varied, perhaps, but all grist for the writer's mill, she says.

For my wonderful Aunt Billie!
Sorry you had to wait so long for this!

CHAPTER ONE

IT WAS A DAY like any other in July on Pelican Cay. It was hot and humid and, according to Trina, the weather girl on the island's on-again, off-again radio station, there was only the faintest hope that a late-afternoon storm would blow in and clear the air.

Carin was grateful for the ancient air conditioner rattling in the window of her small art and gift shop because it kept her cool as she worked, but mostly because its welcome noise brought in customers—day-trippers off the launch from Nassau and week-long vacationers from the local inns and family resorts who came seeking refuge from the sweltering midday heat and lingered because Carin's shop was an island paradise all of its own.

Filled with one-of-a-kind art objects, paintings and sketches, sea glass jewelry, cast sand sculptures and whimsical mobiles that enchanted young and old alike, Carin's Cottage was a haven for those with money and taste and a desire to bring home something more enduring than a T-shirt to remember their holiday by.

Everyone who found their way to tiny Pelican Cay eventually found their way to Carin's. Business was good. Life was sweet.

And she could hardly wait to tell Fiona, the talented but apprehensive young sculptor, that her newest small pieces were headed for Pittsburgh—or would be as soon as Carin finished wrapping them—with the two nice ladies chatting to her about what a lovely place Pelican Cay was.

"Heaven on earth," Carin agreed as she wrapped a small, carved driftwood pelican in blue tissue paper. She put it in a white carrier bag and looked up when the door

suddenly opened. She smiled, hoping for another tourist or
two before the launch headed back to Nassau.

One look and the smile vanished. "Oh, hell."

The two ladies blinked in astonishment.

"I thought you said heaven," one began.

But the other turned toward the door. "Oh," she said.

"My," she said.

"Who's that?" she said.

"The devil himself," Carin answered under her breath.

"Nathan Wolfe," she said aloud, and was grateful she
didn't sound as shaken as she felt.

Nathan Wolfe had always been handsome as the devil.
With his thick, black windblown hair and dark tan, he had
once been the epitome of male beauty.

The years had honed his looks, sharpened them, hardened them. And now he looked as fierce and hard and predatory as his name as he stood in the doorway of Carin's
shop and slowly, behind sunglasses, scanned the room—
settling finally on her.

Carin didn't move. Deliberately she stared back, determined to let him know she wasn't afraid of him. Only when
she was sure she'd made her point did she avert her gaze,
turning back to concentrate on the package she was wrapping for her customers.

They were her priority—not Nathan bloody Wolfe!

But whatever conversation they'd been having before
Nathan had opened the door had gone completely out of
her head. And the ladies seemed much more interested in
Nathan. They stood just drinking in the sight of the hard,
devilishly handsome man who looked like nothing so much
as a gunfighter just stepping into the OK corral.

"I don't suppose we could buy him," the taller one murmured.

"You wish," the other said.

I wish, Carin thought. And she wished they would take
him all the way back to Pittsburgh with them, too.

The taller one studied him a moment longer, but when he didn't seem to even notice her—not once shifting his gaze from Carin—she reached for the bag Carin was filling with their purchases. "Come along, Blanche. We can wrap these back at the ship."

"No," Carin protested hastily. "Don't hurry away. Take your time. Stay awhile." *Stay forever.* If they stayed, maybe Nathan would be the one to leave.

But at that moment he came in and shut the door behind him.

Come on, come on, she thought. *Just get it over with.*

But he didn't move her way. Instead he wandered over to the counter at the far end of the room and began leisurely examining Seamus Logan's coconut carvings, then Fiona's sculptures. Carin gritted her teeth. She watched his easy, nerve-racking grace as he took his time, picking up and studying them all. He moved on then to the handmade toys that the Cash brothers made, Sally's straw weavings, the hand-painted T-shirts and baby rompers that Alisette designed and then he weighed one of old Turk Sawyer's paperweights in his hand.

She'd never thought of Turk's paperweights as weapons before. She did now.

They weren't enemies, she and Nathan. They simply hadn't seen each other in years and years. Thirteen years, to be exact.

And until last September she'd lived in hope of never seeing him again.

But then his brother Dominic had come to Pelican Cay—and Carin had known it was just a matter of time.

But months had passed, and when Nathan didn't come, she began to hope. And now, in the space of a single moment, her hopes had been dashed.

He set the paperweight down and lifted his gaze to study the paintings on the walls—*her* paintings—and with every slow step, Nathan came closer.

Ignoring him as best she could, Carin finished wrapping the last piece of sculpture and put it in the bag. "There you go. I do hope you'll enjoy them—and think of us often. And I hope you'll come back again."

"Oh, we'd love to," one said.

"Especially if you start stocking merchandise like that." The shorter one nodded in Nathan's direction and started for the door.

"He'd be some souvenir," the other agreed with a laugh. Then, eyeing Nathan up and down as she passed, she hurried after her friend. The door opened and banged shut behind them.

In the rattle and hum of the air conditioner, Carin thought she could hear a bomb ticking. She laced her fingers together and took deep, steadying breaths and tried to gather her thoughts—and her defenses.

Thirteen years ago she had been in love with this man. Thirteen years ago he had been gentle, kind, boyish, loving—everything that his hard-edged brother, Dominic, the man she had been engaged to marry, had not.

She'd liked but she hadn't loved Dominic Wolfe. He had been her father's idea of her perfect husband, not hers. But naive girl that she'd been, she'd thought their marriage would work—until she met Nathan.

Knowing Nathan—loving Nathan—Carin had realized that she couldn't marry his brother.

She'd tried to tell Dominic. But he'd told her it was nerves and brushed her aside. She couldn't tell her father—he wanted her marriage to Dominic to cement his business relationship with Dominic's father. Once that had sounded sensible. After she'd met Nathan, she knew it wouldn't be.

So in the end she'd done the only thing she could do—she'd run.

She'd jilted Dominic, had left him at the altar and gone into hiding. She'd been no match for him. He had been too

sophisticated, too strong, too handsome, too hard, too powerful for a girl like her.

Ten months ago he'd looked the same. But Carin had
grown up a lot in thirteen years. Even so she'd had to
muster all her courage to deal with him, to apologize to
him—to explain.

And miracle of miracles, he'd changed, too. He'd been
kinder, more patient, gentler—a word she'd never imagined
using with Dominic Wolfe.

He was married, she'd learned, to the funky, funny pur-
ple-haired Sierra, whom she'd met earlier that day. Sierra
was the last woman on earth Carin would have imagined
with Dominic. But she had obviously been good for
Dominic. She'd changed him.

Falling in love had changed him.

Clearly nothing similar had happened to his brother.
Nathan looked every bit as fierce and hard and powerful
now as Dominic once had. But if she had handled Dominic,
she was determined to handle him.

Behind the counter where he couldn't see, Carin
smoothed damp palms down the sides of her white slacks.
Then she took one last deep breath. "Good afternoon," she
said politely in her best shopkeeper's voice. "What can I
do for you?"

Nathan set down the sailboat and slowly turned to face
her. The years might have been hard, but they had given
him character and even, she noted, a few gray hairs. His
formerly straight nose looked as if it had been broken at
least once. His tan was still deep and, as she could see when
he removed his sunglasses, there were lines at the corners
of his eyes.

It was his eyes that caught and held her. Blue eyes that
had once been soft and loving now glinted like steel as he
met her gaze and answered her question.

"Marry me."

Thirteen years ago she would have jumped at the chance.

Now Carin forced herself to straighten her fingers, to remain calm, steady, centered.

"No."

It clearly wasn't the answer Nathan had been expecting. His jaw dropped. Then he clamped his mouth shut. A muscle ticked in his temple. He looked equal parts annoyance, consternation and fury.

Well, too bad. Thirteen years ago if he'd said those words to her, Carin would have flung herself on him and wept for joy.

But he hadn't.

He'd shared one night with her, then, consumed by guilt at betraying his brother, he'd told her it was all a mistake! She'd loved him body, heart and soul—and he'd simply disappeared.

Nathan hadn't been there to help her tell Dominic she couldn't marry him. And he hadn't been there nine months later when the fruit of that one night of lovemaking—their daughter, Lacey—had been born.

He was here now, Carin knew, only because Dominic had gone home last autumn and told him about Lacey.

And he'd certainly taken his own sweet time to show up! Marry him?

She wouldn't have him on a plate.

"No," she said again when he kept standing there as if he was waiting for her to rethink her answer. "Thank you," she added with icy politeness. For nothing.

For a split second Nathan's hard gaze flickered uncertainly. "I would have come sooner," he said gruffly, "if you'd bothered to tell me."

Carin almost snorted. "As if you'd have wanted to know."

They glared at each other. She was gratified when he looked away first.

"What I wanted didn't matter," he said irritably. "I'd have been here if you'd told me."

"You left. Or had you forgotten?"

"You were engaged to my brother!"

"And I'd just made love with you! For God's sake, Nathan, did you honestly think I was going to turn around two days later and marry someone else?"

"How the hell did I know? You were planning to," he argued. "That's what you were there for. You never said you weren't."

"You didn't give me a chance! You practically bolted out of the bed. Then you went running around the house, throwing your stuff in a bag and babbling about what a mistake it had been!"

A deep-red flush suffused Nathan's face. He picked up one of Turk's paperweights, turned it over and over in his hands, then slammed it down and began to pace in front of the counter.

"Okay," he said at last, "I didn't handle it well. It was a new experience for me. I didn't make a habit of sleeping with my brother's fiancées." He turned and leveled a gaze at her. "I didn't know the protocol."

"I don't think there is protocol," Carin said quietly, meeting his gaze levelly. "I think there's just honesty."

The muscle ticked in his temple again. He rocked back on his heels and jammed his hands into the pockets of his jeans. "Ok. Fine. Let's be honest." His voice was harsh. "It was great, but it was wrong. You were engaged, damn it, and not to me! I felt like a heel afterward, and I thought it was in everybody's best interest if I disappeared."

"Is that what you thought?" Carin said with saccharine sweetness. "You thought I'd just forget?"

"I didn't know what the hell you'd do. I barely knew you!"

"You knew me better than anyone in the world."

She'd been so vulnerable that week before the wedding. She'd been so worried. And she'd found in Nathan the kindred spirit she'd always hoped for. She'd poured out her feelings to him—and he didn't believe he'd known her!

Nathan raked his hand through his hair. "I didn't know what you'd do. But believe me, I was shocked as hell to come back to New York five months later and discover you'd jilted my brother and no one knew where you were!"

"You asked?"

"Yes, damn it, I asked."

"And they said they didn't know, and you left it at that." She said the words scornfully.

"What was I supposed to do? You didn't exactly leave a forwarding address. And I sure as hell wasn't going to press the issue. Your whereabouts wasn't Dominic's favorite topic of conversation."

She could believe that. She'd felt guilty for years. Still did. "So, fine. You didn't know where I was. You should have left it at that." She lifted her chin. "Besides, I didn't go anywhere. I was here all the time."

"Hiding out." Nathan said the words dismissively.

"I wasn't hiding out!" she retorted, stung.

"Right. Sent out cards with your forwarding address, did you?"

She looked away.

"And I'm sure all your old friends from Smith and St. Gertrudis or wherever it was you went to school know exactly where you are now. Your father didn't even know!"

"My father didn't want to know."

"*What?*"

"I called him a week after…after…the wedding didn't…happen. I wanted to explain." It was her turn to shrug now, to act casual, to pretend that what had happened then didn't still hurt. But sadly, whether she wanted to admit it or not, it did. "He didn't want to listen. He told me I was no daughter of his. And then he hung up on me."

"Jesus!" Nathan looked shocked. He paced halfway

down the aisle and scowled furiously. "Nobody told me that."

Carin shrugged. "Maybe no one knew." She couldn't imagine her father had advertised the fact that he had disowned his only child.

Nathan shook his head. "I asked my dad. He didn't know. He just said Magnus said you were okay. That was all. We didn't...talk about it much." Nathan's mouth twisted. "Dominic was...well, not exactly happy."

"I'm sorry." Carin really did regret that. She should have pressed harder that evening before the wedding when he had finally arrived on Pelican Cay and she'd tried to talk to him. She shouldn't have let him brush her off with a grin and an admonition that she'd better go to bed and get her rest because she wouldn't be getting much sleep on their wedding night!

It was that comment, actually, that had made her turn and run.

She couldn't possibly contemplate going to bed with Dominic—making love with Dominic—after her night with Nathan. She *loved* Nathan! There was no way, engaged or not, she could sleep with his brother!

"He seemed...happy..." she ventured "...when I saw him last summer."

"He is. Now."

She winced at the flat accusation in Nathan's tone, but it had the effect of stiffening her spine. "I'm glad," she said. "He wouldn't have been happy with me."

"Because you were in love with me." Nathan didn't look as if he relished saying the words. He tossed them out as if he had to say them, had to confirm them in order to justify his presence here—and his proposal.

"I was twenty-one. A very innocent unworldly twenty-one," she added with a grimace. "A very foolish twenty-one. I've grown up since. I *thought* I loved you. Now I know better."

And if that wasn't entirely honest, it was as close to honesty as she dared to get. She wasn't about to admit that seeing him again had sent her heart somersaulting and that no one but Nathan had ever affected her that way.

It was hormones, she told herself sharply. Sheer animal attraction. Nothing more than a normal response to his male magnetism which, let's face it, Nathan Wolfe still had in spades.

But it was absolutely true—what Carin had said about growing up and knowing better now. It hadn't been love, only infatuation. She'd been enchanted by his dark good looks and his brooding intensity. Mostly she'd been swept away by his enthusiasm, his focus, his dreams and aspirations.

In her circumscribed world all the men she met were like her father—moneyed, high-powered men who ran business conglomerates and whose goal in life was to preserve the family millions and make more. There was certainly nothing wrong with those aspirations, as her father was only too willing to point out to her. His success at achieving them had, after all, paid for their Connecticut estate, their beach house on the cape, her very expensive private school education, and the art and music lessons she'd wanted to take.

Carin knew that. But it had still been refreshing to meet a man who didn't care how many houses he had, who had dropped out of college in his sophomore year and had gone to work on a freighter. That had been the first of many odd jobs. He'd worked as a stringer for a magazine in the Far East, had taken photos on a Japanese fishing boat, had been a deck hand on a copra boat in the South Seas and had washed dishes in exchange for meals and a place to sleep in Chile.

She had listened, wide-eyed and enchanted, to Nathan's tales of a world she had only dreamed about. And he had told her that that's what his life's dream was—to see the world, to experience it, not just read about it…or own it, he'd added disparagingly. He wanted his photos to make it real for people who could never go themselves.

To a young woman who had never had the courage to do what she really wanted to do—who hadn't even *known* what she really wanted to do—Nathan Wolfe had been a hero.

For a week.

Now Carin said firmly, "Trust me, I don't love you now. You don't need to feel any belated compunction to marry me."

"This isn't just about you," Nathan said sharply. "It's about our daughter!"

"*My* daughter. I gave birth to her. I nursed her. I walked the floor with her. I patched up her cuts and bruises and sang her lullabies and read her stories."

"And didn't even tell me she existed!"

"You wouldn't have cared!"

"The hell I wouldn't."

"You left!"

"And now I'm back!"

"Well, we don't need you! So just go away again. Go off to Timbuktu or Nepal or Antarctica. Take your photos. Enjoy your freedom. It's what you wanted!"

"Wanted," he agreed. "Past tense. Like loved."

"What do you mean?" she asked warily.

"I mean it's not what I want now. And I'm not leaving."

She stared at him. "Ever?"

"If that's what it takes." He had the look of his brother again. Hard and implacable. Determined to get his way.

"So you're going to stay here," she said conversationally. "Doing what, If you don't mind my asking?"

"Being a father."

It was the last thing she expected him to say—and it hit her right in the gut. She stared at him. "*You?*"

Kids had never figured in Nathan Wolfe's universe. In

the week they'd spent sharing dreams and hopes and plans, never once had he mentioned wanting a family.

His jaw tightened. "You don't think I can be a good parent?"

"I'm surprised you want to."

"Did you? Want to?"

The question caught her off guard. And the panic she'd felt when she'd discovered she was pregnant appeared unbidden in her mind. She banished it now as she had determinedly banished it all those years ago.

"I always wanted children," she said defensively. "I love my daughter more than anyone on earth."

"I'm looking forward to meeting *our* daughter."

She wanted to say, Well, you're not going to. She wanted to banish him from the island, from her—and Lacey's— life. But she couldn't, and she knew it. He was her daughter's father, and ever since Dominic and Sierra had turned up, Lacey's curiosity about him had been piqued. She'd studied his books avidly, asked a million questions, wondered whether she would ever get to meet him. And Carin had had to smile and act indifferent, as if it wouldn't matter to her whether Nathan appeared or not.

"I'm sure she'll be glad to meet you, too," Carin said stiffly.

"Where is she?"

"Fishing."

Nathan raised a brow. "Fishing?"

"Girls can fish, too."

"I know that. I just didn't think about it. I thought… school or something."

"It's July. No school in July. She went with her friend Lorenzo. He's Thomas's son." Nathan knew Thomas. They were about the same age, and Thomas's parents, Maurice and Estelle, were the caretakers of the Wolfes' house. "They won't be back until late."

Not *that* late actually. Thomas brought his catch in before dinner every day. But Carin wasn't having Nathan hanging around waiting, for the rest of the afternoon.

"I'll just mosey on down to the pier then, shall I?"

"*No!* I mean…no." She'd forgotten Nathan would know that unless a fisherman was going to be gone for several days—in which case he wouldn't be taking a couple of kids—he'd be back in time to sell his catch to housewives looking for fresh fish for dinner. Carin wetted her lips. "You can't just go. I need to talk to her first."

"Come with me. We can talk to her together."

"No. We can't. I can't. I have to keep my shop open." And she didn't want to show up on the quay with Nathan in tow. "Let me talk to her, Nathan. Let me prepare her first. Please."

Nathan jammed his hands into the pockets of well-worn jeans. "Prepare her? How?"

"Tell her that you're here. Have some consideration, Nathan. She thought as soon as you knew about her you'd come. You've known about her for months. You didn't show up until today."

"I had assignments. I had work. I didn't want to come and leave again two days later."

"Fine. Whatever. You did this on your timetable. Give me a chance now."

"All right. You can have the rest of the day."

"But—"

"How long does it take, Carin?" he said impatiently. "Just tell her I'm here. We'll work it out from there."

"We can't—"

"Promise me you'll tell her tonight. Or I'll go down to the pier and tell her myself."

"All right! Fine. I'll talk to her. Tonight," she added grudgingly when he lifted a brow, waiting.

"Do that." He nodded. "And tell her I'll come by tomorrow morning."

She shrugged. "Come whenever you want. You obviously will anyway," she muttered.

Nathan didn't reply He just allowed her a ghost of a smile, then he turned and ambled toward the door. Opening it, he turned back. He leveled his blue eyes on her. "Don't even think of running off."

"As if I would!" she exclaimed hotly.

A corner of his mouth twisted. "See you in the morning," he promised.

To Carin it sounded more like a threat.

So she wouldn't marry him.

Nathan wasn't exactly surprised, since she hadn't even bothered to tell him he was a father! Damn it to hell! He could still get furious just thinking about it! Did she think he wouldn't care that he had a daughter? That he wouldn't have wanted to know?

Even now he could recall the punched-in-the-gut feeling he'd experienced when Dominic had told him he'd met Carin again at Pelican Cay.

Nathan had done his best not to think about Carin Campbell—or the week they'd spent together—for years.

It had been an impossible situation right from the start— the two of them thrown together, more or less alone in the house on the island for an entire week. Nathan, taking a well-deserved vacation from six solid months of being in the field in South America, had shown up at the family house on the island, ready to do his bit as his brother's best man the following Saturday, and had been astonished to find Carin, said brother's quiet, sensitive, pretty fiancée, already there. She'd been sent down early to fulfil a residency requirement for their Bahamian marriage. She'd been there two weeks already—and she'd spent them, as far as Nathan could figure, worrying nonstop about her upcoming nuptials.

"What's to worry about?" he'd asked cavalierly. As

long as it was someone else getting married and not him, he hadn't seen the problem.

But Carin had. Her cheeks had turned a deep-red as she'd admitted, "Your brother."

"Dominic? What's not to like about Dominic? He's handsome, wealthy, powerful, smart." Definitely the best catch of the Wolfe brothers, that was for sure.

"Yes, he is. All of the above," Carin had said faintly. She had barely smiled, and he'd realized she was serious.

He should have realized then she was no match for Dominic. But Nathan had had no experience thinking like an unsophisticated, green girl. Relationships of any sort didn't interest him. Sure, Dominic was hardheaded and used to having his own way, but he was kind, he was honorable, he was the best of men.

"That's the trouble," Carin said when he'd pointed that out. "I don't know anything about men."

"How the hell did you get engaged to him then?"

"Our fathers introduced us."

He should have known. So Dominic was marrying to please their old man. And Nathan supposed Carin was marrying to please hers.

Even so, they had seemed well matched. Both had fathers who were high-powered businessmen, independent entrepreneurs who had used their brains and plenty of hard work to build multinational concerns. Both Dominic and Carin had grown up on the East Coast, had gone to the same sorts of preppy schools and Ivy League colleges, had the same sorts of friends.

And Nathan couldn't imagine that his brother was indifferent to his bride-to-be.

Slender and fine-boned, with long long long blonde hair and wide sea-blue eyes, Carin was your basic, everyday, downright gorgeous female.

If Nathan had been interested in a woman of his own—

which he wasn't—he'd have felt a prick of envy at his brother's lot.

But the last thing Nathan wanted was a wife—especially a wife who would tie him to a corporate lifestyle he had rejected. But Carin was the sort of wife who would suit Dominic to a T. She'd be a terrific accessory to his career and not bad on the home front, either.

So he'd said cheerfully, ''You want to learn about men? You want to get to know Dominic? Hell, I'm just like Dominic—'' perhaps a stretch of the truth there, but in a good cause ''—just stick with me.''

He figured they'd have a good time that week. He would enjoy a little friendly platonic female companionship, would cement his role as favored brother-in-law in years to come, and at the same time he'd do Dominic a good turn.

After all, Dominic had gone to bat for him when Nathan had told their father he didn't want to work for Wolfes', that he wanted to be a photographer instead.

The old man had been downright furious. ''What do you mean you don't want to work for Wolfes'? It's buttered your bread your whole life, you ungrateful whelp.''

Then Dominic had stepped in, pointing out that what Nathan wanted to do was no more than what Douglas had done when he'd built Wolfes' in the first place—be his own man.

''He's the most like you of any of us,'' Dominic had said forcefully.

Not something Nathan cheerfully acknowledged. But it had stopped the old man. It had made him look thoughtful. And the next thing Nathan knew, his father had been beaming and shaking his hand.

''Chip off the old block,'' he'd said, nodding his head. ''Dominic's right. You've got guts, my boy.'' He'd fixed Nathan with a level blue gaze. ''Fine. Go hop your freighter or thumb your way around the world, if that's what you want. It will be hard and long, but it's your choice.''

So Nathan owed Dominic. And showing his wife-to-be a good time and giving her a little confidence had seemed a small chore.

It hadn't been a chore at all.

Carin had been eager to listen to his tales of far-off lands and to ask questions about all his experiences. Very few people, Nathan had discovered, listened as well as she did. He had thoroughly enjoyed basking in her worshipful gaze.

Every day they had gone swimming and snorkeling and sailing. And while they did, he had told her about his family—not only about Dominic, but about their youngest brother, Rhys, and their parents, their mother who had died when they were young, and their father who had been everything to them ever since.

"She taught us to care," he said. "He taught us to be tough."

And Carin had listened intently, taking it all in, nodding and watching him with those gorgeous blue eyes. He told her about the house on the beach out on Long Island where they'd grown up and about the holidays they'd spent here on Pelican Cay when he was a child.

"Dominic has a place in New York," he'd explained. "But only because the offices are there. He isn't as much of a city boy as you might think."

"I don't think he's a boy at all."

Well, no, he wasn't. But Carin wasn't a girl, either. She was a woman.

And Nathan knew it. The more time he spent with her, the greater his awareness of her had grown. His eyes traced the lines of her body. They lingered on her curves. At night it hadn't seemed to matter how much exercise he got during the day, he couldn't settle down, he couldn't sleep. Couldn't stop thinking about her.

She's Dominic's fiancée, he'd reminded himself over and over. And he tried to think about her with his brother, tried to imagine her in bed with Dominic. But his mind left out

Dominic. It only saw Carin. He had fantasies about Carin in bed. And he and not Dominic had been the man in bed with her.

He should have taken off then. Should have started running and never looked back.

He hadn't. He'd stayed. Of course he had stepped up his commentary about Dominic, telling her how his brother had defended his desire to take photos.

But then she'd asked to see them. And when he'd shown them to her, she'd been enchanted, eager to see more, eager to learn about what he looked for in shooting photographs.

And that was when he'd discovered she was an artist.

She'd been shy about admitting it. But when he'd shown her plenty of bad photos he'd taken, she'd relented and allowed him to see her paintings and sketches. They were lively, cheerful, bright, almost primitive paintings and detailed, very realistic sketches. He'd expected something amateurish. Instead she was enormously talented, and he'd told her so.

"What does Dominic think about your work?" he'd asked.

"He wouldn't be interested," she'd said with a shrug. "He only thinks about business."

If he only thought about business when his eager, beautiful, talented fiancée was around, Dominic had rocks in his head.

Nathan hadn't been able to think about anything else.

In fact, whenever he'd thought about the perfect woman for him, Carin was it.

Not that he had said so. He hadn't wanted to make her uncomfortable. Besides, there was no point. Nothing would happen, Nathan had assured himself, because he wouldn't let it.

And possibly nothing would have—if it hadn't been for that storm.

The day before Dominic and his father were to arrive,

Nathan and Carin had gone for a walk after dinner along the pink sand beach. When they'd reached the rocks that jutted out into the sea, he'd held out a hand to help her up, and somehow he'd never let go.

He'd liked holding it, enjoyed running his thumb along the soft smooth flesh, relished the gentle grip she held on his fingers, as if she didn't want to let go, either. It felt right holding her hand. And when they climbed down the other side, their fingers stayed laced together as if by mutual consent. Their hands had known what they were still unable to admit.

When they got back, Nathan remembered telling himself, he would let her go.

The storm had come up quickly, and they were soaked by the time they got back to the house. The wind was chilly, and Nathan had built a fire while Carin changed clothes. Then he'd gone to change his own clothes, expecting to meet her back in the living room and spend the last evening they had together before everyone else arrived lounging in front of the fire.

That's what he'd thought until he'd gone to his room to change. He had stripped down to his shorts when he heard a tap on his bedroom door. "Yeah?"

The door had opened.

Carin had stood before him wearing a towel and a tentative smile. Nothing else. "All my stuff is in the wash and I forgot to put it in the dryer," she confessed. "Do you have some jeans and a sweatshirt I could borrow."

Nathan remembered dumbly nodding his head. He didn't remember saying anything. He didn't think he could have. He'd seen Carin in a bathing suit, of course. He knew—had memorized—those slender enticing curves.

But it was different seeing her wrapped in a towel. It was different knowing that she had nothing on underneath. He remembered the feel of her soft fingers. He wanted to touch the rest of her. His body responded even as his mind tried to resist.

Embarrassed at his sudden fierce arousal, he had turned away toward the dresser. ''I'll get 'em,'' he'd said hoarsely.

But instead of waiting outside his room, she came in. She came to stand beside him—so close that he could see goose bumps on her arms. ''You're cold,'' he'd said. ''We've got to warm you up.''

He hadn't meant to reach for her. He hadn't meant to make love with her. But the next thing he knew she'd been in his arms.

If he shut his eyes now, Nathan could still remember the tremble of her body against his, could taste her cool flesh as his lips had touched it.

Right here. Right in this room.

Nathan jerked back to the present, cursing the desire that flooded his veins, hating the need that seeing her again this afternoon had aroused!

He grabbed his gear and stamped out of the bedroom. He could sleep in any room. He didn't have to stay in there where the memories would haunt him every second.

But the room next to his had been Dominic's. And Carin had stayed in Rhys's. He stood there, clutching his duffel, torn, frustrated, angry—

And heard a knock on the kitchen door.

He clattered down the stairs, expecting Maurice, who was going to help him build a dark room. ''Hey, there,'' he said, glad for the distraction, as he jerked open the door.

But it wasn't Maurice.

It was a girl.

''Hello,'' she said politely. ''I'm Lacey. You must be my father.''

CHAPTER TWO

EVER SINCE DOMINIC had revealed her existence, Nathan had envisioned the day he would meet his daughter, had tried to imagine what he would say to her. And always—every time—their meeting had been at a time and place of *his* choosing.

He'd wanted it to be perfect, knowing full well that, having missed her first twelve years, it never would be.

Still, he'd made an effort.

He'd cleared the decks, finished his assignments, met his commitments. Whenever his agent, Gaby, rang him with new projects, new ideas, new shows, new demands, he turned them down. He wanted nothing on his schedule now but Lacey—and her mother.

He was prepared. Or so he'd thought.

He didn't feel prepared now.

He felt stunned, faced with this girl who wore a pair of white shorts and a fluorescent lime-green T-shirt with the Statue of Liberty and the words New York Babe on it. She had a backpack on her back and sandals on her feet and looked like a hundred preteen girls.

But more than that, she looked like him.

Nathan tried to think of something profound to say or at least something sensible. Nothing came to mind. He had spent much of his adult life in precarious positions—hanging off cliffs, kayaking down white-water rapids, hanging out with polar bears, and tracking penguins in Tierra del Fuego—but none had seemed more precarious than this one.

Now he realized that Lacey was waiting—staring at him,

shifting impatiently from one foot to the other, her hand still stuck out in midair.

Awkwardly Nathan shook it and dredged up a faint grin. "I guess I must be," he said. *Must be your father.*

He felt short of breath. Dazed. Positively blown away. His voice sounded rusty even to his own ears. He stood there, holding her hand—his *daughter's* hand!—learning the feel of it. Her fingers were warm and slender, delicate almost. But there were calluses on her palm. He felt them against his own rough fingers.

From fishing? he wondered. He didn't have a clue. He knew nothing about her. Nothing at all.

She was still looking at him expectantly, and he realized the next move was up to him. "Won't you...come in?"

He felt absurd, inviting his twelve-year-old daughter into his home as if she was a stranger. Fortunately, Lacey didn't seem to see the absurdity of it. She just marched past him into the room, then looked around with interest.

Nathan wondered if she'd ever been in the house before.

He'd always loved it, had thought it was the best place on earth. He had been five when they'd first come to Pelican Cay, and when they'd flown in that first day, he'd thought their little seaplane was landing in paradise. It turned out he wasn't far wrong. Pelican Cay in those days had sand and surf and sun and no telephones to take his father away on business for a week or more at a time.

He and his brothers had spent their happiest hours here. They used to say that it would be the best thing on earth to spend every day on Pelican Cay.

Lacey had. At least he supposed she had.

"Would you...like something to drink?" he asked her. "A soda?" She wouldn't think he was offering her a beer, would she?

"Yes, please." Was she always this polite? Was she always this self-possessed?

He started toward the kitchen, nodding for her to follow.

"Is your…I mean, *where* is your…mother?" Somehow he was sure her visit had not been sanctioned by her mother.

"She teaches a painting class on Mondays," Lacey said. She slipped off her backpack, set it on the counter in the middle of the kitchen. Then she perched on a stool as Nathan opened the refrigerator.

"Pineapple, sea grape or cola?"

"Pineapple, please. It's my favorite."

"Mine, too." Nathan snagged the cans, straightened up and turned around. Their gazes met. And as he popped the tops and handed her the can, they both grinned, sharing the moment and the appreciation of pineapple soda. The knot of apprehension that had been coiled deep and tight inside Nathan ever since he'd discovered he had a daughter suddenly eased.

It reminded him of the feeling he got when he was just beginning fieldwork on a project. The days *before* he was actually there drove him crazy. Once he was involved, he experienced a welcome feeling of relief, a sense of rightness. Like this.

"I'm glad you came," he said, and meant it.

"I'm glad you came," Lacey countered. "I've been needing a father for quite a while."

Nathan's brows rose. "You have?"

"It's difficult to be a one-parent child," Lacey explained. "I don't mean that my mother is a bad mother. She's not. Not at all! She's terrific. And mostly she manages very well. But there are, I think," she said consideringly, "some things fathers are better at."

"Are there?" Nathan was feeling stunned again.

"Mmm. Cutting bait."

He stared at her blankly.

"Fishing." She gave him a despairing look. "You do know how to fish?"

"Of course I know how to fish," Nathan said, affronted.

"I was, um, thinking of something else." As in *fish or...*
"Can't your mother cut bait yet?"

He grinned, remembering Carin's squeamishness when
he'd taken her fishing so she would be able to share one
of Dominic's pleasures.

"She can. She doesn't like to. She doesn't like to fish."

"And you do." It wasn't a question. He could see the
sparkle in her eyes.

"But I always have to go with Lorenzo and his dad, and
then Lorenzo always catches the biggest fish."

"Because his dad cuts the bait?"

"No. Because he gets to go with his dad lots more than
I do. And we always go where Thomas thinks the fish are
biting, and they always are—for Lorenzo."

"I see." Well, sort of, he did. He gathered it had to do
with the amount of time Thomas spent with his son—time
that Nathan hadn't spent with his daughter. But apparently
she wasn't just going to spell it out. Maybe it was the
difference between boys and girls.

"Do you know any good fishing places?"

Nathan rubbed a hand against the back of his neck. "I
could probably find some." He hoped.

"Good." Lacey took a swallow of her soda. "Lorenzo
could come with us, couldn't he?"

"Sure."

"I have your books."

Nathan blinked, surprised by the change of topic, but
even more so by what she'd changed it to. "You do?"

Lacey nodded. "My mother got them for me."

"Why?" He could be blunt, too, Nathan decided.

"When I was little I asked about you, and Mom told me
you were a photographer. I asked if she had any pictures
you took, and she said no. I asked if she could find some.
So on my birthday when I was eight, she gave me one of
your books. Now I have all of them. They're great."

Nathan didn't know whether to be flattered or furious.

Certainly he was flattered that Lacey approved of his work. But he was also furious that Carin had decided that having his books was all of him that Lacey would need.

"But I like Zeno the best," Lacey said. "Did you live with him?"

Zeno was a wolf. He had been, for want of a better word, the hero of Nathan's last book and in some cases, it seemed, his alter ego, as well. Zeno's "lone wolf" status had been similar to Nathan's own.

"I didn't live with him," he said. "But I spent a lot of time watching him, observing, studying, trying to get to know him."

Lacey bobbed her head. "You did. You knew him. He was my favorite."

"Mine, too." The book itself was called *Solo* and dealt with several years in the life of one young lone wolf. The project had grown incidentally out of an earlier book Nathan had done on Northern wildlife. While there he'd come across a small wolf pack with several young pups. One of them, a young male, often wrestled and played with the others, but seemed more inclined to go off scouting around on his own. Intrigued, Nathan had shot a lot of photos of him.

A year later, when a magazine assignment had taken him back to the same area, he had, coincidentally, happened across the wolves again. The young loner had been an adolescent then, and Nathan had shot more rolls of film of the wolf by himself and interacting with the pack.

After that encounter he'd looked for more assignments in the area, always trying to track down the wolf, who by this time he'd begun to think of as Zeno.

Two years ago he'd simply indulged his desire to learn more by taking the better part of a year to live in the woods up there and study Zeno's comings and goings.

Solo had been published this past spring, the story in text and pictures of one young lone wolf. It had garnered considerable critical praise.

It had also fueled a ridiculous amount of comparison between Nathan Wolfe's own life as a "lone wolf" photographer. He and Zeno were somehow connected in the public's perception.

More than one magazine article had asked, Who would be the woman to settle him down? And it wasn't Zeno they'd been talking about.

By that time, though, Nathan had learned of Lacey's existence, and the question of which woman would "settle him down" had already, to his mind, been decided.

It was just a matter of coming to terms with her—and tying up all the loose ends first.

"Are you going to go back and see Zeno again?" Lacey asked him.

"I don't know."

He had planned to. He'd intended to go there again this summer after he'd finished his other jobs. Gaby had been pushing him to do so. But he'd made those plans last summer, before he'd learned about Lacey. For the moment at least, Zeno was going to have to wait.

"I wish you would," Lacey said. "We gotta know what happens to him."

"Maybe," Nathan said. "But I've got work to do now here."

"You're going to shoot here?"

He shook his head. "I'm writing here. I've done the shooting. Now I have to organize the photos for a book."

"What's it about?"

"Sea turtles."

"Oh." Lacey's expression said she didn't think that would be nearly as intriguing as another book on wolves.

"I got to dive with some," Nathan told her.

"Do you know how to scuba dive? I want to learn to scuba dive. Mom says maybe when I'm older, but it's expensive. Hugh said he'd teach me, but she thinks it would be presuming." Lacey wrinkled her nose. "I don't think Hugh would mind. But as long as you're here…"

"Who's Hugh?"

Lacey giggled. "Hugh the hunk. That's what Mom and Florence call him." Lacey giggled.

"Who's Florence?" Hugh's wife, Nathan hoped.

"Lorenzo's mother."

Not Hugh's wife, then. "So what does this Hugh do, when he isn't scuba diving?" What sort of "hunk" was Carin running around with?

"He runs the charter service. He's got a seaplane and a helicopter and three boats. Last summer when Lorenzo had to have his appendix out, Hugh flew him to the hospital in Nassau. When he came home, Hugh took me along to pick him up. It was way cool. Can you fly a helicopter?"

"No."

"Oh." A pause. "That's too bad." Because maybe she was angling to learn how to fly a helicopter, too? "I used to think maybe he'd be my dad," Lacey said.

Nathan scowled. "Why?"

"Because he likes Mom. An' Mom likes him."

And he was a hunk.

"And now she doesn't?" Nathan hadn't even thought that Carin might have a boyfriend. Dominic had only known that she didn't have a husband.

"'Course she likes him. I told you, he's nice."

"But he's not going to be your dad?"

Lacey gave a long-suffering sigh. "You're my dad," she explained.

"Oh. Right. Of course."

Which was true but wasn't the answer to his question: Does your mother plan on marrying Hugh the hunk? He couldn't bring himself to ask that.

"Do you have your book about Zeno here?" Lacey finished her soda, hopped off the stool, carried the can to the sink and rinsed it out. "If you do I can tell you my favorite picture. And you can tell me about when you took it."

"Yeah, I've got it upstairs." He moved to get it. Like a shadow, Lacey came right after him.

"I like this house," she said, looking around his bedroom with interest. "It's big. Lots bigger than our house."

"Yeah, well, there were three of us boys and my folks." He opened the duffel on the floor and began pulling clothes out. There was a copy of each of his books at the bottom. He'd brought them for Lacey, never thinking Carin would already have given them to her.

"I've always wanted brothers and sisters." Lacey perched on the edge of the bed and looked hopefully up at him.

"Yeah, well, um…brothers are kind of a pain in the neck."

She gave a little bounce. "Uncle Dominic is really nice. He came to the shop to see my mom. And then he and Aunt Sierra were here before Christmas. And he and Grandpa came down a couple of months ago."

Grandpa?

"Which Grandpa?" Nathan asked warily.

"The only one I've ever met," Lacey said. "Grandpa Doug."

His *father* had been here? And hadn't even bothered to mention it?

"Grandpa brought me a camera. Want to see it?"

"A camera? Why'd he bring you a camera?" Nathan demanded.

"Because he thought it would be good for me to understand your business," Lacey told him.

Yeah, Nathan thought grimly, that sounded like the old man. Grandkids and business were the two most significant things in Douglas Wolfe's life. Nathan was almost surprised he hadn't given Lacey a share of the company, and he said so.

"He wanted to," Lacey said. "My mom said no."

Nathan blinked. That didn't sound like the Carin he remembered. The Carin he remembered wouldn't have said boo to a goose. But then he recalled that she'd taken her life into her own hands the day she'd jilted his brother. So she'd obviously made some changes.

And so had his father if Douglas was taking no for an answer.

"She said if he wanted to visit, he could visit, but he couldn't buy his way into our lives."

Nathan choked back a laugh, imagining his father's reaction to that. Oddly, he felt both proud of Carin for her stance and indignant on his father's behalf. Because he didn't know what to say, he dug through the books in his duffel until he found *Solo.*

"Great." Lacey took it from him and flipped through it confidently, clearly looking for a particular picture. "This one." She laid the book open flat on the bed so they could both look at it.

It was a photo he remembered well. He had taken it across a clearing with a telephoto lens. In the clearing itself, there were three half-grown wolf cubs wrestling with each other. It had been fun-and-games time for them. And that was all most people ever saw, and they cooed and oohed over the frolicking pups.

But now Lacey's finger unerringly found Zeno watching his littermates from behind the brush on the far side of the clearing. He stood silent. Alone. Apart.

"Did you realize," she asked Nathan, "when you took the photo, that he was there?"

"Not at first," he admitted. "I was caught, like anyone would be, at the sight of the other pups. But as I took shot after shot, I really started to look, to focus. And then I saw him there."

"All by himself." Lacey's finger brushed over the Zeno

on the page. "Do you think he was lonely? Do you think he wanted to play, too?"

"Maybe sometimes he did. Sometimes, though, I think he was happier on his own."

"Me, too," Lacey said. "I mean, I'm like that, too." She slanted a glance up at him from beneath a fall of long dark hair. "Are you?"

Nathan considered that, then nodded. "Yeah, I am."

Lacey nodded. She ran her tongue over her lips. "Then...do you think you'll mind being part of us?"

The question caught him off guard.

But before he could even hazard an answer, she went on. "Because I was thinking you might wish you didn't know...about me."

"No," Nathan said flatly. He sat down on the bed beside her and looked straight into his daughter's big blue eyes. "Don't *ever* think that," he said firmly. "Not for a minute. I'm glad I know about you."

Their gazes locked. Seconds ticked by. It was like being weighed and measured, judged for his intentions. And Nathan knew, however long it took, he had to hold her gaze.

Finally a smile spread slowly across Lacey's face. "I'm glad you know about me, too," she said, then sighed. "I didn't think you wanted to."

"Why not?"

"Because you didn't come. After Uncle Dominic and Aunt Sierra were here the first time, I mean."

Nathan looked away, wondering how to explain what he wasn't sure he understood himself. When Dominic had first told him about finding Carin again, he'd been astonished at his reaction. He'd so determinedly "forgotten" her that he was completely unprepared for the sudden clench of his stomach and the flip-flop of his heart at the sound of her name.

And he'd felt awkward as hell about those feelings in

front of his brother. Dominic's old pain was fresh enough in Nathan's memory to make all his guilt flood back. And even though Dominic was happy now and glad to understand at last why Carin had jilted him, Nathan hadn't been able to come to terms with the new circumstances that quickly.

He'd resisted all thought of renewing his relationship with Carin.

And then Dominic had mentioned Lacey.

He'd been deliberately vague, mentioning her name casually, hinting at a possibility that had frankly taken Nathan's breath away.

He had a daughter? He'd been poleaxed by the idea. It had reordered his reality and had paralyzed him at the same time. He'd prowled the beach near their Long Island home for hours afterward, had driven miles. Had tried to think. But his mind had been a blur.

There was no way he could explain to Lacey the roller coaster of emotions he'd ridden that night and for weeks after he'd learned of her existence. A part of him had wanted to grab the next plane to the Bahamas. A saner, more rational part had refused to let him.

He needed to get his house in order, to weigh the implications, to decide what would be best for his daughter. And while he did that, he went on with his life.

He fulfilled the assignments he'd already committed to, wrote the articles he'd agreed to, took the pictures that would go in his next book. And all the while—no matter where he was—his mind was grappling with the knowledge of his daughter.

"I had commitments," he said finally. "Things that I'd agreed to do before I knew about you. Photo assignments. Articles. People were counting on me." *And your mother definitely was not.* "So I did my job. When I came I wanted to be ready to stay. I didn't want to have to leave again as soon as I got here."

Lacey nodded happily. "That's what Grandpa said."

The old man had certainly been sticking his oar in, Nathan thought. But in this instance he was glad. "He was right."

"I'm glad you're staying." She gave a little bounce on the bed. "For how long?"

As long as it takes, Nathan thought. He wasn't sure what the answer was. But he wasn't leaving until he and Carin and Lacey were a family.

"I've got a book to write. Pictures to choose. I'll be doing that here. You can help."

Lacey's eyes lit up. "I can? Really?"

"Well, you can't make all the decisions, but you can have some input. You said you were taking pictures, right?"

"Right. I brought some. An' I brought my camera. They're in my backpack. Want to see them?" She looked eager, and then just a little nervous, as if she might have overstepped her bounds.

But Nathan was delighted. "Of course. Show me."

They went back downstairs and Lacey opened her backpack. Her camera was a good basic single-lens reflex, not a point-and-shoot. Every setting had to be done manually.

"Grandpa said you'd want me to start the way you did," Lacey told him. "Learning how to do everything."

Good ol' Grandpa. It was true, of course. It was exactly what Nathan would have wanted. He handed the camera back to her.

"He said it was exactly the same in business," his daughter informed him. "A person needs to know how to do things herself before she starts taking shortcuts."

"Yeah," Nathan said. "Let's see your pictures."

Lacey hesitated. "I don't focus real good."

"You'll learn."

"And sometimes I wobble a little."

"So do we all."

"And some of 'em are too light and others are too dark."

"It happens. Not every shot is a prizewinner, Lace. I throw out way more than I print."

"Really?" She looked at him, wide-eyed, as if that had never occurred to her. And at his solemn nod, she breathed a sigh of relief and began pulling out envelopes of photographic prints.

Nathan spread them on the island, and they pulled up stools and sat side by side, looking at them. She was right— many of them were out of focus, many were too dark or too light. On some the camera had clearly wobbled. But she had a nice sense of composition. She had an eye for telling detail.

There were pictures of the harbor and the village, of Maurice blowing a conch shell to call the women to buy fresh fish, of Thomas, Maurice's son and the father of Lacey's friend Lorenzo, cleaning fish on the dock. There were lots of pictures of a boy Lacey's age, mugging for the camera, walking a fence like a tightrope, sitting astride one of the old English cannons near the cliff. Lorenzo, no doubt.

There was a particularly well-composed picture of a row of colorful shirts flapping on a clothesline in the wind and, behind them, a row of pastel houses climbing the hill, their colors pale echoes of the flapping shirts.

Nathan edged that one away from the others. "This is really strong."

Lacey's eyes lit up. "You think?"

"Oh, yeah."

More confident now, she pulled out more envelopes from her backpack and opened them up. Suddenly Nathan found himself staring at Carin.

Close-ups of Carin looking stern, looking pensive. Laughing. Rolling her eyes. Sticking her tongue out at the camera. Long shots of Carin walking on the beach or sitting on the sand or working in her shop.

And a particularly wonderful one of Carin on the dock, her feet dangling in the water, as she turned her head and looked up at her daughter and smiled.

It was a smile Nathan remembered, a smile that, deep in his heart, he had carried with him for the past thirteen years. It was the smile she'd given him so often that week they'd spent together, an intimate, gentle smile that touched not just her mouth but her eyes, as well.

For years, in his wallet, he'd carried a picture of that smile. The photo, one he had taken during their week together on the beach, had become worn from handling and faded from exposure to all kinds of weather. Two years ago he'd had his wallet stolen in a street bazaar in Thailand. The inconvenience of having to get his driver's license re-issued and his credit cards changed was annoying. But the loss of that photo more than anything had left him feeling oddly hollow and alone.

Now, unbidden, his fingers went out and touched the one Lacey had taken.

"It's the best one, isn't it?" she asked.

"It's…very good. The way the light…" His voice trailed off because his reactions had nothing to do with the way the light did anything.

It was all Carin. He picked it up and stared at it. She could have smiled at him like that today. She could have thrown her arms around him, welcomed him…

"You can have it if you want," Lacey offered.

"No, that's okay." Hastily he set it back down, steeling himself against an ache he refused to acknowledge. He felt trapped suddenly, cornered by emotions he didn't want to face.

He shifted from one bare foot to the other, then drummed his knuckles nervously on the countertop. "Well, those are good," he said briskly, gathering the Carin photos into a pile and tucking them firmly back into the envelope. "Let's see what else you've got."

But before Lacey could pull out any more envelopes, there was a knock on the front door.

"That'll be Maurice. I can talk to him later."

But he was wrong again.

It was Carin, pacing on his porch. When he opened the door she whirled to demand, "Where's Lacey?" Her voice was high and shrill, like nothing he'd ever heard from her before.

"She's, uh…I—"

"Where is she?" She pushed past him. "Lacey!" She strode into the living room, looking around wildly. "Lacey Campbell! Where are you?"

"She's in the kitchen. Cripes, Carin, relax. She's—"

"I'm here, Mom." Lacey appeared in the doorway, clutching her backpack, looking worried.

"See," Nathan said. "She's fine."

But Carin didn't even look at him. She was glaring at their daughter. "I told you he was coming by tomorrow, didn't I?"

"Yes. But I wanted to see him tonight."

"And the world runs according to what you want?"

"I left you a note."

"Not good enough."

"I'm almost thirteen years old!"

"Then start acting like it."

"*He* was glad I came. Weren't you?" Lacey turned to him.

Shoved straight into the middle, Nathan swallowed. "Of course. But—"

"See!" Lacey said triumphantly to her mother.

Carin shot him a fulminating glare. "It doesn't matter whether he was glad or not. I'm your mother and I didn't give you permission."

"Well, he's my father and he—"

"Doesn't want you to start a fight with your mother," Nathan said firmly, getting a grip at last. If there was one thing he did know about parenting it was that the two of them needed to present a united front. "I was glad to see you," he said to Lacey. "Very glad. But glad as I was, if your mother said tomorrow, she meant tomorrow. You shouldn't have come without asking."

"But—"

Nathan steeled himself against the accusation of betrayal in her look. "It might be tough being a one-parent child," he told her firmly, "but you'll find out it's not always a picnic having two, either. Especially when they stick together."

Lacey scowled. She looked from him to Carin and back again. Her shoulders slumped.

Nathan hardened his heart against it. "Go on with your mother now," he said, feeling every inch the father Carin had never given him a chance to become. "I'll see you tomorrow."

"But—" She turned beseeching eyes on him.

"Tomorrow, Lace. Unless you don't want me to show you that fishing spot."

Lacey's eyes narrowed, as if she weren't sure she believed him. She waited hopefully for him to cave in. When he didn't, she shook her head sadly. "You're as bad as Mom," she muttered. Then, shouldering her backpack, she loped past him out the door.

Watching her go, Nathan felt guilty and parental at the same time. He supposed it was a fairly common feeling. Once Lacey had gone, he looked at Carin.

Her arms were crossed like a shield over her breasts. "Thank you," she muttered, her tone grudging.

"Don't fall all over yourself with gratitude."

"Don't worry. I won't."

Her intransigence annoyed him. "Oh, come on, Carin. No harm done. She's fine. And you can hardly blame her for wanting to meet me."

Carin's eyes flashed. "I blame her for not following the rules!"

"I remember when we didn't always follow the rules, Carin."

Their gazes met. Locked. Dueled. Minds—and hearts—remembered.

"Carin—" He tried once more, said her name softly this time.

But she tore her gaze away. "Good night, Nathan."

And she hurried down the steps and almost ran up the drive after their daughter.

CHAPTER THREE

"HE'S SO COOL, Mom," Lacey said over and over as they walked home.

As soon as she was sure that her mother wasn't furious anymore, Lacey hadn't stopped singing Nathan's praises. All the way over the hill and along the narrow road through the trees and into Pelican Town she chattered on.

"He told me about Zeno. The wolf Zeno," Lacey qualified, because the mongrel dog she had taken to feeding a few months back and who now slept on the porch was, amazingly enough, called Zeno, too.

"Did he?" Carin responded absently.

"And he liked my photos! He said they were good. Did you know he has to throw out a lot of his, too?" Lacey hopped around a pothole and grinned over her shoulder at her mother. "He says he throws out way more than he keeps."

"I'm sure that's true."

She wasn't really listening to her daughter. She was busy cringing at how frantic she'd sounded and feeling furious that he had sided with her so willingly—even though, she acknowleged, she'd have been even more furious if he hadn't.

"He even said I could help him pick photos for his next book." Lacey opened the gate to their tiny front garden. "D'you want to see which ones of mine he really liked?"

"Tomorrow," Carin said.

"But—"

"Tomorrow, Lacey," Carin said in her she-who-must-be-obeyed voice. "Go get ready for bed. It's nearly eleven o'clock."

She could see that Lacey was humming with energy and the desire to talk till dawn. But Carin needed peace and quiet and she needed them now. Apparently, one look at her face and Lacey must have figured that out. Heaving a theatrical sigh and grumbling under her breath, her daughter went up the stairs.

Carin sank onto the sofa, stared at the slowly whirling ceiling fan, drew a deep breath and felt the adrenaline fade. She was spent, frazzled, completely shot.

Was this what having Nathan back in her life was going to do?

Dear God, she hoped not.

She'd thought she was ready to deal with him. But she hadn't expected this.

The Nathan she'd expected would have railed at her about not telling him about Lacey, but would actually have been relieved that she hadn't. He would have gruffly offered her financial assistance, would have complimented her on how well she had raised their daughter, and would, after a few hours—or at the most, a few days—have taken off for parts unknown.

That Nathan she could have dealt with.

This Nathan made her nervous.

This Nathan seemed both implacable and reasonable. She'd expected Lacey to be charmed by him. What woman between the ages of three and ninety-three wasn't?

But she hadn't expected him to plan to take their daughter fishing!

Of course she was sure it had been Lacey's idea. But Nathan would enjoy it. They would bond.

Hadn't she herself bonded with him under similar circumstances? Carin remembered well the times he had taken her fishing. His quiet competence and serene enjoyment out on the water had put her at her ease, and his patience as he taught her everything she needed to know had calmed her at the same time it had caused her to fall even deeper under his spell.

It was his patience that worried her now.

What if he really did intend to stick around? What if she had to see him day after day, week after week?

Dear God. It didn't bear thinking about.

Lacey finished brushing her teeth, and Carin heard the floorboards squeak as her daughter crossed the hall to her bedroom, so she climbed the stairs to act sane and sensible and calm and maternal—and hope she convinced Lacey even if she didn't convince herself.

Lacey was in bed, covers tucked up to her chin. Carin hoped she wasn't going to start in again on how wonderful Nathan was.

She didn't. She said instead, "I was afraid he wasn't going to come."

All the bounce was gone now. This was the reflective Lacey. Usually her daughter was eager, cheerful and fearless—much more outgoing than Carin, so that sometimes she forgot that Lacey had insecurities, too. Sometimes it seemed as if she didn't.

Now she realized that Lacey might just be better at masking them. Lacey wasn't one to talk about her fears, and she'd certainly never before confided this concern about her father. She'd asked lots of questions about Nathan—especially since Dominic had appeared last year—but she'd never seemed to fret about him.

Carin had been apprehensive, of course, when she'd had to introduce Lacey to Dominic. But the two of them had hit it off quite well. And while Lacey had asked questions about her father and his family after meeting Dominic and Sierra and, later, Douglas, she'd never asked, "When's my father coming to see me?"

Carin had been pleased and relieved, convinced that Lacey simply hadn't cared enough to ask. Now she realized that the really important questions might be the ones Lacey didn't ask. Her heart squeezed just a little.

"Would it have mattered so much?"

Lacey levered herself up on her elbows. "Of course it would matter! He's my father! I want to know him. I've *always* wanted to know him!"

The ferocity of her tone cut Carin to the bone. It challenged the most basic decision she'd made—not to tell Nathan about their child.

And yet she knew, given the same circumstances, she would do the same thing again. Given who Nathan was and what he wanted to do with his life, she'd had no choice.

He might think differently now. He might blame her now. But thirteen years ago, keeping her pregnancy a secret had been the right thing to do. If she'd told him, she'd have effectively tied him down to a life she knew he'd hate, to obligations he hadn't chosen. If she'd told him, he might have married her.

But he would never have loved her.

He *hadn't* loved her, even when they'd made love.

She made herself reflect on that for a long moment because that had been the other fact on which she'd based her decision. Even when she'd found out she was pregnant, she knew she couldn't have begged Nathan for marriage— not when she'd given him her heart and he'd only shared his body. It would have destroyed them both.

In the end there had been only one thing to do. And the truth was, she admitted to herself, she had barely considered Lacey's needs at all.

Later she'd assured herself that it would be better for Lacey to have one parent who loved her than have two where one of them might resent her very existence.

Now Carin took a careful, steadying breath and let it out slowly.

"Well, he's here now," she said with far more calm than she felt as she smoothed the light cotton blanket over

Lacey, then bent to give her daughter a kiss. "So you can enjoy getting to know him."

"I will," Lacey vowed, and settled back against the pillows again.

On a normal night, once Lacey had gone to sleep, Carin would have finished up her bookwork from the store, then made herself a cup of tea and taken it out on the porch to sit in the swing and unwind from the day.

Tonight she couldn't settle. She tried to do her bookwork and couldn't concentrate. She made a cup of tea and couldn't sit still to drink it. She paced around the house, picking things up and setting them back down again.

Finally she went outside and flung herself down on the swing, grabbed her sketchbook and tried to funnel some of her restless energy into ideas for her work. But all her drawings became sharp-featured, dark-haired men, and she ripped them out of the sketchbook, crumpled them up and tossed them aside, wishing it were as easy to get rid of Nathan.

A creaking noise at the gate made her look up. A pair of yellow eyes glinted in the darkness. "Ah, Zeno," she said as the gate was nosed further open. "Come here, boy."

A dark shape shambled toward the porch. He was a little taller than an Irish setter, a little wirier than a terrier, a little more spotted than a dalmatian, a little less mellow than a golden retriever. He had turned up one day, full-grown, and no one knew which visiting boat he'd come off.

Her friend Hugh McGillivray, who ran Fly Guy, the island transport company, had begun calling him Heinz because he was at least fifty-seven varieties of dog. But Lacey had named him Zeno because he had appeared on their doorstep about the same time Nathan's book, *Solo,* had come out.

"He looks nothing like a wolf," Carin had protested.

"Looks aren't everything. Are they, Zeno?" Lacey had

said stubbornly, hugging the gangly animal who had grinned and furiously wagged his tail.

"He's not ours to name." Their house wasn't close to big enough for a dog the size of a wolfhound.

"He's nobody else's," Lacey rejoined practically. "Not unless someone comes back for him. Besides," she added, apparently deciding that an outside dog was better than no dog at all, "he doesn't have to come in. He can just come around."

Which was pretty much what he did. Zeno the dog seemed to have no more interest in settling in any one place than Zeno the wolf had. He moved from place to place, from house to house—life was a movable feast for Zeno—and pretty soon everyone on the island knew him, fed him and called him by the name Lacey had given him. Mostly he divided his time between their place and Hugh's, because Hugh had a mostly border collie called Belle who had apparently caught Zeno's eye.

Tonight, though, Belle must have had other plans as Zeno was looking hopefully at Carin. She scratched his ears and rubbed under his chin. It was soothing, petting the dog. It calmed her, centered her, slowed her down.

"Thanks for coming," she told him with a wry smile.

Zeno grinned. His tail thumped on the porch. He looked toward the door. Carin knew what he wanted.

"It's late," she told him. "You must have eaten. Didn't Hugh feed you? What about Lorenzo?"

But Zeno cocked his head and whined a denial.

Carin sighed and rolled her eyes. "Okay, fine. Let me see what we've got." Giving his ears one last scratch, she went inside to check the refrigerator. She found leftover peas and rice from dinner plus a bit of the fish Lacey had caught. Carin crumbled it into a bowl, carried it back through the living room and started to push open the screen door.

"Here, Zee—"

Nathan was on the porch.

So much for calm and settled. Carin's fingers automatically clenched the bowl in her hand. Instead of going out, she let the screen bang shut between them. "What are you doing here?"

"We need to talk."

"No, we don't."

"Yes, we do. Invite me in or come out here."

Zeno, whining at the sight of the bowl, offered his opinion.

Nathan reached for the door handle.

Carin beat him to it. "Fine. We'll talk out here." She yanked the door open and stalked past him onto the porch. Zeno pushed between them, his eyes fixed on the bowl, his tail thumping madly.

Nathan reached down and absently scratched his head. "Who's this?"

"A dog."

"No? Really? I'd never have guessed." Sarcasm dripped. "What's his name?"

Carin didn't want to say, knowing full well what he'd think. But if she didn't, Lacey undoubtedly would. "Zeno," she said defiantly. "Lacey's choice."

A corner of his mouth lifted. "Somehow I didn't imagine it was yours."

"He turned up about the same time your book did." She put the bowl down so that Zeno would have to stay between them to eat. Then she straightened up again, wrapping her arms across her breasts as if they could protect her.

"I was surprised Lacey had read my books."

Carin shrugged. "She was curious."

"About them or about me?"

"About what you did. Your job." She turned away from him and stared out into the darkness. Down the hill she could hear the faint sounds of steel drum music coming from the Grouper Bar and Café. The night breeze, which normally she looked forward to, seemed chilly now, and Carin rubbed her bare arms to ward off goose bumps.

"She seems interested," Nathan said after a moment.

"I guess." She still didn't look his way, but she didn't need to in order to know he was there, right on the other side of Zeno. It was almost magnetic, the pull he had over her. She'd never felt that way about any other man. She didn't want to feel that way about this one. Didn't want to fall under his spell again.

"What do you desperately need to talk to me about?" she said when he didn't speak.

"Lacey. Fishing. This parenting bit. How we're going to handle it."

"I handle this 'parenting bit' just fine, thank you."

"Good for you. But you're not handling it alone anymore. There are two of us now. And you're going to have to remember that. We need to present a united front. We don't argue in front of our daughter."

"Don't tell me how to parent!"

"I backed you up tonight."

"I said thank you."

"And I'll expect the same from you when I tell her something."

"If I agree with you, I will."

"Whether you agree or not," Nathan said evenly.

"No way! If you think you can just waltz in here and take over and expect me to back you up—"

Nathan lifted a brow. "Like you took over and never even told me we had a child?"

"You wouldn't have wanted—"

"You didn't let me decide what I wanted!"

"So I'm the bad guy in this? I'm the one everybody blames?" Carin said bitterly.

First Lacey, now Nathan. As if she'd taken on single parenthood for thirteen years to spite them both.

"You're not the bad guy, Carin," Nathan said gruffly.

"I'm sure you did what you thought was the right thing at the time."

She snorted. "Thank you very much for the vote of confidence."

"Jesus, what is it with you? I'm trying to give you the benefit of the doubt!"

"Don't bother."

He drew a breath, then let it out and sighed. "Look, Carin. I didn't come here tonight to fight with you. And I didn't come to Pelican Cay to make your life miserable. I came because my daughter's here."

If Carin had ever dared hope he'd come back for *her*, she knew now that she'd hoped in vain. It was only Lacey he'd come for.

She swallowed the hurt, told herself it didn't matter, that she wasn't surprised. Which she wasn't.

"And you're determined to do your duty by her." Her tone was mocking. She couldn't help it.

"Yes, damn it, I am."

"Bloody noble of you. And unnecessary. We don't need you."

"Lacey does. She said so."

Hell. Oh, hell.

"Well, *I* don't need you. And I don't want you!"

"Don't you?"

His quiet challenge made her glare at him in fury. "What are you saying?"

"That once upon a time, you damned well wanted me!" And he stepped around Zeno, who never even looked up as Nathan hauled her into his arms and kissed her.

It was a kiss to remember—a kiss so like the passionate kisses they'd shared so long ago that it was as if all the years between vanished in an instant. As Nathan's hot mouth pressed hers, persuaded hers, opened hers, Carin's mind fought the surge of desire, the onslaught of memory. But her body did not.

Her body wanted it—wanted him.

For years she'd told herself she had imagined the hunger in the kisses they'd shared. For years she'd almost believed it.

But it wasn't true. She hadn't exaggerated. This kiss was as fierce and possessive and hungry as his long-ago kisses had been. And it touched that same chord deep inside her, and she responded. Desire and need and hunger and passion all resonated, reverberated, began to grow.

Blood pounded through her veins, her heart hammered against the wall of her chest. And against her will, against her better judgment, against everything she had been telling herself for years, she opened to him. Her lips parted, savored, welcomed.

And then, heaven help her, she was kissing him back.

Nathan groaned. "Yesss." The word hissed between his teeth, and he wrapped his arms around her more tightly and pressed his hard body against hers. And far from frightening her away, the pressure of his arousal incited and encouraged her own. Her own hunger, unsatisfied for so long and now awakened, was ravenous. She deepened the kiss, couldn't stop herself, needed it, needed *him!*

And then quite suddenly, Nathan wrenched himself away.

Carin stared at him, stunned, the night breeze cold on her burning flesh.

"There," he said raggedly, "I'd say that pretty much proves it." His breathing came quick and harsh. The skin over his cheekbones was flushed and taut.

Dazed, Carin shook her head. "Proves what?" She ached, abandoned and bereft.

"I said you wanted me once, Carin. You still do. We'll start from there."

"So," the gruff voice on his cell phone said the minute Nathan answered it. "When's the wedding?"

"Dad?"

Douglas Wolfe was the last person Nathan expected to hear when he'd grabbed the phone off the bedside table. And yet, the moment he heard his father's unmistakable baritone, he didn't know why he was surprised.

Just because the old man had never rung him on his cell phone before—and as far as Nathan had known, didn't even have his number—didn't mean that Douglas wouldn't have it and use it when he chose to.

"Of course it's me. Who were you expecting?" Douglas gave a huff of impatient indignation. "So, did you set the date?"

How his father even knew he'd proposed was a mystery to Nathan. But Douglas Wolfe hadn't run an internationally respected company for thirty years by being unaware. He had tentacles everywhere.

"The old man's an octopus," Dominic had once said, a note of respect and awe in his voice.

Nathan hadn't given a damn then about his father's far-reaching tentacles; they'd had nothing to do with him. Now they did. He raked a hand through his hair, wondering if the old man had the house bugged or if he could just read minds.

If so, he ought to try reading Carin's.

"No," Nathan said flatly. "We didn't set a date."

"Why the hell not? You dallied around a whole year just getting down there."

"I had obligations."

"You have a daughter!"

"I know that," Nathan said roughly. "And I didn't want to come and have to leave again right away. I took care of my responsibilities elsewhere, and now I'm here. I spent this evening with my daughter."

"Ah, you met her? Isn't she a peach?" Douglas's whole tone changed, and Nathan could hear his father's obvious delight. "Pretty as a picture. Reminds me of your mother."

There was just a hint of wistfulness in his father's tone as the older man recalled Nathan's mother who had been the love of his life. "Beth would have loved her," Douglas said. "She's smart as a whip, too, that girl. Got a good head on her shoulders. Polite, too. Wrote me a thank-you letter after I, er, stopped to see her in the spring." He said that rather quickly, as if he wasn't sure he ought to be admitting to having visited his granddaughter.

"She showed me the camera you gave her," Nathan said so his father would know he was aware of the visit. "Thanks."

"Made sense to give her one," Douglas said briskly. "She was interested."

"She's taken some pretty nice shots."

"Figured she might. Reckon she comes by it naturally, what with you being a photographer and her mother an artist." Douglas paused again. "That Carin's got talent."

"Yes."

Douglas waited for him to amplify. He didn't.

Finally, impatiently, Douglas demanded, "So when *are* you going to set the date? Dominic will need to know in order to set aside some time, and Rhys will have to apply for leave."

"Sorry. Can't help you."

"What's that supposed to mean? By God, boy, she had your child. I don't care if thirteen years has gone by, Lacey is a Wolfe!"

"I know that!"

"Well then, do your duty and ask—"

"I asked." The words hissed through Nathan's teeth. "She said no."

The sputterings of disbelief on the other end of the line should have been comforting. Dominic, Nathan was sure, would have been heartened to know the old man was on his side. And even their younger brother, Rhys, wouldn't have seen Douglas's meddling as a liability.

Only Nathan had consistently turned his back on their father's commands. He hadn't finished college. He hadn't gone into the family business. He hadn't shown any interest in any of the girls Douglas had wanted him to date. Instead he'd taken his camera and left. He'd made his own way in the world ever since.

It had been a point of pride to do things his own way.

And in the old days he would have taken Douglas's demand that he marry Carin as reason enough to pack his bags and head for the hills. Even now Nathan found that the instinct ran deep.

But for once, unfortunately, he agreed with his father's assessment of the situation. He was Lacey's father and he wanted to be part of her life. More than a peripheral part.

Easier said than done.

"She said no?" Douglas was still sputtering. "I'll talk to her," he said.

As if that would help. Nathan was almost tempted to say, Be my guest.

He could just imagine how Carin would react to Douglas's corporate power tactics. She'd run from them once already when she'd jilted Dominic.

There was nothing to stop her running again.

But having seen her today, Nathan didn't think she'd run this time. The Carin Campbell he'd met today wasn't merely older, she was stronger. She wasn't a girl anymore. She was a woman. There was a resilience and a determination in the grown-up Carin that she'd lacked all those years ago. She had no trouble speaking her mind now.

He had no doubt she'd speak it to Douglas if he attempted to interfere, too. And Nathan didn't need any more complications than he already had.

"You stay out of this," he told his father.

"I'm only trying to help." Douglas sounded aggrieved.

"Fine. Then don't meddle. Leave us alone."

"Left you alone for a year."

Nathan ground his teeth. "And you'll keep on doing it now. Trust me, Dad, you sticking your oar in won't help at all."

"She likes me. Said so. Said it was good for Lacey to know me. Told me I could come and visit anytime. I could just sort of drop in and—"

"No!" Nathan said sharply. He drew a steadying breath. "No," he said again, more moderately. "Thank you. I appreciate the support, but I'll handle it."

Douglas didn't say anything for a long moment. Then he sighed. "I damned well hope so."

To be honest, Nathan did, too.

CHAPTER FOUR

WEDNESDAYS were Carin's day to paint.

Last month she had promised Stacia, her agent, a dozen more paintings for the show Stacia had got her in New York City right before school started. That meant a lot of hard work.

So every Wednesday Fiona Dunbar did behind-the-counter duty while Carin stayed home and painted.

But that wasn't going to happen today.

Fiona had arrived, of course, bright and early to pick up the cash box and anything else Carin wanted to send to the shop. She was standing in the kitchen, drinking a cup of coffee and talking animatedly about the collection of flotsam and jetsam she was going to use for her next big sculpture, when Carin heard a noise on the porch and turned to see Nathan at the screen door.

This morning he wore a pair of faded denim jeans and a chambray shirt with the tails flapping. His sunglasses were parked on top of his thick, tousled hair, and Carin thought he looked like an ad for Ray●Bans, gorgeous as ever and well rested to boot.

Clearly he hadn't tossed and turned all night. The kiss that had kept her awake for hours obviously hadn't affected him!

But then, it wouldn't, would it? He didn't love her.

Well, damn it, she didn't love him, either, Carin vowed. Not anymore. She steeled herself against reacting to him now.

Fiona had no such compunction. Always a connoisseur of male beauty, Fiona gave Nathan an appreciative once-over and murmured, ''Well now, where'd you find him?''

"He's here to pick up Lacey."

Fiona stared. "*Lacey?* Since when is Lacey going out with gorgeous guys old enough to be her father?"

"He is her father."

Fiona's jaw dropped. "That's Lacey's *father?* That gorgeous...I didn't know Lacey's father was coming," she said accusingly.

"Neither did I." And she wouldn't have announced it in any case. "Lacey will be right back," she said to Nathan, not bothering to invite him in. "She went to borrow some fishing gear from Thomas."

"Good." He didn't wait for an invitation. He stepped into the kitchen and smiled at Fiona, who looked at Carin expectantly.

"Aren't you going to introduce us?"

Carin introduced them. Fiona didn't only admire his looks, she was disgustingly flattering about Nathan's photos and his books and articles and how pleased she was to meet him. And Nathan was his most charming, too, saying he'd noticed Fiona's sculptures in Carin's shop. He'd thought they were eye-catching and appealing—even the weird ones made out of stuff Fiona had found on the beach. They were well on their way to forming a mutual admiration society when Lacey at last appeared.

"Hey, wow! You're early." She beamed when she saw Nathan already there. "I got some stuff from Thomas." She waggled the rod, coming dangerously close to decapitating Fiona. "I thought I'd bring my camera, too. So I can take pictures. And maybe afterward you could show me some of yours?"

"Don't pester," Carin warned Lacey, who seemed about ready to offer yet another suggestion.

"I never pester," Lacey said indignantly. "All set?"

Nathan nodded. "All set."

They started out the door.

"Wait." Carin snagged Lacey's neon-lime-green ball

cap off the hook by the door and thrust it at her daughter. "And don't forget sun screen."

"I won't." Lacey rolled her eyes.

"And wear your life jacket. You do have life jackets?" Nathan nodded.

"And don't stand in the boat and—"

"If you're so worried that we can't manage without you," Nathan cut in, "why don't you come along, too."

"No! Thank you. I have work to do."

"Mom paints on Wednesdays," Lacey said. "She's got a lot to do 'cause she's having a show."

Nathan's brows lifted. "A show? Where?"

"In New York City," Lacey said proudly.

The brows hiked even further. He looked at Carin for more details.

She shrugged. "It's no big deal."

It was a huge deal, and sometimes she thought she'd made a mistake agreeing to it. A successful one-woman show in New York City would take her to a whole new level. She'd had a couple of shows in Nassau and one in Miami. But Stacia hoped to broaden her market.

But if the critics panned her work or the sales weren't there, Carin knew she would regret it. She had agreed to the show only because the offer had come after Dominic had discovered her whereabouts. There was no longer any point in keeping a low profile. And she'd hoped that the show would result in more money in case she needed to fight Nathan in court.

She didn't imagine she would have to—couldn't believe he would want custody of Lacey—but it would be better to have a nest egg than not.

"Where?" Nathan asked now.

She told him. It was just a small gallery in Soho. But he'd heard of it.

"I'll have to go," he said. Which would be fine with her because she had no intention of going.

"Dad," Lacey said impatiently. It amazed Carin how she

could say the word so easily, as if she'd been saying it all her life.

"Coming," Nathan said just as easily. "You won't mind if I don't bring Lacey back until after dinner, then? Since you're going to be painting all day."

Hoisted by her own petard. Carin pressed her lips together. "Fine. If that's what you want."

"It's what we want, right, Lace?" Nathan took the ball cap Lacey held and clapped it on her head. "Come on, kid. We've got dinner to catch."

Giggling and grinning over her shoulder at her mother, Lacey followed her father out the door.

"Welllllllll," Fiona said when the door shut after them, "I can certainly see why you went to bed with him!"

Carin flushed. "I was young and foolish and it was a mistake. Except for Lacey."

"Of course." Fiona nodded, then slanted Carin a glance. "You had very good taste. He's lovely."

"It's purely skin deep," Carin said. Of course that wasn't entirely true, but she was not getting into a discussion about what had attracted her to Nathan in the first place.

"The bones aren't bad, either," Fiona said with a grin, "speaking as a sculptor, of course. Still got the hots for him?"

"Of course not!"

Fiona's grin turned wicked. "Protesting just a bit too much?"

Carin clamped her mouth shut.

Fiona added a little more coffee to her cup and settled against the kitchen cabinet. "When did he show up?"

"Yesterday." Pointedly Carin glanced at her watch. "I think you might want to head on over to the store. Turk brought paperweights by yesterday. You can price them and put them out in a display."

"Okay." Fiona nodded, sipping her coffee. "How long's he staying?"

Carin sighed. "Who knows? Who cares? Tommy Cash is supposed to be bringing some toys into the shop this morning. You'd better get a move on."

"You'll feel better if you talk about it."

"I'll feel better if you go open my shop and I can get to painting!"

Fiona tut-tutted. "So testy this early in the morning."

"I've got work to do."

"Fine." Fiona took one last swallow of coffee and poured the rest down the sink. "If you ever want to talk about it. About *him*—"

"I will certainly let you know," Carin said. Not. "Now I really have to get to work. I need eight more paintings at least."

Fiona picked up the box of paperweights and, shaking her head at Carin's one-track mind, pushed her way out the screen door. "Down, Zeno."

He was waiting on the porch, angling for breakfast. But when Carin shut the screen again, he followed Fiona toward the gate.

"I'll bring you a sandwich for lunch," Carin called after her. "Ham or grouper?"

"Ham." Fiona opened the gate. Zeno, spying Carin's neighbor's cat, forgot all about breakfast and shot through the gate after it. The cat took one look, darted under the fence and hid. Zeno barked, paced, prowled, hovered.

Ordinarily Carin found his antics amusing. This morning, feeling hunted herself, her sympathies were all with the cat.

She took a cup of coffee with her and went out back to her tiny studio. She had three paintings in varying stages of progress. She had twenty or thirty sketches that she should be working from.

She started to work on a painting of some children playing on the quay. But the children made her think of Lacey. Lacey made her think of Nathan. Nathan made her remember last night, made her remember the kiss.

She couldn't think—or paint—for remembering that kiss.

She set aside that painting and tried another, this one a landscape of the windward beach. It was a wide-angle painting done from a photo she'd snapped when Hugh had taken her up in his seaplane. But her eye was drawn to the rocky promontory where she and Nathan had once stood together, hands clasped, hearts beating as one.

And that brought her to Nathan again. And the kiss.

So she moved on to a landscape of higgledy-piggledy houses perched on the hillside above the harbor. But somehow even the houses reminded her of days long ago when the two of them had walked side by side through the narrow streets, when they'd shared an ice cream, licking madly before it melted in the Bahamian summer sun.

Everywhere she looked, there was Nathan.

Desperate, she got out her sketchbook and tried to figure out other ideas she wanted to develop. She flipped through the photos she'd taken last week, hoping for renewed inspiration. She had shot several rolls of film and had easily half a dozen island scenes that she could work on—children playing in the street; a cricket game on the "cricket grounds" with Daisy the resident horse-and-lawn-mower watching the game; a bunch of happy diners at the Grouper, sitting under palm trees decorated with tiny, colored fairy lights; a shot of two little boys riding the old cannons that had sat on the point, defending the island, for almost 350 years.

They were nothing fancy—just bread-and-butter shots— but they had always captured her imagination before.

Not now.

Now her mind's eye didn't see cricket players or children in the street or little boys swinging their legs on the cannons. It saw Lacey's grin as she'd followed Nathan out the door. It saw Nathan's broad shoulders and strong back. It saw Nathan's back as it had been thirteen years ago, bare and tanned and smooth—

"Argh!" Carin flung the photos aside and raked both hands through her hair.

My God, it was nearly two o'clock and she had nothing—*nothing!*—to show for her day's work. Fiona had asked when Carin brought her the sandwich and Carin had said, "It's coming."

But it wasn't coming. All she could see in her mind was Nathan.

Damn it! Even when he wasn't here, he was here!

Well, fine. If she couldn't be creative, she'd go for a walk. She'd do leg work, make some sketches, get raw material. In the wide-open spaces she'd have other things to distract her.

She put on a pair of sandals, grabbed her sketchbook and her sunglasses and set out.

The air was stifling, steamy and hot, like getting slapped in the face with a hot wet towel—minus the towel. There wasn't a tiny bit of moving air anywhere. The flag hung limp. Even the water in the harbor was flat and still.

Carin headed toward the beach on the far side of the island. If a breeze existed, that's where it would be. The tarmac road burned through the thin soles of her sandals as she walked up the hill. She wasn't outside three minutes before the sweat was running down her back and making damp patches on her shirt.

"You crazy, girl? What you doin' out in the noonday sun?" Carin's neighbor, Miss Saffron, who was eighty if she was a day, looked up from her rocking chair on her shady front porch and shook her head as Carin passed.

"Just out for a little inspiration." She lifted her sketchbook in salute.

Miss Saffron chuckled. "If I be you, crazy girl, I'd be gettin' all the inspiration I need from that man was kissin' you last night."

Her blush came hotter even than the beating sun. Carin wished the tarmac would open and swallow her up. Instead she listened to Miss Saffron's cackling laughter all the way up the road.

She walked past the cemetery and the library, then turned

up Bonefish Road, which led round past the cricket ground, over the hill and through the trees, eventually turning into a path that led through the mangroves down to the beach.

There she found a breeze at last. Tiny waves broke against the shore. To her right there were signs of civilization—a half dozen strategically placed beach umbrellas sat in front of the newly refurbished and gentrified Sand Dollar Inn, an island institution recently turned yuppie since Lachlan McGillivray, Hugh's brother, had added it to his hotel empire.

Carin turned away from it, started to walk, and found no more focus than she'd found trying to paint. The only thing that would help was exertion—making so many demands on her body that she couldn't think of anything at all.

It wasn't smart. She could die of sunstroke. But it was better than spending the rest of the afternoon trying *not* to think of Nathan. So she ran.

She ran. And ran.

She ran until sweat poured down her face. She ran until her breaths came in painful harsh gasps. She ran until she reached the rocks. Two miles. Maybe more. She was exhausted, bent over, gasping for breath. But her mind was clear. She felt calmer, steadier, stronger. Her demon had been exorcized.

Carin shut her eyes and breathed a long, deep cleansing breath. *Yes!*

Then she straightened, turned and began to amble back the way she'd come—and saw, for the first time, the tall dark-haired man and the slender girl in a lime-green cap coming toward her.

Damn!

So much for steadier, stronger and calmer. All Carin's sense of emotional well-being vanished as she realized she'd run right past Nathan's house. Now he would think that she'd come to spy on them!

"Mom! Hi! What're you doing here?" Lacey waved madly, then came running up to her.

"I finished early," she said, struggling to breathe easily. It wasn't really a lie. She had finished. Just because she had nothing to show for it, didn't mean she hadn't tried. "So I thought I'd come for a run."

"In this heat?" One of Nathan's brows lifted.

"I'm quite used to it."

"We finished early, too," Lacey told her. "Dad said we'd caught enough fish to feed an army and he didn't want to clean them all. He knows a great fishing spot! Better'n the one Thomas took me and Lorenzo to!"

"Really?" Now it was Carin's turn to raise a brow. It didn't seem likely that Nathan would know any such thing, just having returned to the island yesterday.

Nathan shrugged modestly.

"We're goin' for a swim now," Lacey went on. "An' then we're gonna cook the fish. Dad says he's good with a grouper." She grinned. "You can eat with us if you want to, can't she?" Lacey turned eager eyes on Nathan.

"I wouldn't want to intrude," Carin said quickly, not looking to see what Nathan's reaction to Lacey's impromptu invitation was.

"You wouldn't be," Lacey said.

"You're welcome to eat with us," Nathan seconded.

But Carin didn't want to eat with them. "I'm…having a guest for dinner," she improvised.

Lacey looked surprised. "Who?"

"Hugh."

She only hoped he was home. If he was, there was no doubt that Hugh McGillivray, Pelican Cay's "best-looking bachelor"—his own description—would say yes to pulling up a chair to her table tonight. Hugh was notorious for trying to wangle dinner invitations. He also made no secret of his attraction to her—an attraction that Carin generally discouraged.

Well, one meal wouldn't get Hugh's hopes up. She just prayed he wasn't already eating at someone else's house.

"Bring him," Lacey said promptly. "Hugh's just a

friend," she explained to her father. "Remember, I told you about him. He's the one who flew Lorenzo to Nassau."

"Right." Nathan looked at Carin. "Bring him along." There was an edge to his voice. Still Carin hesitated.

"Come, Mom. Please," Lacey begged. "It'd be fun."

It wouldn't be fun at all. But maybe if she brought Hugh, Nathan would think she and Hugh were an item. Maybe he'd realize that he didn't need to stay around Pelican Cay, that Lacey didn't need a full-time father.

"I'll ask Hugh," Carin said. "I'll let you know."

"Seven o'clock," Nathan said. "I can pick you up."

"Hugh has a car. Or we'll walk."

Nathan looked as if he might argue, but Lacey grabbed his hand. "C'mon, Dad. Let's swim. And I want to show you how I can stand on my hands."

Carin swallowed the temptation to tell Lacey not to brag. She should be pleased that daughter and father were forming a relationship, forging bonds, making connections. But she turned away at the sight of Nathan's fingers curling around their daughter's as he allowed himself to be led toward the water. She couldn't look. It made her wish...

She didn't want to wish.

"Dinner?" Hugh looked amazed, then delighted at Carin's invitation. "You're inviting me to dinner?"

A grin cracked his handsome face as he looked up from the boat engine he was working on. Hugh McGillivray had dancing blue eyes and thick dark hair, cheekbones to die for and a once-broken nose that merely added to his appeal. And even with a streak of engine grease on one cheek and another on his bare muscular chest, it was true, what he always claimed—that he was the best-looking bachelor on Pelican Cay.

Or he had been until yesterday, a tiny voice piped up in Carin's brain.

"Yes, dinner," Carin said firmly, ignoring the traitorous voice, not wanting to admit that, even now, in her eyes

Nathan was far more appealing. "Tonight. If you don't have other plans." *Please God, don't let him have other plans.*

"Sounds great," Hugh said cheerfully. "I'll bring the beer."

"Not necessary," Carin said quickly. At Hugh's look of surprise, she shifted from one foot to the other. "It's, um, it's not at my place. Well, it was going to be, but…there's been a change in plans. My, um…that is, Lacey's…father…is on the island…visiting…and he took Lacey fishing and they asked if we'd like to come to dinner." She said all this in sort of a jerky stop-and-go jumble and wasn't surprised when Hugh cocked a brow.

"Invited *us*?" Clearly he was reassessing the invitation and didn't believe her one bit. Carin couldn't blame him.

"Invited me," she clarified. "But I didn't want—I said I was inviting you to dinner—" she flushed a little admitting that "—and Lacey said bring you, and Nathan said yes, do. And, well…you know."

Hugh knew. "Right," he said. "So you want me to go as your boyfriend?"

Carin felt the heat in her cheeks increase. "I don't—I mean, it's not what you think," she said lamely.

Hugh tilted his head. "Oh? And what do I think?"

She put her hands on her hips. "You think I'm still attracted to him. I'm not!"

Hugh's silence told her what he thought of that remark.

"Of course he's attractive," Carin allowed, because it was impossible to deny that Nathan was a damned attractive man. It was the fact that he didn't love her and had left her that she found *un*attractive! "But I'm not attracted to him."

"Uh-huh."

"I'm not!"

"I understand." Hugh nodded solemnly, though there was an unholy light in his eyes. He started to rake a hand through his hair, then looked at the grease on it and wiped it on his disreputable cutoffs instead. "I get it. You've finally become attracted to me. And about time." His grin flashed. "Taste comes to Carin Campbell at last."

"Don't you wish?" she teased.

"Don't I," Hugh agreed with just enough seriousness to make her wonder as she sometimes did, if he was serious or not.

As long as she'd known him, he'd had one girlfriend after another. None had been serious. None had lasted. The only single woman between eighteen and forty she knew he hadn't dated was her. And not because he hadn't asked. He had. She hadn't been interested.

"We'll be friends, Hugh," she'd told him. "That will be better."

"Sez you," he'd complained.

But they'd been friends for four years. Maybe she'd made a mistake asking him to have dinner tonight. She didn't want to spoil that by changing things now.

"You're a gorgeous guy, Hugh," she began, "but—"

He held up a hand to stop her. "Don't. If you're asking me out to dinner, don't start putting qualifications on it."

"No. I just—"

"Don't, Carin," he warned her, a rough edge to his voice. "What time do we have to be there?"

"Seven. But if you'd rather not—I don't expect—"

"I'm looking forward to it," he said firmly. "I'll be interested to meet Lacey's father." The speculative look on his face was further cause for concern. But before Carin could say anything, he told her, "Right, seven it is, then. I'll pick you up at quarter to."

"Ok." But as Carin started away from the boat dock, she still worried. She tended to think of Hugh as her pal, a carefree, devil-may-care guy, whom every woman on Pelican Cay lusted after—save her—and who wouldn't be caught no matter what. Certainly that was the impression he was always at pains to give.

His reputation, well known among the island's fairer sex,

was that he was a terrific playmate—and bedmate. But in his own words, he'd "never met a woman he didn't like, nor one who made him think in terms of happily ever after."

But Carin also remembered that two years ago he'd taken her flying one afternoon, determined to show off his new toy—the seaplane that he had added to his fleet of charter vehicles. Carin had never taken off or landed on the water before. She'd loved it, had been eager to have him do it again and again.

And while they were soaring through the wild blue yonder getting ready to make yet another approach, and the plane had banked and Carin had taken half a dozen shots out the window, exclaiming all the while how wonderful it was, Hugh had said, "You could do this all the time if you married me."

Carin had laughed. She'd rolled her eyes and said, "Oh, yes. Sure. Right." Because, of course, he wasn't serious. Hugh was never serious in matters of the heart.

He'd laughed, too. He hadn't pursued it. He'd never uttered the word *marriage* again. But every once in a while Carin had caught him looking at her intently, his expression always unreadable.

It had made her wonder more than once if she'd been wrong.

But then immediately she thought, surely not. Hugh McGillivray went through women like she went through tubes of cadmium blue. He was a tease, a charmer and her pal. He could have said no, after all, she told herself. It wasn't as if she was leading him on. He knew she wasn't interested in serious stuff. And neither was he!

"Hey, Carin!"

She slowed and glanced back over her shoulder. Was he going to change his mind?

Hugh was standing beside his disemboweled engine now, looking grubby and sweaty and handsome as sin. And she wished, not for the first time, that she could muster for him a hundredth of what she felt every time she looked at Nathan Wolfe.

"What?"

He grinned. "Wear some sexy little black number with no back, why don't you?"

Lacey had said Carin and Hugh the hunk were "just friends."

It didn't look like that to Nathan.

They weren't exactly holding hands and smooching in public, but when they arrived for dinner they were very definitely a couple. Carin had obviously made an effort to dress up for the occasion. She was wearing a sundress in varying shades of blue. It skimmed her narrow waist and flared at her hips, and it had such thin shoulder straps that it was obvious she wasn't wearing a bra. While the dress wasn't backless by any means, it displayed a lot of smooth, tanned skin, which Nathan watched Hugh the hunk touch as he escorted Carin up the steps.

That annoyed him. It annoyed him further that when she introduced them she called Hugh "my very good friend".

She called Nathan "Lacey's father".

Which he was, of course. But prior to that he had to have been "Carin's lover", hadn't he? He'd been tempted to say so. And he might have if Lacey hadn't been in the room.

Instead he'd got Hugh a beer and Carin a glass of wine and chatted about the fishing expedition he and Lacey had gone on, while he watched the fish he was cooking and tried not to watch Hugh lean back against the deck railing and casually slide an arm behind Carin, obviously staking his claim.

"I think maybe we'll eat out here," Nathan said abruptly. "How about helping me move the table, Hugh?"

"I just set the table, Dad," Lacey moaned.

"It's too nice an evening to eat inside," Nathan said firmly. "Come on." He went in through the sliding doors and was gratified to have made Hugh follow.

After they got the table and chairs moved and Hugh was about to settle back next to Carin again, Nathan suggested she give Lacey a hand. "She made a fruit salad and we've got some garlic bread in the oven that you could bring out."

"I'll help," Hugh said.

"Great." Nathan thrust a platter into his hands. "Hold this for me."

He put Carin at one end of the table, himself at the other and had Hugh and Lacey sit on either side. At least Hugh the hunk wouldn't be able to put his hands on Carin during the meal.

But the connection remained.

When they talked about fishing, Carin said, "Hugh's a great fisherman," and began a story about a time Hugh had taken her and Lacey fishing and they'd had great success because he knew right where to go.

"We didn't do that well," Hugh protested modestly. "Carin thinks less is more because she doesn't like baiting hooks," he told Nathan with a grin.

"I remember," Nathan said tersely. He looked down the table at Carin. "I think I was the first to ever take you fishing, wasn't I?"

Carin paused, a forkful of salad halfway to her mouth. "Were you?" she said. "I don't remember."

Liar, Nathan thought. And he said it with his eyes. He wasn't sure whether he was gratified or not when Carin looked away.

They moved on from fishing to talking about the island economy.

"It's picking up," Hugh said. "Tourist dollars are coming in. They're staying longer, spending more."

"They have more options now," Carin said. "It's not just my place and Miss Saffron's straw shop and the pineapple store and lunch at The Grouper anymore."

Which is pretty much the way it had been—minus Carin's store—when Nathan had been growing up. Pelican

Cay had been a place to come to for complete relaxation, to get away from it all.

"Obviously things have changed," he said gruffly.

Carin nodded. "There are plenty of things to do now. Those who want to can do an afternoon dive or go on a sightseeing boat trip around the island. Three days a week they can take a historical walking tour. The museum is open most afternoons. We've had several historians rave about what a good little collection we've got going."

"An' if they don't want to go to the museum, Hugh will take them up in his plane or sightseeing in the helicopter," Lacey said eagerly.

"And next month we're starting horse carriage tours," Hugh put in.

"So much for peace and quiet," Nathan muttered.

"There are off-islanders who come for two weeks a year and hate the way things have changed," Carin said—meaning him and those like him. "But those of us who have to make a living aren't complaining. We're delighted Hugh and his brother have opened things up."

"It's a matter of balance," Hugh explained. "We're not trying to turn the place into Nassau. We liked Pelican Cay just the way we found it. But we could afford to come and go as we pleased. People who were living here, most of them were barely making it. They needed a few more opportunities."

"And Hugh and Lachlan gave them to us. I got my agent, thanks to Hugh." Carin smiled at him, and Hugh smiled back and winked at her.

Nathan's teeth came together. "Agent?" he said. "What agent?"

"Stacia Coleman. She's a friend of Hugh's. She's in New York."

"I've heard of her." Stacia Coleman was one of the younger up-and-coming agents in the business. His own agent, Gabriela del Castillo, had introduced him to her last fall at a gallery opening in Santa Fe.

"Stacia's sharp," Gaby had told him later. "She has a good eye and good instincts."

Years ago when he'd first seen her work, Nathan had thought Carin had talent. The paintings he'd seen in her shop yesterday had supported that impression. Even so, he was surprised to hear that she was selling her work not just on Pelican Cay, but through Stacia Coleman, as well. Stacia didn't take on friends' friends. She promoted bonafide artists.

"Stacia's arranging a show for Carin next month," Hugh said. There was a note of pride in his voice. "In New York City."

"I'll have to go."

"It's not a big deal," Carin said, just as she had before. She actually looked embarrassed.

"The hell it isn't," Hugh objected. "It's fantastic. You don't get a one-woman show in a New York gallery if you're second rate."

"No, you don't," Nathan said. "Congratulations."

He'd known about her shop. Dominic had mentioned it after he'd visited the cay, months ago. "Arts and crafts stuff. Mobiles, seashells, dust catchers."

"Wonderful pieces," Sierra had countered, giving her husband a playful swat. "You philistine. She has one-of-a-kind pieces. Not touristy shlock at all. Come see the painting I bought."

She'd dragged Nathan into the living room of their Fifth Avenue apartment and pointed to a vibrant, primitive beach scene that complemented the paintings his mother had done even as it outshone them. Whoever had painted it was no amateur.

"Carin painted it," Sierra had informed him.

Nathan had admired it, but he hadn't studied it long. He'd been too blown away by Dominic's other news—that Carin was on Pelican Cay, that she'd been there for the past twelve years, and that she had a daughter called Lacey who looked just like him.

Now he thought about Carin's talent and Carin's promise—and how she'd buried it for all these years in Pelican Cay. Did she regret it? He certainly couldn't tell from her expression.

"So we might get to go to New York!" Lacey said eagerly.

"Not likely," Carin said. "New York isn't exactly my cup of tea."

"But I've never been there," Lacey argued.

Even Hugh argued. "You have to go. It's not every day you get a show like that. Besides, Stacia wants you there."

"I know, but—"

"I'll go with you. Lend moral support," he promised her and reached out to squeeze her hand.

Carin blinked, as if surprised at the offer. But then she smiled. "Maybe."

"Goody!" Lacey cheered.

"Peachy," Nathan growled under his breath.

"I beg your pardon?" Carin looked down the table at him.

He shoved his chair back and said through his teeth, "I said I think I'll bring out some fresh peaches for dessert."

He didn't have any peaches, but he banged around the kitchen until he felt less likely to rip Hugh McGillivray's head off. And then he went back with a couple of fresh pineapples and offered them. "Sorry. Fresh out of peaches. This is all I could find."

"I don't need anything else. It was a lovely dinner. Thank you." Carin sounded like the poster girl for Miss Manners.

"Yeah, it was great," Hugh agreed. "Maybe not as great as whatever Carin would have cooked." He gave her a wink and a grin, then looked back at Nathan. "But it was a pleasure to meet you."

Nathan wasn't going to say it had been a pleasure to meet Hugh. "Glad you could come." That was at least close to the truth. It was, as his father always claimed, smart to size up the competition.

Carin stood up. "We should be going."

Nathan glanced at his watch. "It's not even nine-thirty."

"Some people got up extremely early and had a long exhausting day." Carin glanced at Lacey, who was trying her best to swallow a yawn.

"I'm fine!" Lacey protested when she could open her mouth without her jaw cracking. "I'm not tired!"

"I didn't say you were. It happens that *I* had a very long day." Carin yawned, too.

Nathan wasn't sure if she was faking it or not. Maybe she figured she'd been polite long enough. Maybe now she was desperate to get back to her place, get Lacey to bed, then have mad passionate sex with Hugh McGillivray.

Nathan's jaw clenched so tight that he could feel a muscle pulse in his temple. He drew in a deep lungful of air and let it out jerkily. "Whatever you want."

Carin was still smiling her poster girl smile. "I think we'll just go on, then. Unless you would like us to stay and help clean up the dishes?"

"No."

Wouldn't want you to miss your date for hot sex by helping with the washing up.

His terse reply caused Carin to blink, as if she didn't have a clue what he thought.

Hugh stood up quickly and eased Carin's chair back for her. Then he turned to Lacey. "C'mon, Lace. Time to hit the road."

Like he was her father, Nathan thought, his fingers balling into fists.

Lacey sighed, but she muffled another yawn, which meant, Nathan realized, that she really was tired.

"Get your fishing stuff," Carin directed, "and your backpack and whatever else you brought."

"I'm leaving my photos," Lacey said. "Dad says we'll look at them tomorrow."

"Tomorrow you're helping Miss Gibbs move all those books at the library. Remember?" Carin reminded her.

"Oh, Mom! I don't have to. You know that. It's voluntary. She'll understand."

"No, she won't. She's relying on you. The books need to be moved, Lacey. And you said you'd help. They're refinishing the floor," she told Nathan, "and they need to move all the books to one side. Then next week, they'll move them to the other side. The librarian, Miss Gibbs, asked the kids to help. And Lacey—" she turned her gaze on their daughter now "—volunteered."

"But I—"

"Good for her. I'll help," Nathan said.

Lacey laughed delightedly. "Will you? Oh, cool!"

"Oh, for heaven's sake, Nathan. You don't need—" Carin began.

"The books need to be moved." Nathan quoted her words back to her, arching a brow, daring her to deny what she'd just said.

She clamped her lips together.

Getting no denial, he shrugged. "So I'll help. Do me good to volunteer, too. Since the island is going to be my home now...." He stared hard at Carin, making his point, then for good measure turned his gaze on Hugh, as well.

He was gratified to see the other man's obvious surprise.

"Then Lacey can come back here with me after," Nathan went on smoothly, "and we can go over her photos. We didn't have time today. Give you a chance to do your painting," he said to Carin. "And Lacey needs to help me on my book, too."

Her mouth opened as if she were going to argue. Then she shrugged those nearly bare shoulders. "I'm sure Miss Gibbs will be delighted to have your assistance. And that's nice that you and Lacey can work on your book. But I won't be painting. I'll be working in the shop. I only paint on Wednesdays." She stepped through the open sliding door into the house, heading straight for the front door, then turning once more to say politely, "Thank you again for the lovely meal. Say thank you, Lacey," she instructed their daughter.

"Thanks, Dad." Lacey flashed him a grin that, thank God, didn't look forced.

He reached out and gave her ponytail a tug. "Anytime, kid."

Hugh stepped around Nathan and opened the door for Carin, then turned back and offered Nathan a grin and a handshake. "Hope we meet again soon." Pause. "Carin and I will have to have you for a meal."

It was a blatantly territorial comment and Nathan knew it. He shook Hugh's hand, pistols at dawn not being an option. But nothing required that he respond to that ridiculous remark, so he didn't.

"Night, Dad." Lacey said brightly, turning to grin up at him. "It was a great day, wasn't it?"

"Yeah, great," Nathan echoed hollowly. He managed a smile. Just. And one last tug of her ponytail.

For her he was glad that it had been. For him, seeing Carin walk away with Hugh's hand pressed possessively at her back, the blessings had been decidedly mixed.

CHAPTER FIVE

ELAINE, Lorenzo's seventeen-year-old sister, hurried into the shop at ten minutes past nine. "I'm sorry! I'm sorry! I'm sorry I'm late!"

Carin, who was dusting, blinked. "Late? For what?"

"Nathan said to be here at nine."

"*What?* Nathan said *what?*"

"To be here at nine. That you needed me to work every day." Elaine looked delighted. "I'm so glad. I was so sick of waitressin'. My feet hurt sooooo bad."

Carin stared at her. "When did you see Nathan?"

"Saw him yesterday afternoon. Him an' Lacey came by to talk to my dad after they went fishing. Oh, you mean about workin'? Didn't see him. He called last night. Said you had a big show in New York an' you needed more time to paint. I was that happy, I can tell you!"

"Ah." Carin hesitated. "Um."

"What you want me to do? Want me to dust? If your cash register is like The Grouper's I won't have any problems with that." Elaine was so eager that Carin couldn't simply say, There's been a mistake. Go home.

But there had definitely been a mistake! And Nathan Wolfe had made it! How dared he?

"Just...yes, here." Carin thrust the duster in Elaine's hand. "I need to make a phone call. I'll be right back."

There was a phone by the register, but Carin went to the one in the back room. She punched out the number of Nathan's cell phone, which he'd given her yesterday. She'd been sure she would never need it. She was wrong.

"What do you think you're doing?" she demanded when he answered.

"Ah, Elaine arrived."

"Yes, damn it, she arrived! And you're just going to have to get down here and tell her you've made a mistake and she has to go home. And you'd better hope she hasn't given notice at The Grouper!"

"I gave it for her. Stopped in this morning when Lacey and I were on our way to the library."

"What!" Carin was outraged. "You had no right!"

"Elaine asked me to. And you need time to paint. You said so," he reminded her.

"That doesn't mean you're supposed to hire someone to work for me! I can't afford—"

"I'm paying her."

"No!"

"Well, she's not going to work for nothing."

"You're not hiring my help! You presumptuous bastard! You—"

"Stop shouting in my ear. Ms. Gibbs can probably hear you all the way across the room. This is a library, you know."

"I don't want—"

"You don't want me here. That's the bottom line. Too bad. I'm staying. And I'm trying to make life a little easier for you."

"Then leave," Carin muttered.

"Look, Carin, I know you don't think much of me. So be it. You never gave me a chance. You shut me out. Well, now I'm back. And like it or not, you're stuck with me."

"That doesn't mean—"

"It means I'm taking an interest in Lacey's life. Lacey's life involves you. You've got a terrific opportunity here. I'm trying to give you a chance to benefit from it. I'll keep Lacey during the days so you won't have to worry about her. Elaine will take care of the shop. And you can paint."

Carin's jaw tightened. He was so reasonable. He was so right, damn it! "You can't pay her."

"We'll discuss it later. Go paint."

"I—"

But there was just dead air. He'd hung up.

Damn it! Carin fumed, she paced, she fussed. She didn't want to be beholden to Nathan Wolfe. She didn't want him running her life.

But it was true, what he'd said—this gallery show was a once-in-a-lifetime opportunity—and Stacia did want more paintings. In fact, she'd called this morning to see how Carin was coming on them.

"Good," Carin had said, which was only a small lie. "Moving right along."

"Wonderful. Glad to hear it. When will you be finished?"

"I'm not sure yet. Can I call you in a week or so?"

"A week?" Stacia sounded worried. "I'm going to be out of the city for a few days. How about I call you when I get back? I'll need to come down so we can pack them up for shipping."

Ordinarily Stacia wouldn't be bothered doing any such thing. It was outside the realm of her job. But she was sure Carin had enormous sales potential.

"You're a phenom ready to be discovered," was what she'd said. And she was pulling out all the stops to make sure it happened—even going so far as to say she would come to the island herself and make sure that the paintings were packed and shipped properly since there was no "pack and ship" on Pelican Cay.

Stacia had a lot invested in her in terms of time and effort and expense. Of course, she stood to get plenty in return if Carin was the success Stacia thought she would be.

But that meant Carin had to come through with enough work to make mounting the show worthwhile. And that meant she should have hired an Elaine weeks ago, but she hadn't had the money to do so.

Now Nathan was taking Lacey and offering to pay Elaine.

"I can pay him back," Carin said aloud now.

"You talkin' to me?" Elaine called from the front of the shop.

Carin took a breath. "No. I was talking to Nathan." She would pay him back. And he wouldn't be able to stop her. "Here," she said to Elaine. "Let me show you the ropes."

Elaine learned things quickly. By ten Carin felt she could leave her on her own in the shop, giving her the admonition to call if she needed anything.

Elaine shook her head. "Nathan said not to bother you."

Carin narrowed her gaze on the young woman. "Call me," she said. "Or I'll fire you."

Elaine flashed a broad grin. "Well, when you put it like that…"

Carin went home. Zeno, hoping for a snack, tagged along after her. She gave him a bit of ham and left him sitting on the porch. Then, somewhere between fierce and furious, she headed for the studio to tackle her work.

Lacey couldn't have been happier.

As the days passed and she went fishing with her father or shot photos with her father or just walked on the beach and talked to her father, she couldn't have had a better summer.

Carin couldn't have been more of a wreck. Of course she was happy that Lacey was forming bonds with her father. But for herself, as she heard daily the tales of Nathan and Lacey fishing, helping move books at the library, taking photos in the cemetery or going swimming or snorkeling, Carin felt bereft.

She felt hollow. Lonely.

And she couldn't help thinking about what it would have been like if they could have done these things together as a family—the three of them.

That was stupid, of course. If they had been a family, Nathan would never have been able to do what he'd done. He wouldn't have been able to pursue his dreams, find his path, focus on his goals. He would have grown to resent her—and their child.

Too, if she'd announced she was pregnant with his child, she would have caused a huge rift between him and Dominic. Lacey talked a lot about her dad and his brothers when they were growing up. She loved to recount the "Nathan and Dominic and Rhys stories" that her father told her. It was clear they loved and respected each other. And there was no way Carin would have wanted to come between them.

So it was just as well she'd kept her mouth shut. Just as well she'd accepted her fate—and there was no sense in bemoaning the fact that they had no memories together.

But you could have now, some niggling little inner voice kept telling her. *You could have said yes when Nathan asked you to marry him.*

But she was selfish. She didn't want Nathan marrying her out of duty. In her heart she was still a romantic. She wanted to marry for love.

She was thinking about this when Hugh stopped by on Friday after work. He stuck his head in the studio and asked, "How's it going?"

And Carin said wearily, "It isn't," because thinking about Nathan had depressed her and she hadn't been able to paint much for the last half hour. She decided to take a ten-minute break and have a cup of tea before sending Hugh on his way.

Now he was leaning against the kitchen counter with a bottle of beer in his hand. watching her sympathetically as she paced and muttered. "I don't know how I'm going to get this done."

"You're trying too hard. You need to relax. Come out to dinner with me."

"I can't. I've got to work. But every time I try I start to think. And then I stop working. I don't know what to do!"

"Kiss me."

"What?" She stared at him as if he'd lost his mind.

"Kiss me," Hugh said. "Now." He set the beer on the counter, took two steps across the room and hauled her into his arms.

Carin was so amazed she let him. She wrapped her arms around him to keep her balance, and was the recipient of a deep hungry kiss.

"Hard at work, I see," a voice drawled from the front porch. "Don't let me interrupt."

Carin froze at the sound. But Hugh took his time finishing the kiss before he drew back and looked over Carin's shoulder at Nathan.

"Not a problem. We can continue later," he said smugly. "Looking for Lacey?"

"As a matter of fact, I'm not. I'm looking for her mother. I came to see if you—" he looked pointedly at Carin and not at Hugh "—wanted to join us for dinner, seeing as how you've been working so hard all day." Scorn positively dripped. "Figured I'd give you a ride over. Lacey thought it might save you a little time if you didn't have to cook. Give you more time to paint." His gaze narrowed and his tone became even more scathing. "But I see you've got other, more important things to do."

Carin flushed guiltily and was annoyed that she was reacting at all. It wasn't his business what she was doing! Or with whom.

"Hugh stopped by after work and I took a few minutes' break," she began.

"You don't owe me any explanations."

"You're damned right I don't!"

"So don't waste your breath. Are you coming with me for dinner or are you going to be too busy going to bed with lover boy?"

"Now there's a thought." Hugh grinned.

Carin glared at him, then at Nathan. "I'm going to paint, damn it. So you can both just get out of here now."

Hugh sighed. "Ah, well, I can wait," he said easily, then bent his head and dropped a light kiss on her lips. He winked as he sauntered out the door past Nathan and down the steps. "See you later, sweetheart."

Nathan didn't budge. "So, *sweetheart,* are you coming or not?"

"Not," Carin said. "I need to work."

Nathan regarded her through narrowed eyes. "You'd better work," he said. "You'd better be painting your sweet little heart out."

As Carin watched, he turned on his heel and stomped down the steps. At the bottom of the steps he turned and looked back up at her. "I'll have Lacey home at nine. So whatever you and lover boy get up to in the meantime, you be sure to be painting by then. Fair warning."

As he drove away, Carin stuck her tongue out at him.

Dominic called to see how it was going.

"It's not," Nathan said testily.

Rhys called to offer advice.

"It's not the same as with you and Mariah," Nathan said with all the patience he could muster. "Mariah *told* you when she was pregnant. She *wanted* you to be part of Lizzie and Stephen's life."

Obviously, his brothers talked to their father. Next thing Nathan knew the old man was on the phone.

"What do you want?" Nathan growled.

"Nothing," Douglas said airily. "Just called to shoot the breeze."

"Uh-huh." And pigs could fly. "And you're not going to ask about my love life?"

"Don't have to, do I?" Douglas said. "I think it's pretty clear from your tone that you don't have one."

Nathan ground his teeth.

"Sure you don't want me to come down and lend a hand?"

"Yes, damn it, I'm sure. And no, damn it, I don't!"

"Giving you a hard time, is she?" Douglas said, sounding almost sympathetic.

"I don't want to talk about it."

He knew what he was doing. He hoped. Besides, for the moment progress on the Carin front was at a standstill. There was nothing to talk about. She was painting—or so she said. And he was spending the days with Lacey.

He and Carin talked stiltedly when he picked Lacey up or dropped her off. Occasionally Hugh was there when Nathan brought her home.

"Helping you paint, is he?" Nathan found himself snarling more than once.

She didn't answer. It was hard to pick a fight with someone who ignored your provocation. And she did seem pretty paint-spattered much of the time, so he didn't have much of a leg to stand on.

Still, having to leave Lacey there with her mother and Hugh didn't make for restful evenings.

Actually, it made Nathan nuts. He took to going to The Grouper after he dropped Lacey off. There was sure as hell no point in going back to his place. All he'd do there would be to pace the floor and mutter things about Hugh McGillivray's maternal ancestry. Knocking back a beer or two or three with the locals was a much better idea.

At least, though his relationship with Carin was nonexistent, he and Lacey were getting on like a house afire.

He spent most days with Lacey. The day after the dinner at his house, they'd helped Miss Gibbs move library books. Then they'd gone back to his place and had begun to look at slides and talk photography. They did that now almost every day. She was smart as a whip and she had a good sense of composition. When he explained something, she asked questions, and she got the point.

Every day he spent with her, he learned more about her—and her mother—and felt twin twinges of anger and sadness that he hadn't had a part in her life until now. He blamed Carin. Sometimes he wanted to throttle Carin.

But if he was honest, he understood why she hadn't told him.

He'd been so focused in those days. He knew he was going to be a photographer, knew in his gut he could do it. But he also knew how much it would demand of him, how hard the work would be, how single-minded he'd have to be.

Fighting his father's determination that he go into the family business had been nothing compared to the obstacles he'd had to overcome to get where he was. He hadn't needed more obstacles.

Carin had known that.

It wasn't easy looking in the mirror when he thought about how self-absorbed he'd been.

He wasn't self-absorbed now. He wasn't single-minded. Gaby, his agent, was calling him every few days making offers and suggesting ideas—all of which would mean traveling—and every time, Nathan said no.

"I'm staying put," he told Gaby.

He was enjoying his time with Lacey. He was opening up the world to her. And she was opening up a particular small slice of it for him.

She was an eager student. She always wanted to take photos. Every day, no matter what else they did, they spent time doing that. At first he just let her take photos that interested her. But after a few days of that, he suggested she start looking for specific things. Patterns, themes, specific subject matter.

They shot trees, they shot flowers, they shot buildings

and birds and kids and fishermen. They shot old men at work and playing dominoes under the shade trees.

Sometimes they picked a topic—heat, water, happiness, symmetry—and spent the day shooting whatever they saw that expressed it.

In the evenings they developed the black-and-white film together. They took the slides to Deveril's, which had an overnight developing facility, then spent the next morning comparing the differences and similarities in the way they viewed things.

It was as instructive for Nathan as he hoped it was for Lacey.

He was fascinated to discover what interested her, to learn more about the way she looked at the world. And she rose to every challenge he offered, focusing on it, thinking about it, trying to see what she could bring to it that would be something he hadn't thought of. Sometimes she wanted it too much, tried too hard.

"Don't push it," he advised her. "It's about vision and about potential, but it's mostly about patience. You've just got to be there. The opportunity will come."

It was true in photography. Great photos came to those who were prepared, who knew what they were doing and were prepared to wait.

And as the days went by and nothing seemed to happen, he hoped to God it was true in life—in his life—with Carin.

His theory, which was not at all the theory subscribed to by his father or even by Dominic, for that matter, was that showing up and sticking around were half the battle.

"It's all about opportunity," he told himself, just as he'd told Lacey about photography.

But as one week went by and then another, he didn't see any opportunities.

Lacey did her best to try to throw them together. It was no secret their daughter wanted them together, even though she never said so outright.

"Don't push," Nathan advised her when she was trying to get her mother to come to dinner with them one night. "It doesn't do any good. She might show up because you asked her to, but it won't be because she wants to."

"I know, but—"

"And she'll go home irritated and more resistant than ever."

"Maybe, but—"

"So we'll just cool it," Nathan counseled. And tried to take his own advice.

But as the days passed, it got harder and harder to simply bide his time.

As the days passed Carin thought Nathan would get bored, get fed up, get antsy, be ready to leave.

Instead he stuck around.

Not only did he stick around, but he and Lacey bonded completely. They fished and swam and wandered all over the island, according to what her glowing daughter told her every evening. He listened to her and talked to her. He took her seriously. As far as Lacey was concerned, she could not have a better father.

"I wish he'd been here before," she said more than once. "He wishes he had been here before, too."

Carin tried to take that with equanimity. "Really? Did he say so?"

"No. 'Cause he's too polite. But I know he feels that way. I can just tell."

Which, of course, made Carin the bad guy of the piece. Good old Nathan wasn't even complaining because she'd done him out of twelve years of their daughter's life. Perversely it made her angry.

It was hard, too, because she felt such conflict. She didn't want to feel beholden to Nathan, and yet she was. He was saving her bacon by taking Lacey every day, by having hired Elaine, by allowing her to paint.

Even so, it was hard to feel grateful. She didn't *want* to feel grateful. And yet she knew she owed him.

More guilt.

And then there was Hugh. Carin was grateful to him, too. He made a point of stopping around in the evening along about the time Nathan would be bringing home Lacey. He stood in her kitchen, beer bottle in hand, acting like he'd been there all evening, giving her intimate little smiles and winks designed to make Nathan believe she and Hugh were an item.

He kissed her, too. And she let him—in front of Nathan. She told him they were friends. He said of course they were friends. But then he winked at her. And he kissed her. And there was something in the way he looked at her.

Even more guilt.

Oh, God, what a mess everything was!

The painting, wretchedly slow as it was, was the most successful part of her life! At least when Stacia had called on the weekend, she'd been able to say, without lying, that she had two paintings finished and the others were coming along.

"Terrific!" Stacia had been delighted. "I'm so glad. Do you want me to get you reservations for a place to stay?"

"No. Thanks. I still don't think we'll be able to make it." Every spare penny she had was being put away to reimburse Nathan for Elaine's salary.

"But you could use a holiday," Stacia argued.

"That wouldn't be a holiday," Carin said truthfully. The very notion of going to her own opening scared her spitless. "A holiday is where you have a good time."

Stacia laughed. "Keep painting. Let me know when you're getting close to finished and I'll be down."

"Will do."

No, she wouldn't go to New York. But maybe they could take a vacation to another of the islands. Stay a week or two before school started.

And when they got back, with luck Nathan would be gone.

Surely he had to leave sometime. He couldn't just stay on the island forever. A man who made his living traveling to the four corners of the earth wasn't going to be able to do that on an island five miles long and half a mile wide. The subject matter just wasn't here.

"Once you've seen one lizard, you've seen them all." Carin smiled to herself.

Maybe she could ask when he dropped Lacey off tonight. Since Hugh wasn't here—he'd flown a charter to Nassau and would be returning tomorrow sometime—it would be good to have another distraction. Something to annoy Nathan.

Since he got annoyed every time she brought up the possibility that he might not spend the rest of his life on Pelican Cay, that would be a good one.

But shortly before nine, when she heard the car pull up out in front, the engine kept on idling even as the car door shut. Half a minute later, Lacey banged into the house and the car drove away.

"No Nathan?"

"Dad's got company. Her name is Gaby."

"Gaby?" What kind of name was that? It called to mind blonde bimbos with big boobs.

"His agent," Lacey said.

"Oh." The blonde bimbo disappeared as fast as she'd come. "Well, that's nice," Carin said briskly. Nathan's agent arriving had to be a good sign. "When did she arrive?"

"This afternoon. We had dinner with her."

"And is she here to get your father to go back to work?" Carin asked, hoping she didn't sound as eager as she was.

"He is working," Lacey said, offended. "He works every day on his book."

"I mean in the field. She must want him to go and take more photos."

Lacey hunched her shoulders. "Dunno. They didn't talk about that. You don't think he'll leave, do you?"

"I don't know." Clearly Lacey wanted him to stick around. Carin didn't want to get in the middle of an argument about it.

"He's got a lot to do on his new book," Lacey said. "The one he's picking out photos for. And she was talking about him doing a show at her gallery this winter."

"Gaby has a gallery?"

"Uh-huh. In Santa Fe. It has a Spanish name." Lacey scrunched up her forehead, thinking. "Something about sombreros?"

"Sombra? Sombra y Sol?" Even Carin had heard of Sombra y Sol. It was one of the best-known galleries in Santa Fe.

"Yeah, that's it. Sombra y Sol."

"I thought it belonged to Gabriela del Castillo."

"Yeah." Lacey bobbed her head. "Gaby."

That was Nathan's Gaby? Though Carin had never met Gabriela del Castillo—having lived in a Caribbean backwater for a dozen years, that was a given—she'd certainly heard of her.

Gabriela del Castillo was a force to be reckoned with.

The widow of famous art patron, agent and entrepreneur, Enrique Castillo, she took over his gallery and his business after his death a few years back. At first, gossips said she was coasting on her late husband's coattails. But it hadn't taken Sra del Castillo long to dispel that notion. She had an eye for talent—and she was a terrific marketer.

Gabriela del Castillo was highly respected in the art world now. Sombra y Sol displayed some of the finest photographers in the world as well as some of the most successful artists in other media. It was one of the galleries Stacia had mentioned when she'd told Carin that if her show in New York was a success they might be able to take her work elsewhere. Carin had privately thought Stacia was aiming a little high.

It didn't surprise her that Gabriela del Castillo was Nathan's agent. It did surprise her that Sra del Castillo was humoring him about his staying on Pelican Cay. But maybe she would crack her whip after she'd been here a couple of days. Carin envisioned her as an elderly, ramrod-straight Spanish matron with snapping black eyes and an astute business mind.

"He showed her my photos," Lacey said. "She liked them. She says I'm a chip off the old block. Maybe she'll show my photos someday."

"Maybe," Carin said. "How long is she staying?"

"Dunno. They were going to The Grouper. He said he was going to take her out for a little local color."

Carin grinned. "Well, I hope she enjoys it."

It was hard to imagine a seventyish widow enjoying the steel band at The Grouper, but maybe Nathan was trying to broaden her horizons a little. "Is she staying at the Mirabelle?"

The Sand Dollar was a hip, yuppie spot on Pelican Cay while the quietly elegant Mirabelle, tucked away by a cove at the south end of the island, was the poshest small inn on the island. It was one of several that Hugh's brother, Lachlan, had bought in the past year. The Mirabelle was where all the VIPs stayed when they came to Pelican Cay.

Lacey shook her head. "She's staying at Dad's."

Carin was surprised to hear that. But then, maybe Sra del Castillo was a family friend. Perhaps she and her husband had been friends of Nathan's father. Douglas had to be about seventy now. And from what Carin remembered of him, he had his finger in many pies. She wouldn't be surprised if Sombra y Sol was one of them.

"Well, I'm sure she'll find it comfortable and quiet," she said. "She must be tired if she just arrived today."

Lacey shrugged. "I guess."

Carin yawned. "I'm tired, too. Time for bed. What time is your father picking you up tomorrow?" she asked as she shut off the light in the kitchen and shooed Zeno out onto the front porch.

"He's not," Lacey said as she climbed the stairs. "I'm going fishing with Lorenzo and Thomas."

Carin stopped, one hand on the newel post. "What? Since when?"

Lacey looked back at her. "Dad called Thomas and asked. He and Gaby have work to do. They said I'd be bored. And Thomas said it was okay."

"And he didn't think to check with me?"

Lacey lifted her shoulders. "He said he didn't want to bother you, on account of your painting and all."

"So he imposed on Thomas?"

Lacey looked offended. "Thomas is glad I'm coming. He says I'm a 'civilizing influence' on Lorenzo." She turned again and went up the steps.

Carin, following, shook her head. "I wonder. Well, I guess…if Thomas agreed. But I still think your father should have discussed it with me."

"He says you never want to talk to him."

It was true, of course, but galling that he had mentioned it to Lacey.

Still she went off to bed, heartened and blessing Gabriela del Castillo for her arrival. It wouldn't be long now and Nathan would be gone. Carin felt better than she'd felt since Nathan had appeared back on Pelican Cay.

The morning went well. The painting went well.

Knowing that Lacey was with Thomas and Lorenzo and not with Nathan somehow freed up a little of her creativity. Knowing that Gabriela del Castillo was at this very moment most likely leaning on Nathan to get back to work freed up some more.

Carin actually got some work done after Lacey left in the morning.

It was the first time in a long long while that she'd been able to focus, to think, to feel as if she were "in a zone" as far as her work went. She even whistled while she worked, contemplating the departure of Nathan as she did so.

She would have worked straight on through the afternoon, but Elaine expected her to bring lunch. She had done it every day, using it as an excuse to check on things, to see how Elaine was doing, to answer any questions the young woman might have.

Ordinarily, too, it was a nice break because she was getting so little done that being allowed out of the studio for twenty minutes or so was a treat.

Today she grumbled as she assembled Elaine's lunch and bundled it into the basket of her bicycle. It wasn't far to the shop, only a few blocks. But it was quicker to ride Lacey's bike there and back, and today—for once—Carin was actually in a hurry.

She pedaled off toward the shop, focusing on the new painting that was taking form in her mind. She didn't see Miss Saffron's cat dash across the road.

She didn't see Zeno race after him—not until he was right in front of her. She slammed on the brakes, jerked the handlebars and swerved just in time to see Nathan, his hand on the small of the back of an absolutely gorgeous blonde woman, going into the grocery store.

Carin, gaping, wobbled wildly, swerved madly and hit a pothole.

The bike flipped. So did the lunch.

So did Carin.

And then she went splat.

CHAPTER SIX

"*CARIN*! Good God, Carin! Are you all right?"

Asinine question. Of course she wasn't all right!

She'd flipped right over the handlebars of the bike! If he shut his eyes Nathan could see it still, in slow motion, Carin sailing through the air, arms flailing in an attempt to get her balance—and lay now in a crumpled heap in the road.

"Go inside. Tell 'em to call the doc." He didn't look to see if Gaby followed his directions or not. He had already hurdled the stair railing and was sprinting down the street toward Carin.

She was conscious. She was moving. She was scraped. He saw blood and he could hear her swearing a blue streak, saying words that would have shocked him if he hadn't been tempted to say them himself.

"Don't move," he instructed as he crouched beside her. "Damn it, Carin! Stay still!" he commanded when she struggled to get up.

"Bloody, bloody—! Oh, hell! Owwww!" She was scrabbling on the ground, trying to pick herself up, but one arm wasn't cooperating. And Nathan was afraid to touch her for fear of making things worse.

She had an abrasion on her cheek. Her legs were scraped, her hands bloody. And her arm—oh, God—her arm!

"Stop moving, damn it!" Nathan snapped at her. "You've broken your arm."

Carin looked at him, stricken, white as a ghost. Only her lips and lashes had any color. "I haven't! Oh damn! Oh hell! Oh—" She swore desperately. "I can't have broken my arm!"

"You have. Stop moving."

"You're not a doctor! What do you know?"

"I know you aren't supposed to have an elbow halfway down your forearm."

She jerked her gaze down and really looked at it for the first time. Then she looked back at Nathan, went even whiter, and her eyes started to roll back in her head.

"Damn it, Carin! Don't faint!" He did his best to get her head down, trying to avoid her arm, easing his around her, feeling her whole body tremble. He had no doubt that she was in shock. "It'll be okay. Gaby's got 'em calling for the doc."

"Gaby," she mumbled and shook her head as if she was dazed.

"My agent," he explained. "That's her name." It seemed stupid to be talking about Gaby now. He wanted to see how badly Carin was hurt.

But people began appearing to stand around—Lyle from the grocery store, Emmalyn from the bakery, Otis who ran the hardware store. And Miss Saffron, holding her damned cat. Zeno was there, too, looking worried.

"Is she all right?"

"Carin, you ok?"

"Oh, Carin!" It was Elaine. "You're hurt! You're not dyin'?"

Carin saw her and dredged up the faintest of smiles. "Not dying," she affirmed. "Your, um, lunch." She managed a weak wave of her hand on the unbroken arm toward the contents of the bag that had been in the basket of the bike.

"Forget the lunch." She stopped at the sight of Carin's arm. "Your arm! It's your *right* arm!"

The significance of this seemed to hit Carin at the same time it hit Elaine—and Nathan. Her right arm.

"I can't paint!" There was panic in Carin's tone now. "Oh, my God, I—"

"Here's the doc," Nathan broke in as Maurice pulled up in his Jeep and Doc Rasmussen climbed out.

He ran quick, practiced hands over her and turned to Maurice. "Call Hugh. Tell him we need to get her to Nassau." As he spoke he put a temporary splint on Carin's arm.

"Hugh's already in Nassau," she said weakly.

"We'll get him back here," Nathan promised. "Call McGillivray and tell him to get his ass home."

Maurice shook his head. "Be lots faster if Molly takes her."

"Who's Molly?"

"Hugh's sister," Carin answered. "Yes, Molly can do it."

Nathan noticed she wasn't arguing about having to go to the hospital. But he wasn't sure about Hugh McGillivray's sister. He'd met Molly McGillivray one day when he'd needed some work done on his boat's motor.

Lacey had said she knew who could fix it—and had taken him to see a girl she'd introduced as Hugh's sister.

Nathan had hardly believed it. Hugh had dark hair and blue eyes and was, even Nathan had to admit, pretty damned good-looking. The girl he'd met had carrot-red hair, freckles enough for a dozen Irishmen, and looked like a seventeen-year-old boy! She'd been wearing cutoff jeans, a baseball cap, and a T-shirt advertising a bar. With a smear of grease on her cheek and a wrench in her hand, she looked like a poster child for Tomboys R Us.

She'd fixed his engine in no time flat.

Now he said, "How many sisters does McGillivray have?"

"Just Molly."

Nathan had been afraid of that.

But Doc Rasmussen nodded. "Let's get her in the car. Call Molly and tell her we're coming. Maurice, you can drive us."

Nathan would have objected, but Carin, of course, was already trying to rise on her own, with Doc doing his best to support her.

Nathan stepped in. "Here," he said and scooped Carin into his arms before she could protest. "Open the door, Maurice."

Carin was still trembling as, slowly and carefully, Nathan carried her to the car and eased her into the front seat. He felt a shudder run through her before he got her settled. "You okay?"

She nodded shakily. Her head fell back against the head-rest and she closed her eyes for a brief second before opening them again and meeting his gaze. "Yes. Thank you."

"No thanks necessary," Nathan said gruffly. "Doc can ride with you. I'll take my own car."

"You don't need to come," Carin said quickly. "You need to be here. For Lacey. She's out fishing with Lorenzo and Thomas. Of course you know that. You set it up." She sounded aggrieved.

Nathan wasn't going to get into that with her now. "I'll see you at McGillivray's."

"Lacey—"

"Lacey will be fine."

She woke up in the hospital.

At least she supposed she was at the hospital.

She felt dazed and fuzzy-minded and her mouth tasted terrible. She looked around. She was in a private room, which didn't seem right. There was no way she could afford a private room. Even dazed and confused, she knew that.

She moved her gaze slowly—it was almost the only thing she could move—trying to take it all in.

Her arm was in plaster halfway to her elbow. There were ominous metal screws sticking out of the plaster. One leg was raised on pillows. Her hands were bandaged. Her lips felt cracked. There was something stuck to her cheek.

Every muscle in her body hurt. Even when she blinked, she could feel it.

"Look who's awake."

Her head jerked around and she almost screamed at the pull of the muscles. And very nearly screamed again at the sight of Nathan, unshaven and bleary-eyed, standing over her.

"Wha-what are you doing here?" Even her throat hurt. Probably because they'd stuck some tube down it while they had her knocked out.

"Watching you."

"Well, don't." If there was ever a time she didn't need him around it was now. She knew she sounded petulant and probably even childish. "Just let me alone."

"Thought you might like to know how Lacey is."

Her gaze snapped back to him. She started to sit up. "What's wrong with Lacey?"

"Nothing's wrong with Lacey," he said quickly, his tone soothing. "You were worried when we left, so I thought I'd stay around and let you know she was fine. I figured you'd want to know."

"Yes. Of course. Thank you. Where is she?"

"At Maurice and Estelle's. Hugh will bring her by later." His jaw tightened briefly. "We ran into him at the airfield and he insisted on coming to the hospital with us. When you were out of surgery, he flew home. He'll tell Lacey."

"And he's bringing her?"

"Later today. And he'll take her home again."

Knowing that Lacey was all right eased Carin's mind. That didn't help, though, when it came to her arm. She looked at the cast with the pins, and then at her leg. "What did they do to me?"

"Rasmussen called in an orthopedic surgeon, who set your arm. He put a couple of pins in it, said it would heal faster that way. Your ankle is sprained. X-rays came back negative for breaks on that," Nathan reported. "You've got some abrasions. Lots of grit in your skin. They picked that out while you were unconscious." He nodded at her face and at her gauze-wrapped hands. "It should heal up pretty fast. Doc said a couple of months and you'd be good as new."

"A couple of months?" Carin tried not to wail the words. "My show..."

"Don't worry about your show."

"Easy for you to say," she muttered.

"Ah, good. You're awake, dearie." A nurse appeared in the doorway, a bright white smile on her ebony face. "How you be feeling, then?"

"Just ducky," Carin muttered. But it was actually nice to see someone other than Nathan.

"Pain medication wearing off?" The nurse shook a pill out into a tiny paper cup and gave it to Carin. "You just take this. You feel better soon." She held a glass of water so Carin could sip it and get the pill down. "You get lots of sleep now an' you heal right up," she went on. "Don't worry 'bout a thing. Your husband, he take care of things for you."

The water went right up Carin's nose. She coughed and snorted and gasped and every muscle in her body screamed. "Oh, dear. Oh, dear. You drink too fast. Go slow. You got to go slow, dearie," the nurse said, completely mis-understanding the reason for Carin's coughing fit. The nurse put the glass out of reach and waited until Carin had stopped choking. "There now. You go slow."

"He. Is. Not. My. Husband." Carin wheezed out the words. She shot Nathan a fulminating glare.

The nurse looked surprised, then as her gaze turned to Nathan, she looked accusing.

In return Nathan looked both implacable and inscrutable. Whatever he had told the doctors and the hospital staff, it had apparently involved him being a close relative.

Now he shrugged, as if to say, Want to make something of it?

Clearly the nurse didn't. "You want more water now you stopped choking?" she asked Carin.

"No. Thank you," Carin added after a moment, banishing the rude child. She gave the nurse a wan smile and was rewarded with a pat on the hand.

"Don't you fret now," she said. "Whatever he is, he cares about you." Then, giving Nathan a smile, too, she headed for the door. "You need anything, you push that button," she pointed to the one by Carin's hand. And then she was gone.

And the two of them were alone again.

"Go away," Carin said after a moment.

Nathan didn't bother to answer. He didn't bother to move, either. He just sprawled in the chair by her bedside, looking tired. His dark hair was ruffled and uncombed, as if he'd run his hands through it. Dark stubble shadowed his cheeks and jaw. He was wearing a rumpled long-sleeved blue shirt and a pair of jeans faded at the knees to almost white. They were what he'd been wearing when she'd seen him right before she'd gone sailing over the handlebars of her bike.

"What time is it?" she asked wearily, when it was clear he wasn't going anywhere. There was some light coming through the window, but not much. It looked to be getting dark.

Nathan glanced at his watch. "Just past seven."

"I've been out six hours?"

"Eighteen. It's seven in the morning."

She stared at him. "Seven in the morning. Tomorrow? I mean, I've been here since yesterday?"

Nathan nodded. "Yep."

"And you've been here…"

"Since we brought you in."

No wonder he looked as if he'd been run over by a truck.

And Carin didn't even want to think what she must look like. "You should go home," she said.

"I will." But he still made no effort to move.

"Don't you have a hotel room?"

"Didn't need one. They let me stay here."

All night? He'd sat beside her bed all night? Carin was mortified and felt oddly teary at the same time.

"Well, you didn't need to," she told him.

"I promised Lacey I would."

And what could she say to that? Her fingers curled around a handful of sheet, and she shook her head, overwhelmed, exhausted, hurting even though the pain killer was beginning to take effect. It made her feel woozy. Her eyes shut.

"Go to sleep," she heard Nathan say. His voice seemed to come from far away. "Get that rest the nurse was talking about."

She strove to open her eyes. "You—" But of their own accord her lids closed again. "You should go…"

The last thing she heard was Nathan say, "Don't worry about me."

Nathan was doing enough worrying for both of them.

Whatever "opportunity" he'd been waiting for, he'd never imagined this one. The sight of Carin flying over those handlebars was one he would take to his grave. And the vision of her chalk-white face and the way her eyes went all glassy from shock still had the effect of a punch in the gut every time he called them to mind.

He hadn't left her side except for the time she'd spent in the operating room. Then he'd paced the hallway cursing and muttering, calling himself seven dozen kinds of a fool for being so damn "patient" so damn long.

He should have just hauled her off to a justice of the peace as soon as he'd arrived. It was what his father and Dominic would have done.

It was fine to let people go their own way if they didn't matter to you. But Carin mattered!

He loved her.

The moment he realized it was frozen forever in time as if he'd framed a shot, clicked the shutter and captured the mind-boggling amazement that came with it.

He had told himself he'd come for Lacey. He had a daughter; he wanted to know her. And Carin? He hadn't let himself think about Carin.

When he couldn't help but think about her, he'd focused on his anger at her not telling him, on his pain that she hadn't loved him enough to trust him to do the right thing. And after he'd got here and faced further rejection, he'd done his best to get his heart to reject her, too.

But it wouldn't. Because his heart knew what his head had tried to deny—that he had come because of Carin. Lacey had been a part of it, the catalyst, but not the deepest reason.

That had been Carin all along.

He'd had a lot of time to think about it during the fifteen hours or so, after his epiphany. He had sat by her in the recovery room. He'd walked alongside the gurney when they'd taken her back to her room. He'd scarcely left her side since. He'd answered questions from the doctors and nurses. He'd fielded visitors—and she'd had several, including Hugh, who had run into his sister at the airfield.

Hugh had come up to the room right after she'd returned from recovery and had insisted on seeing her. "Lacey will want to know how she is," he'd said.

"Getting along," Nathan had replied. But he knew that Hugh was right, that Lacey would expect a report and that it would be better for her if she knew Hugh had actually seen her mother. So he let Hugh in.

"For a few minutes." He'd stayed right by her side, and he'd made sure Hugh understood that he was in charge.

Hugh hadn't seemed inclined to dispute it. There were

no grins and intimate glances. He kept a respectful distance from Carin's sleeping form, standing at the foot of the bed, looking pale and worried and shaken, but uninclined to fight Nathan for the place of responsibility.

On the contrary, after he'd looked at Carin, he'd turned his gaze toward Nathan and said, "You're staying?" he asked as if he already knew the answer.

"Yes."

"I'll bring Lacey tomorrow."

Nathan had wanted to say that it wasn't necessary. But of course Hugh's offer was sensible and was what Carin would want. So he'd agreed. "That'd be good."

Hugh nodded and looked back at Carin, then sighed. "What a mess." Then noting how Nathan had stiffened, he grinned faintly. "Not Carin."

"Definitely not Carin."

"She's going to be crazy when she realizes she won't get enough paintings finished."

"I'll take care of it."

As soon as Hugh left, Nathan had used the phone in the room to call Gaby. He'd told her to call Carin's agent to tell her what happened, to see what could be done. And then he'd gone back to sitting beside Carin.

He wished he could at least hold her hand. But both hands had been bandaged and she was asleep and there was nothing he could do at all.

Only sit there and know that he loved her.

He wouldn't go away.

They were going to keep her in the hospital three days. Three!

It was ridiculous, Carin told the nurses, the doctors, everyone who came to see her. Everyone knew they were sending people home from the hospital the moment they'd pinned them back together these days.

"Not here," said Dr. Bagley, who had done the surgery.

"Not my patients. You stay until I say you are ready. You cooperate, maybe you go home tomorrow."

And since there was no way she could go without help, Carin stayed—and cooperated.

But she didn't need Nathan bloody Wolfe staying with her!

She told him that. She told the nurses and doctors and everyone else who came to see her, too. Often. Hourly sometimes.

No one paid any attention. Not even Hugh. He came bringing Lacey the afternoon after she'd had surgery, and she'd tried to get him to take Nathan home with him. "He doesn't need to be here," she'd said. "I don't want him here."

But Hugh only shrugged and said not very helpfully, "He says he's staying."

Something had happened between Nathan and Hugh while she'd been asleep. There was no convincing Nathan that Hugh meant anything to her anymore. It didn't take a genius to figure that out.

So she tried to enlist the aid of the nurses. "Tell him to go away," she said to each of them in turn. "He's invading my privacy."

"Ah, dearie, you know you'd miss him," said one.

"Send that great hunk of handsome away? Not on your life, ducks," said another.

"Only if I can take him home with me," said the youngest, batting her lashes and slanting hungry grins Nathan's way.

"Don't be daft," the senior nurse said to Carin. "Without him you'd be in a ward, not in a private room. I'd give my arm for a man who cared that much for me. Hasn't left you once."

"You need a change of clothes and a shower," Carin told Nathan.

"I took a shower," Nathan said, nodding toward the

bathroom attached to her room. "And Gaby brought me a change of clothes just this morning."

"Good for her," Carin said sourly.

Nathan just grinned at her. "See? Clean jeans. Fresh shirt. Brought me my shaving kit, too. I'll shave when you take a nap."

Carin could see, now, that he had cleaned up. And though he obviously still looked tired, his stubbled jaw only made him look rakish and more handsome than ever. She felt like an ugly witch by comparison.

"Gaby's looking forward to meeting you."

"What!"

"She'll be along in a little while. She couldn't stop this morning. Had a business meeting this morning. But when they get things sorted out, she'll be along to see you."

"She doesn't need to stop and see me," Carin said hastily. "What does she want to meet me for?"

"Because I've told her all about you," Nathan said.

Whatever that meant. Carin didn't even want to think. She didn't have time in any event because moments later the door to her room opened and the beautiful blonde Carin recognized as Gaby came in.

She wasn't alone, either. There was another woman with her. She came running toward Carin, long, dark hair flying.

"Oh, my God, Carin! You poor thing! I didn't believe it when Gaby told me!"

Carin gaped. "*Stacia?* How did you—" Nathan's agent had told hers that she was in the hospital? Oh, dear God. "I was going to call you," she began, trying to sound calm and in control to Stacia, all the while shooting Nathan a furious glare. "I've got…got two of the paintings done. I know that's not—"

"Not to worry," Stacia said, patting her unplastered arm. "You need to rest. To get well. You need to take care of your arm. Even your hands are bandaged." She was tsking, making horrified sounds.

"I'll be all right," Carin said. Dr. Bagley hadn't told her she wouldn't be. He'd said she might need some therapy, but she could do that. "I just can't get all six of the paintings done now, though."

If Stacia dumped her, Stacia dumped her. This show had been going to be her "big break," and she might never get another. But there was no crying over what had happened. It had happened—and she simply had to go on from there.

"No problem," Stacia said, giving an airy wave of her hand.

Carin blinked. "No…problem?"

That wasn't what Stacia had been saying the last time they'd talked. "You think you've got enough to make the show go on?"

"Of course," Stacia said emphatically. "It's all sorted out. It will be wonderful." She beamed at Carin, then at Nathan. "Having such a wonderful photographer's work as a complement to your paintings will bring patrons out in droves."

"What!" Carin tried to sit bolt upright, but gasped at the pain and sank back against the pillows to stare aghast at Stacia. "What are you talking about?"

"Nathan's offer. You know we needed more," Stacia said, perfectly matter-of-factly. "I told you that. I told you six more large pieces minimum. Better ten. Or lots of smaller ones. So you finished two more. And Nathan offered his work to fill in the gaps. Island shots, right?" She looked at Nathan for confirmation.

He looked a little uneasy, as well he might. If looks could kill, Carin thought, he'd have been worse off than she was.

"I don't need Nathan bailing me out," she said to Stacia.

Stacia blinked, then said, "Oh, but you do. We don't have enough otherwise."

"Then we won't do it!"

Stacia just looked at her. For a full minute she didn't say a thing, just looked, and let Carin realize how stupid and petulant and childish she sounded. It didn't even take thirty seconds. Irritably she did her best to shrug.

"I don't like to be beholden," she said irritably. "I wanted to do it on my own."

"But circumstances don't permit. And you will," Stacia assured her. "In time, you will. But for now, this is perfect. It will showcase your work in the company of a man who shares a vision with you. Different media, same subject. Wonderful. And I hear that your daughter has done some fine work as well."

"Lacey?" Carin looked from Stacia to Nathan to Gaby.

Gaby was nodding. "She's very talented. We thought we might feature all three of you." She beamed. "A family affair. Island Eyes."

While Carin listened, stupefied, they chatted on, as if it were really going to happen. They talked about logistics and shipping and framing and all the practicalities that meant they were serious. They discussed Lacey's work as if they were familiar with it. They mentioned different pieces. They talked about balancing her work and Nathan's with Carin's paintings.

Every once in a while they consulted Nathan. But they talked as if Carin weren't even in the room. When the nurse appeared, she took one look at Carin's pained expression and misunderstood the situation completely.

"Out," she said to Gaby and Stacia. "You're tiring my patient."

They didn't seem to mind. "We can finish this over lunch," Gaby said cheerfully. "No sense in bothering Carin about it."

"Of course not." Stacia came over and patted Carin's hand. "Don't you worry about a thing. Gaby and Nathan and I will take care of everything."

"We certainly will," Gaby seconded. "It was lovely to meet you at last, though I'd have preferred other circumstances," she added. "And don't worry. Everything will be fine. We'll see to it."

Carin looked from one woman to the other, and finally at Nathan. "No reassurances from you?" she asked sarcastically.

He shrugged, but met her gaze steadily. "Trust me," he suggested.

She didn't.

Not an inch.

How could she when he just bullied his way in and took over her life?

First he insisted on staying with her the whole time she was in the hospital. Then he arranged for his agent and hers to get together and come up with this ridiculous combined show, this "family affair," which everyone else seemed to think was wonderful and which Carin knew was a sham.

They weren't a family, damn it!

But when she pointed that out to Nathan, he said, "We could be."

And she knew that was his way of saying he was still willing to marry her. Obviously the Wolfe notion of duty ran very very deep.

She found out just how deep when she finally got out of the hospital and Hugh flew her home to Pelican Cay.

Of course it was too much to hope that Nathan wouldn't be with her every step of the way. Even when she had Hugh right there to help her, Nathan insisted on carrying her across the tarmac and helping her into the helicopter.

"Where's Lacey?" she demanded. Lacey had flown over with Hugh once, but she'd been so stricken by the sight of her mother all banged up that Carin had told Hugh not to bring her again until she was ready to come home.

Lacey needed to feel that her mother could cope. And seeing her in the hospital, barely able to do anything for herself, didn't lend itself to the notion of coping. After three days she was better. She could feed herself. She could hobble around—just. She had thought Lacey would be here to witness her progress and her return home.

But Nathan just said, "She's getting the house ready for you."

And Carin had to be satisfied with that. In fact, it was probably just as well Lacey hadn't come, since the mere trip to the helicopter wore Carin out.

She tried to appreciate the beauty of the island as Hugh took off and eagerly pointed things out to her. But the combination of fatigue and pain medication got to her before they'd gone far, and she felt her eyes close.

When she woke up, she found her head against a warm male chest. She jerked and looked up and found herself staring into Nathan's blue eyes.

"You okay?" he asked.

She pulled away and tried to sit up. "Fine. I'm fine."

She managed to stay awake until Hugh set the copter down on the small landing field near the cricket grounds. Then he carried her bags to his waiting van and Nathan carried her.

"I can walk," Carin protested.

But Nathan ignored her. "Humor me," he said. "I love carrying wriggling females."

She shot him a look of annoyance and stayed perfectly still to spite him, then realized that was exactly what he had in mind.

He tucked her into the second seat of the van and clambered into the back one, then reached up and slung the door shut. "All set," he told Hugh who was in the driver's seat.

Hugh put the van in gear, and they rumbled out of the field and onto the road. Carin was leaning forward eagerly now, looking forward to seeing the town, to seeing her house, to being home again. It felt as if she'd been gone a year, not merely a few days.

''Hugh! My house is that way!'' She pointed to the right fork when Hugh took the left.

Hugh just kept driving, bouncing them along the rutted road toward the far end of the island.

The penny dropped. ''Oh, no.'' Carin protested. ''You're not taking me to Nathan's!''

''You can't stay at your place,'' he said practically.

''Certainly I can! Stop this car! Hugh, turn around!''

But Hugh neither stopped nor turned. He wound through the jungly woods heading directly for Nathan's place.

''Damn it!'' Carin shoved herself up, making her arm hurt. ''You can't kidnap me like this!''

''Fine. We'll just go back to the copter and take you back to the hospital.''

''Take me home!''

''Can't.'' He shook his head. ''Doc said you need care.''

''I'll get care. Lacey can—''

''Lacey's a child,'' Nathan said firmly. ''And you are an adult. So why don't you try acting like one.''

Carin glared at him, furious at being told off that way. ''How dare you! She's my daughter! She can—''

''No doubt she can,'' Nathan cut in. ''*Our* daughter is bright and capable and she would probably bend over backward to do whatever you wanted her to do because you're her mother and she realizes how much you've done for her. But—'' he fixed her with a hard level stare ''—I would hope you're not selfish enough to ask her to do it.''

Carin opened her mouth, then closed it again. She sat, rigid, glaring at him, hating him for putting her at such a disadvantage, for being right, for making her feel like a fool. She didn't speak, just glowered.

He didn't back down. ''She's at my place now, fixing up a room for you, making it nice for you. She and Estelle have been working on turning my dad's office into a bedroom for you so you can be on the main floor and you won't have to climb stairs, which you would have to do at your house…''

''I could have,'' Carin said sulkily.

''And the very least you can do,'' Nathan went on, ''is to be grateful to her for her efforts. You can stop acting like a spoiled child and start acting like a mother.''

Carin felt as if steam was going to come right out of her ears. ''I'm *not* selfish! You're the one who's being selfish! Pushing into our lives, taking over, shoving into my gallery opening, forcing me to stay at your place—''

''Get it out of your system now,'' Nathan said implacably. ''Because you'd better not carry on like this in front of Lacey. Bad enough you're doing it in front of Hugh.''

Hugh? Dear God, she'd forgotten about Hugh, driving silently on toward Nathan's, listening and not responding at all.

''Whose side are you on?'' she asked him now.

His gaze flicked up, and their eyes met in the rearview mirror. He looked abashed and apologetic. ''Nath's just trying to help, Carrie.''

Carin arched a brow. ''Nath?'' she echoed. ''Are you two buddies now?'' She looked at Hugh accusingly.

''We've, um, talked…''

''Talked? And what did he tell you? Did he tell you he's trying to run my life?''

''And you're making it such a pleasure,'' Nathan said dryly.

Carin flushed and glared at him.

''The doc said you couldn't be going up and down stairs and you had to have someone with you or he wouldn't let you leave. You know I don't have any place to put you up. And Lachlan's place is full this time of year. And it would be a hell of an imposition on Estelle and Maurice.''

''I know that,'' Carin muttered.

''So Nathan said you could stay with him.''

"Out of the kindness of his heart," Carin grumbled, disbelieving.

"Exactly," Nathan said, his tone gruff but something of a smile lurking at the corners of his mouth. Their gazes met. Something electric seemed to sizzle between them.

If she were healthy and whole she would run a mile, Carin thought.

"You're doing this for Lacey," she told Nathan sternly. *Not for me.* "Right, Nathan?"

He just looked at her. "What do you think?"

CHAPTER SEVEN

SHE WAS IN TROUBLE being at Nathan's 24/7.

But she was stuck and she knew it.

As the doctor had predicted, she couldn't manage on her own. It wasn't just climbing the stairs in her house with her badly sprained ankle that she couldn't have done. She couldn't do simple things like cooking a meal or washing dishes. She certainly couldn't frame her pictures or work at the store.

Just getting through the day was a struggle.

"Accidents do that," Nathan said, taking her weakness in stride and with far more equanimity than she did.

Of course he did, she told herself, because he was getting what he wanted!

But why any sane man would want to be stuck with a cranky, annoying invalid and an exuberant twelve-year-old girl she couldn't imagine.

Nathan seemed to take her crankiness and Lacey's endless enthusiasm in stride, too.

He pretty much ignored the first and he actually encouraged the second. Mostly he seemed to be able to cope.

She wanted to be furious with him, to hate his bossiness and his presumptuousness and his general all-around taking over of her life.

But it was hard to hate the man who carried her to the bathroom, when she needed to get there, because she couldn't use crutches and her leg wouldn't let her put weight on it at first. It was hard to dislike him when he cooked her dinner and brought her breakfast and fixed her lunch. And it was hard to stay angry with a man who got up in the middle of the night to check on her and who every night bedded down on the sofa in the living room so he would be close enough for her to call if she needed something.

She wanted to turn away from him, to fight him, to resist him and, damn him, he was making it almighty difficult.

Of course, from the start she'd been cornered into calling a truce. After what he'd said about Lacey worrying about her, she'd had no choice. And once they got there, she'd understood what he meant.

Lacey had been standing on the porch, practically bouncing with joy at the sight of her mother. She had been so eager to have Carin back home, so obviously worried about her, and so delighted that they would all be there together at Nathan's and that "everything would be all right now," that Carin knew she had to try to make sure it was.

That meant she couldn't fight with Nathan when Lacey was around. But the fact was, as the days went by, she couldn't seem to fight with him, anyway.

He was still bossy and interfering and thought he knew best. But he was also making their daughter feel happy and secure. He was allowing Lacey to be a child instead of her mother's caretaker.

Carin was grateful for that.

At the same time, though, it made her want more. It made her want things she'd wanted years ago, when she'd been starry-eyed and in love.

And she didn't want to want that. Loving Nathan and not being loved in return simply hurt too much.

Still, at the moment she couldn't change things. She had to stay here until she was well enough to go home. When at last she and Lacey were on their own again, she would do what she could to restore the distance between herself and Nathan.

In the meantime…in the meantime she was living dangerously.

Oh, yes.

Every day she felt herself sucked further into the web of desire. It was, in some ways, like the week they'd spent together all those years ago. She hadn't wanted to want him then, either. But what her mind knew, her body disagreed with, and her heart…her heart was torn.

Watching Nathan day after day—studying him surreptitiously when he was cooking dinner in the kitchen or out on the deck repairing a railing or at the desk in the living room, bent over his light table picking over his slides—was a treat and a torture at the same time.

She'd always liked looking at Nathan. And his lean, agile young man's body had matured well. He was still lean, though not slender. His shoulders were broader than she remembered, his arms were harder and more muscular. There was a bit more hair on his tanned chest.

Nathan's chest, Carin decided—purely from an artist's perspective, of course—was a work of art. She knew that some men worked hard at the gym to achieve masculine perfection.

Nathan's beauty was a by-product of working hard. And wherever he moved—whether around the kitchen or the garden, on the beach or in the water—he did so with an effortless masculine grace.

He had always been a man who was comfortable with his body.

And it was all too easy to remember what he'd been like in bed.

Carin knew she shouldn't think about that. But it was impossible not to.

She was a captive of her injuries, stuck in the house where they'd slept together with far too much time on her hands. It was too easy to look at him and remember. The days were hot, the nights were barely less so. She saw a lot of Nathan's bare, tanned skin.

She touched it, too. At night when he came to check on her, he was usually bare-chested and wearing only a pair of shorts. Before she could walk and he carried her into the bathroom or out onto the deck, she felt those strong hard arms supporting her. Her body was pressed against the firm warm wall of his chest.

She remembered when he'd been hot with passion, remembered when their bodies had linked, when their hearts had beat together, when, however briefly, the two of them had become one.

They weren't restful thoughts.

She tried to stay out of his way.

"You don't have to stop and fix lunch for me," she'd protested when he'd brought her a sandwich and a cup of soup the day after she arrived. It was enough that he had cooked dinner for them the night before and had brought her breakfast in the morning.

"I'm fixing lunch for me," he'd said patiently. "Easy enough to make two sandwiches."

She would have looked foolish if she had made an issue out of it. So she'd thanked him politely and had eaten the lunch—which had been very good—and every day after that he brought lunch to her in her room or carried her out onto the deck on nice afternoons so she could enjoy the weather.

Bad. Worse, instead of disappearing again, he sat and ate with her.

She couldn't tell him not to. It was his deck.

Nor could she refuse to answer the perfectly polite questions he asked her and take part in the perfectly pleasant conversations he began. So they talked. Carefully at first, as if they were treading in a minefield, which in many respects they were.

At first Lacey had hovered around every minute, obviously afraid that leaving them alone together might be a disaster. But as the days passed and the truce endured, like any twelve-year-old, she got bored with spending every minute with her parents. She went to Lorenzo's. She went to Marcus's. She went to the shop and helped Elaine or she went to see Hugh and Molly. In other words, she resumed her regular life.

She had already gone and they were eating lunch one afternoon when Nathan asked Carin about her painting.

"I remember thinking you had talent when I saw the stuff you showed me," he said. "But you didn't have a 'style' of your own then."

"You're right. But then I met Gretl."

And she told him about Gretl Hagar, the internationally known Austrian folk artist who had spent a winter on Pelican Cay when Lacey was small.

"Miss Saffron owned the shop then. And I was working for her," Carin told him, "and dabbling in various artsy things when I could. Gretl used to come by the shop and play with Lacey and talk to me about her work. She encouraged me to find what I liked to do. I told her I didn't have a lot of time to do anything, except when Lacey was napping. And she said to come to her place and she would play with Lacey a couple of mornings a week and I could work."

Nathan's brows lifted. "Gretl Hagar played with Lacey?" Obviously, even he knew who Gretl was.

Carin nodded, smiling as she remembered that winter. Gretl had been so kind, so supportive.

"She said it was important to mentor. Someone had helped her get started. She helped me. I've tried to do that, too. Though I'm not nearly the caliber of artist Gretl is."

"You're very good," Nathan said flatly.

"What about you?" she asked. "Did you have a mentor?"

He thought a minute. "Mateo," he said. "Mateo Villarreal."

"I remember Mateo Villarreal."

He looked surprised. "You do?"

"Well, I remember your mentioning him. You'd been

climbing with him before you...before you came here for the wedding.''

And just like that, the years seemed to fall away. The ''Do Not Touch'' and ''Do Not Mention'' signs vanished and the past came rushing back.

When she'd first met Nathan he'd just come back from an Andean expedition with Chilean mountain climber Mateo Villarreal, a man so well-known that even a non-climber like Carin had heard of him.

During the week they'd spent together, Nathan had told her plenty of Mateo stories. Mateo, he'd assured her, made a guy like Dominic look easy-going. Mateo was intense, focused, demanding and absolutely reliable. Also very funny. It had been easier to think of Dominic as a ''whole person'' and not just a scary one when she'd heard Nathan's stories about Mateo.

She hadn't gone through with the wedding, though, because in telling the stories, Nathan had endeared himself to her even more. One Mateo story she remembered particularly well because it had, in a way, made her reevaluate her own situation.

In those days, Nathan had said, he hadn't been much of a climber. He'd had to push himself to keep up with Mateo on even a moderate climb. Of course, the climb itself wasn't what he'd gone for. Nathan had been after photos. He'd told her there was a particular route he'd wanted to climb and Mateo had said no, he wasn't ready.

Nathan had argued. ''A man needs to test himself.''

But Mateo had been adamant. ''There's testing and there's foolishness. And it's crucial to know which is which. It's fine to stretch. But you need to respect your limits.''

It was respecting her limits that had made Carin jilt Dominic. In the abstract, the notion of being married to Dominic Wolfe had been thrilling. He was gorgeous, wealthy, strong, capable, responsible—everything a woman could want in a man.

He was like Everest. Both towering and tempting.

Not a challenge in which a novice could succeed. And the closer she'd come to their wedding day, the clearer that had become.

During the week before the wedding, Nathan had attempted to show her the softer side of Dominic—the human side, the gentle side. He'd shown her that Dominic had traits that made him human, that she could relate to.

It wasn't Dominic she'd doubted in the end.

It was herself.

Facing marriage to Dominic, Carin had learned her limits.

Now she wondered if she was pushing the limits again— sitting here talking to Nathan, feasting her eyes on him, enjoying his company.

She finished her glass of iced tea. ''I'd better let you get back to work,'' she said abruptly. Nathan looked startled. A flicker of something—annoyance? irritation?—crossed his face. But then it was a mask of politeness again.

He stood up. ''I'll take the dishes into the kitchen. Do you want to stay here or would you like me to carry you back to your room?''

Carin shook her head and stood up carefully. ''I'll walk.''

She didn't need him touching her. Didn't need more memories or more temptation. It had been a week since her accident. It was time she did what she could for herself. She took a halting step.

Nathan's jaw tightened as he watched. ''Carin.'' His tone was warning.

She shook her head. ''I'm fine,'' she said fiercely. ''Go take the dishes into the kitchen.''

He didn't move, just stood there, prepared to catch her if she fell.

She wouldn't fall!

She saw a muscle ticking in his temple as she made her way past him and slowly limped into her room.

Enough.

Nathan wanted to tell Carin he'd had enough. Wanted to step in right now and tell her how it was going to be—that she was going to let him carry her across the damn room, that they were going to talk about what had happened between them all those years ago, logically and rationally for once. Then they were going to put it behind them, marry each other, turn the three of them into a family, and that was going to be that.

A hundred times since her accident he opened his mouth to say those things. And every time he'd back away again.

His father could have done it. Dominic could have done it. Hell, even Rhys probably could have done it!

Nathan couldn't.

He wanted to marry her. No question about that. If he'd come back out of duty first and a healthy curiosity about the one woman he'd fallen hard for in his whole life, that wasn't why he was here now. He was here because he loved Carin Campbell.

But he couldn't ask her to marry him now because, damn it to hell, when he married her, he wanted her to love him, too!

She didn't. Not anymore.

Once she probably had. He understood now—with maturity and the experience that came with years of casual dating—that while other girls might hop into the sack with a man just for the fun of it, Carin had never been one of them.

When she'd made love with him that night, she'd been doing exactly that—making love.

And he understood now what he hadn't understood then—that he'd loved her, too—in his way.

But he hadn't been in any position to do anything about it then. In fact, what had happened between them that night had scared him to death.

It wasn't only betraying his brother's trust that had been wrong. It was that he'd become involved with Carin. He'd told himself he was merely entertaining her while she waited for Dominic. He'd charmed her and teased her and talked to her—and found himself drawn ever deeper by his attraction to her.

He'd wanted her. And he'd had her with no thought as to what the consequences might be.

He'd overstepped his limits.

It went back to exactly what Mateo had been telling him when they'd gone climbing. There were some things that were, for the time being, out of his reach.

"You're not ready for that peak," Mateo had told him.

He hadn't been ready for Carin, either.

And as soon as he'd made love with her, he'd known it was wrong. He'd felt gut-punched. Queasy. Desperate. Guilty. Every bad thing he could imagine.

If he'd never fully understood the Sunday school story about forbidden fruit, he'd had firsthand experience of it when he'd made love to Carin.

He couldn't undo what he'd done. And heaven help him, he had still wanted her—as wrong as it was. So he'd done the only thing he knew how to do at the time.

He'd run.

He'd gone as far and as fast as he possibly could. He'd turned his back on all of them, consumed with guilt, with knowing he'd overstepped. If he couldn't undo it, still he'd tried desperately, with the naiveté of youth, to put things back as best he could.

It couldn't be done.

The world had changed.

Carin had changed. At the time, of course, Nathan hadn't had any idea how much. Now he knew that by taking her love when he'd had no right to it—when it should have been beyond his reach—he had completely altered her life.

He hadn't realized then that he'd also altered his own.

Now he did. And he was still trying to put things right, knowing even as he did so that the odds were against him. He'd had his chance with Carin all those years ago. He'd blown it. He had no right to expect her to look kindly on his efforts now.

Still he couldn't stop trying. Couldn't walk away. He'd promised Lacey he wouldn't. But this was about more than Lacey. It was about Carin and him. It was about second chances and trying again.

He was smarter now. Older. More mature. He had something to offer her—if he could only get her to see it.

Sometimes—like at lunchtime—he thought he was making a bit of progress. Sometimes she was like the old Carin, eager and interested, easy to talk to. Sometimes they could have a genial conversation.

And then, all at once, she would pull back, the way she had this afternoon. One minute they'd been talking comfortably about Mateo Villarreal, and the next minute the wall between them had slammed back down again. He was on one side, she was on the other, and she wouldn't even let him touch her.

He'd enjoyed the conversation. He'd been looking forward to touching her. Having the excuse to carry Carin from one place to another was a pleasure—and a pain.

It was wonderful to have her in his arms, to touch her soft skin and rest his chin against her silky blonde hair. He lived for those moments, for being close enough to breathe in the scent of her, to surreptitiously rub his nose against her hair, to accidentally on purpose brush his cheek against its softness, to rub the pad of his thumb along her arm, to let his fingers slide down the backs of her bare legs.

He prowled the house, irritable and unsettled, needing to work on his book, unable to focus on it at all.

Talk to me he wanted to demand.

But he didn't think he wanted to hear anything she might have to say.

And nothing he could say apparently made the slightest difference to her.

He had to show her. Had to prove that he had changed. Had to convince her by his actions.

But first he needed a cold shower.

The door creaking open startled him.

It wouldn't have awakened him had he been asleep. Of course he wasn't. He'd barely slept, it seemed, since Carin had come to stay. At first he'd deliberately stayed awake to hear her if she needed him to help her, to carry her.

But she didn't need him now. Not like that.

But he stayed awake anyway. Couldn't help it. It was too easy to lie in bed and remember lying there with her. Too easy to think about her creamy smooth flesh because he'd been touching it lately.

And all the cold showers in the world didn't help if the minute you had one, you started once more thinking about the woman who had made you need the shower. So Nathan was awake and restless when the door creaked open and soft limping footsteps came down the hallway.

He stopped breathing. But his heart still thundered so loudly that he wondered if she could hear it.

Was she coming to him?

That had been one of the cold-shower fantasies—that one night she would find her way from her bed to his. Now, hearing her footsteps, Nathan wanted to sit up, to reach out to her. His aroused body ached for her.

The footsteps slowed, then paused at the archway into the living room. He swallowed. He could see her silhouetted in the moonlight as she looked toward him.

Should he move? Shouldn't he?

Still she stood there, one hand braced on the doorjamb. Nathan took a slow, careful even breath.

Come to me. As she'd come to him all those years ago.

He shifted, made a sound, wanted her to know he was awake.

She jerked and stepped back from the doorway.

"Carin?" He couldn't *not* speak. His voice was ragged. "You okay? You, um, warm enough?"

On that long-ago day she'd been cold after the storm and he'd warmed her. God, he wanted to warm her again, wanted to take her into his arms and—

"I'm fine," she said quickly, her voice sounding raspy. "I...I was just on my way to the bathroom. Sort of using the wall for balance. Sorry if I bothered you." And she hobbled quickly away.

He stayed where he was, cursed his foolishness. Maybe he shouldn't have said anything, maybe she would have come closer, maybe...

The water ran in the bathroom, then the door opened and she limped back, quickly this time, and went straight past the archway to the living room. She didn't pause or look his way.

The door to her room shut with a decided click.

Nathan let out a harsh breath. He flung himself over onto his side. Hell! He tried to put her out of his mind; he tried to forget.

He needed another cold shower, but he'd be damned if he would advertise his distress. He glanced at his watch, sighed, shifted against the sheets, twisted, turned and finally hauled himself up off the sofa.

His body was taut with arousal. He stared toward Carin's room, willing her to open her door again, willing her to stand there in her shift in the moonlight, willing her to want him the way he wanted her.

But the door stayed shut.

And finally there was no help for it. Nathan eased open

the sliding door, grabbed a towel off the railing and went swiftly down the steps, headed toward the beach.

The cool night air did little to assuage his hunger, the colder ocean water into which he flung himself helped only a bit.

He got through the night. But first thing in the morning he took himself off early to spend the morning working on a new project, a sort of architectural history of the island's houses. It was a far cry from the work he usually did, but he was enjoying it—or he would have been if he hadn't wanted to enjoy something else—making love to Carin!—more.

If he were smart he would stay away all day, but as lunchtime approached he picked up some conch fritters from Perry at the fish shop and headed home. With a salad and a cold beer, they'd be an unexpected treat. He knew Carin liked them as much as he did and he was looking forward to seeing her grin of delight.

"Hey," he called as he bounded in the door. "Guess what I've got!"

She wasn't in the kitchen, so he headed for the deck. Most days lately she had been setting the table for the two of them out there. But the table was bare and she wasn't on the deck, either.

"Carin?" He went back in and headed for her room. "Carin? Are you okay?"

The door was ajar. He pushed it open—and stood stockstill and stared.

The bed had been stripped, the quilt haphazardly folded at the bottom. The desktop was bare. The closet doors were open. Her clothes were gone.

"What the—!" Nathan whirled around and sprinted out of the room and up the stairs to Lacey's room.

It was just as bare.

"Carin!" It was a bellow now.

He banged Lacey's closet doors open, kicked the corner of the bedstead, cursed and charged back downstairs.

And then he spotted it—on the kitchen counter. A note. A *note,* for God's sake! A *thank-you* note!

"'Dear Nathan,'" he read through clenched teeth. "'I want you to know how much I've appreciated your hospitality. It has been a great help. I'm doing so much better that I don't want to impose any further, so Lacey and I are going home. We really appreciate…'" Blah, blah, blah.

He crumpled the note. Slammed his fist on the counter! Flung the bag of conch fritters clear across the room!

Then he jumped in his car, whipped it around and drove straight back to town. He slammed on the brakes in front of her place, practically knocked Zeno over as he pushed through the gate, took the steps two at a time and banged open the door without even knocking.

Carin was sitting on the sofa eating a piece of toast. She looked startled, then resolute, then damned guilty.

"What are you doing?" she demanded.

"*Me*? What am I doing? You're the one who picked up and stole out without a word to anyone! Just what the hell do you think *you're* doing?"

"Eating lunch," she said deliberately misunderstanding. "Would you like some?"

"Damn it, no, I wouldn't like some! I brought you lunch at home! Conch fritters! Come on, we're going back."

"No, we're not. I'm not. We imposed on you long enough. I'm fine now."

"Oh, yes, I can see how fine you are." Her arm was still in the cast and in the sling. She was still wearing a T-shirt—his T-shirt!—because she couldn't fasten buttons well.

"I need to get by on my own. It was time."

"So you snuck out," he accused her.

Her lips tightened into a firm line. "I did not sneak out!

I just didn't want to argue. You told me we shouldn't argue in front of Lacey," she reminded him.

"How do you know we would have argued?" He was prowling around her living room. It was barely big enough to swing a cat in. He nearly tripped over the rocking chair as he swung around and glowered at her.

"Educated guess," Carin said dryly. "If I'd said I wanted to go home today, would you have said, oh sure, I'll drive you right over?"

Nathan scowled and scuffed his toes on the braid rug. "I would have tried to make you see reason. That's *not* arguing."

"Right. If *I* do it, it's arguing. If you do it, it's making me see reason." Carin shrugged equably. "I didn't want to see reason," she said reasonably. "So I called Maurice and asked him to come get me."

"Just like last time," Nathan said bitterly.

Carin stiffened. "It is not at all like last time. I wasn't running away today. I was coming home. Besides, you and I were not getting married."

Nathan stared at her in stony silence. He felt betrayed, as if she'd pulled the rug right out from under him.

"Why?" he demanded. "Was it so hard living with me?"

She hesitated. "You were very kind. I—"

"Kind!" He spat the word. "I didn't do it to be kind, damn it!"

"I know that," Carin said, an edge to her voice.

"Then—"

The front gate banged. "Here comes Lacey. We are not arguing in front of Lacey."

Nathan opened his mouth.

"Your rule," she reminded him.

Nathan swallowed a retort as Lacey burst through the door. "Hi, Dad! How come we're back here, Mom?" She gave Nathan a brilliant grin, which faded a bit as she looked at her mother.

Good, Nathan thought. Let her explain.

"This is where we live, Lacey," Carin said evenly. "We were only staying at Nathan's while I was recovering."

"You're not recovered yet." Lacey apparently had no rule about not arguing.

"I'm recovered enough. Aren't I, Nathan?" Carin's gaze went straight to Nathan, challenging him to back her up.

He shoved his hands into the pockets of his canvas shorts. "If you say so."

"I say so," Carin said. "And that is that."

She'd known she was living dangerously all the time she'd been at Nathan's. But it was true, what he'd said—she hadn't had any choice. Not a viable choice, anyway.

She couldn't make Lacey take care of her. She couldn't impose on Estelle or Fiona or Hugh. And until she'd been able to hobble around, staying in her own place—even with help—would have been difficult in the extreme.

So she'd stayed at Nathan's. And she'd steeled herself against him as best she could. It had been hard once she'd begun to feel better, once her mind had become less preoccupied with pain and more with the persistent presence of Nathan Wolfe.

As soon as she could put weight on her leg, she'd refused to let him carry her—even though she nearly went stir crazy staying in the house. He'd offered several times to carry her down to the beach.

"You can sit on a towel on the sand and watch Lacey swim," he'd said.

And it had been very tempting. It would have got her out of the house. It would have permitted her some time on the beach. It would have been lovely to sit in the sun and watch Lacey swim.

But she would have been in Nathan's arms all the way

there and all the way back. *And* she would have had to watch Nathan swim.

It was bad enough seeing Nathan in shorts and T-shirts every day. With the heat, there was rarely any reason for him to wear more than that. But if she'd taken him up on his offer to go to the beach with them, she would have seen him in less.

She had enough trouble remaining indifferent to Nathan. She didn't need to see his hard abs and bare chest. She didn't need to watch his bathing trunks mold to his masculine frame and watch water stream down his belly and disappear into his trunks. She had enough memories. She didn't need that!

The night before she'd packed up and made Maurice come and get her, she hadn't been able to sleep because of those memories. They'd had her shifting around on her bed, agitated and uncomfortable. It was too hot, she'd told herself. It was too humid. There were half a dozen reasons why she couldn't sleep.

Finally she'd got up to use the bathroom and get a drink of water. Ordinarily when she did so, she tried to get from her room to the bathroom as quickly and quietly as possible.

Last night she'd been quiet, but she hadn't moved quickly enough. The moonlight had tempted her to slow down as she passed the archway to the living room. And a glimpse of the sculpted masculine form sprawled on the sofa had immediately drawn her eye, had made her pause and stare.

The silvery light streaming in the window highlighted the planes and threw into shadow the angles of Nathan's muscular body. He was lying on his back, his only covering a pair of light-colored loose-fitting boxer shorts. But their looseness didn't completely mask the swell of his masculinity.

Carin couldn't help herself. She stopped. She looked. And then Nathan had moved and spoken to her.

Dear God, he'd been awake! He'd seen her standing there ogling him!

At least he'd only thought she needed help! Quickly Carin had assured him she was fine and had limped rapidly away.

That had been bad. What had followed was worse.

If she had been restless before her trek down the hall, after Nathan had spoken to her, Carin hadn't been able to sleep at all. She'd been awake and staring out into the moonlight through the sliding glass door to her bedroom when another door had opened and she saw Nathan, still wearing only his boxers, step out onto the deck.

As she watched, he had grabbed one of the towels hung out to dry on the railing. Then, slinging it around his neck, he hurried down the steps and in seconds had disappeared through the trees onto the path that led to the beach.

He was going for a swim? At two-thirty in the morning?

Why? Because he was as restless as she was? Because he was remembering things, too?

It was possible. It was even likely. She didn't question that he was still attracted to her. She didn't doubt that he'd be delighted to go to bed with her. He just wouldn't love her.

Carin wanted love.

But three-quarters of an hour later, when she saw him come out of the trees and into the clearing wearing nothing but the towel around his shoulders, she found herself tempted to settle for less.

Dear God, he was beautiful.

She would love to paint him, to capture the hard lines of his body silvered in the moonlight, to catch his catlike grace as he strode across the grass and mounted the steps. But more than that she wanted to touch him, to feel once more the strength and hardness of his body beneath her fingers. She wanted to run her hands over his hair-roughened skin. She wanted to trace the line of his jaw with her lips. She wanted to touch them to his chest, to kiss her way down the arrow of hair that ran down the middle of it, that arrowed directly toward his very visible masculinity.

She wanted to touch him there.

Carin sucked in a sharp breath at the heat in her own body, at its readiness to know him fully, to let him touch her!

Love.

She wanted *love,* she reminded herself.

And that's when she knew that come daybreak she had to move out.

Living dangerously was one thing. But she was in danger of crossing the line from dangerous to foolish.

Because it would be foolish indeed—as well as all too easy—to settle for sex with Nathan Wolfe.

CHAPTER EIGHT

THE BANGING on the front door woke her. Carin struggled up, dazed, then worried. It was just past seven. Who would be knocking at this hour?

All she could think was that something had happened to Miss Saffron. The old lady didn't have a phone. Maybe she'd fallen and someone had found her and needed to call Doc Rasmussen. She fumbled into her robe, cursed her cast and, not even bothering to comb her hair, she hurried down the stairs and jerked open the door.

It was Nathan. He grinned at her.

Carin stared, nonplussed, aware of her uncombed hair and hastily donned robe in the face of his freshly shaved bright-eyed face. "Nathan? I thought—" She dragged a hand through her hair. "What are you doing here?"

"Picking up Lacey."

"Now? It's seven o'clock! She's not even up."

"Well, if you were at my house, I could have woken her and you wouldn't be bothered."

He was baiting her, Carin knew. She deliberately didn't respond to it. "I'll get her up. You can come back later."

Instead he stepped past her into the living room. "No problem. I'll have a cup of coffee while I'm waiting."

"I didn't make coffee this morning." Carin followed him into the kitchen, wishing she could just grab him by the collar and throw him back out the door. It had been bad enough being around Nathan at his place. There, at least, the rooms were big enough that it didn't seem as if they were on top of each other. Here it did. As he got out coffee mugs, then turned to look in the other cupboard for the coffee, he literally brushed right against her. Carin jumped back.

Nathan didn't even seem to notice. "You want a cup, too?" He found the coffee and began measuring it into the coffeepot.

"No, I do not." She glared at him. "I'm going up to get dressed."

"Don't bother on my account." He gave her a grin that had the effect of annoying her even more.

She banged on Lacey's door, then took refuge in her room. It took her a long time to get dressed, partly because the cast made things difficult and partly because she was so flustered that she couldn't seem to manage to button her shorts or do something with her hair. Ordinarily she would have asked for Lacey's help. But she wasn't going to ask this morning.

If she did, no doubt Nathan would be the one to button her shorts or braid her hair!

Besides, she decided, if she took enough time he and Lacey would be gone before she came back downstairs again. In fact, it was true.

A few minutes passed and Lacey clattered downstairs, a few more and she'd obviously grabbed breakfast because she sang out, "See you later, Mom!"

"See you later," Carin called back and breathed a sigh of relief.

Five hours later Nathan was back.

"We ran into Thomas and Lorenzo at the dive shop when we got back," he said. "She went off with them. So I brought lunch."

"I don't need you bringing lunch." Carin said testily as he came in carrying a bag that she recognized as being full of conch fritters. Her mouth watered. Her stomach growled.

"Thank you, Nathan. I'm really glad you thought of me sitting here by myself with no food in the house," he said in a mock falsetto as he walked right past her into the kitchen and began opening her cabinets.

"I do, too, have food in the house!"

"Not according to Lacey." He got out plates, set them on the table, opened a drawer, took out silverware and began dishing up lunch.

Lacey was a traitor, Carin thought grimly. They had *some* food in the house, and Maurice would have gone shopping for her.

"Lacey is a picky eater," she grumbled.

"Good thing you're not," Nathan said cheerfully. "Otherwise these conch fritters and cole slaw would be going to waste." He plunked several fritters on her plate and added a dollop of cole slaw alongside them, then sat down and began to eat.

He was back again at dinner. And the next day it was exactly the same. She might as well not have moved out at all. Nathan was bound and determined to make them dependent on him.

Lacey was already under his spell. And Carin knew that she only had so much resistance. If he kept this up, she was afraid she would be in danger of succumbing.

She couldn't allow it!

And she could just sit here and hope that his work would take him away. Undoubtedly eventually it would—but not soon enough.

So if he wouldn't leave, she would.

She had told Stacia she wasn't coming to New York, but now it sounded like a very good idea.

It would be a treat for Lacey, who had been all for it from the moment the show had been proposed. It would make Stacia happy. And given what—or rather, who—she was facing here, dealing with millions of New Yorkers seemed far less stressful.

She called Stacia and said she would come.

"Well, you've seen sense at last. Hooray. I'll make the arrangements."

"Wonderful. Thanks." She didn't say a word about Nathan.

She didn't say a word *to* Nathan, either.

She didn't want him deciding to come along. This was her trip—hers and Lacey's. And if she felt the tiniest bit guilty because his photos were in the show, too—and had in fact saved the show for her—well, he'd had other shows, and she needed some space.

She didn't even say anything to Lacey about the trip. She didn't want her telling Nathan. Besides, she wanted it to be a surprise.

She only told Hugh because she needed him to take them to Nassau. "Bright and early Monday morning," she said.

She didn't say they needed to leave early because she wanted to be gone before Nathan showed up.

On Monday morning she got Lacey up early.

"It's barely six," Lacey grumbled. "Dad didn't say he was coming early today."

"It's nothing to do with your father," Carin said. "Come on. Get up. It's a surprise."

Lacey rubbed her eyes, looking disgruntled, then curious. "A suprise? What kind of surprise?" But she was dragging herself out of bed.

"You'll see."

Now that they were actually going, Carin was feeling excited, too. She'd packed a bag for each of them last night after Lacey was asleep, then called Fiona and asked her to feed Zeno while they were gone.

Now, when Lacey came downstairs and saw the bags sitting by the door, she looked at her mother, wide-eyed. "We're going on a trip? Where are we going? Are we going to New York?"

"Wait and see," Carin said, smiling, as Hugh pulled up out front.

"Are we going to Nassau?" Lacey pressed.

"You'll see," Carin said. "You'll love it."

But she had no idea how thrilled Lacey would be—or how shocked *she* would be—when they got to the landing field and Nathan was standing by the helicopter, grinning at them!

Carin opened her mouth as he opened the door of Hugh's car and winked at her.

"No arguments. Not in front of Lacey."

It had been sheer luck that Stacia had called his place to talk to Carin about the arrangements for the trip to New York. Obviously, she'd thought Carin and Lacey were still living with him.

"Trip?" Nathan had echoed when she'd rung.

"For the opening. It's next week, you know. I was badgering her to come and she kept saying no. Then, all of a sudden she finally said yes. I suppose," she'd added, "I have you to thank for that."

Very likely, yes, Nathan thought grimly.

"She didn't mention if you were coming, too," Stacia went on. "Are you?"

"I am." Oh, yes.

"Wonderful. I told her I'd make arrangements for a place to stay and—"

"Not necessary. We'll be staying with my family."

"Oh, of course. That will be lovely for you." Stacia's tone told him how delighted she was.

Nathan doubted Carin would feel the same.

She hadn't argued with him in front of Lacey, but she hadn't exactly been sweetness and light personified since then, either.

Lacey had been delighted enough not to notice that her mother was grinding her teeth.

Nathan had noticed. He'd noticed, too, that she'd deliberately ignored him, clambering into the helicopter to sit on the seat next to Hugh's dog, Belle, his "copilot," leaving Nathan to sit with Lacey in the back.

He didn't mind sitting with Lacey. His daughter's enthusiasm delighted him and, as far as Nathan was concerned, it justified what he'd done, arranging things without Carin's knowledge. She wouldn't have agreed if he'd told her—and it was all too clear how happy Lacey was.

As the helicopter lifted off, she was practically bouncing off the seat in her excitement.

"See! There's the school! And our house, and Lorenzo's, and Maurice and Estelle's! Oh, look! We're going to see your place!" She gave another bounce as Hugh aimed the copter toward the seaward side of the island. "See it, Dad? Mom? Do you see?"

"I see," Nathan said.

Carin glanced that way, but she didn't say anything. She sat, stiff and unyielding all the way to Nassau, her good arm wrapped around Belle.

So much for taking charge and controlling her own destiny. So much for putting space between them. So much for the trip for two—just her and Lacey—to New York.

Of course Nathan was coming along because Stacia—of all people!—had called him and asked if he was coming. Naturally he'd said he was. And because he was Nathan, naturally he'd told Stacia not to bother making arrangements, that he would handle that end of things.

"Handle them how?" Carin asked.

"Well, we can't go to a hotel," he said practically. "My brothers would be offended."

And Carin knew without asking that Nathan had no intention of staying in a hotel no matter how much she argued, which she couldn't do anyway since Lacey was sitting next to her, all ears.

"Don't say we're going to stay with Dominic."

The very thought appalled her. Stay with the man she'd jilted? Talk about uncomfortable situations.

"No. His place isn't really big enough. We're going to stay with Rhys and Mariah."

Carin barely remembered Rhys, though she felt pretty sure he would remember her. "He's married again?" She knew his first wife had died.

"To Mariah. She's Sierra's sister. You'll like her."

"Does she have purple hair, too?" Lacey asked avidly. She thought Sierra's purple locks were absolutely fascinating.

Carin thought they were pretty amazing, too. She still found it hard to believe that Sierra, with her purple hair and funky day-glo clothes, was Dominic's wife. But they'd certainly seemed deeply in love when she'd met them on the island last autumn.

"I don't know what color it is now," Nathan answered Lacey. "You'll have to wait and see. Dominic's picking us up."

It should have been horrible.

In scant moments she was going to be face-to-face with the man she'd jilted. She'd seen him before—twice—but both times had been on Pelican Cay. She'd never presumed to set foot on his turf. And even though Dominic had professed to have forgiven her, who knew what he really felt? And would he and his wife really want to welcome her into their home?

Carin knew Sierra was "unusual." But did her unusualness extend to welcoming her husband's ex-fiancée? Carin tried to imagine and couldn't. Why on earth couldn't Nathan have left well enough alone?

"I've got your tote bag," Nathan said over his shoulder, steering Lacey ahead of him and checking behind him to make sure Carin was following as they disembarked. As if she might duck out and vanish given a chance.

If it weren't for Lacey, she would have been tempted. She didn't want to have to smile and make small talk with Dominic. She didn't want to go back to his Fifth Avenue apartment and act like she was glad to be there.

What she wanted was to strangle Nathan for forcing her into this.

But she couldn't, she thought grimly. Not in front of Lacey.

The next thing she knew Dominic was striding toward them, his hard face lightened by a broad grin and his whole tough demeanor softened by the baby girl he held in one arm. He gave Nathan a punch on the shoulder, then wrapped his free arm around his brother's neck and gave it a friendly squeeze.

"Took your own sweet time coming to see us, didn't you, bro?" When he released Nathan, he wrapped Lacey in a one-armed hug and said, "My God, you're like a weed. You've grown a foot since spring." And then he released her and looked at Carin, smiling still as he held out a hand to her. "Welcome home."

It had been years since Carin had thought of New York City as home. And yet Dominic was right. She'd felt that eager longing prick her as the city had come into view. She'd been like Lacey as they'd left Pelican Cay, her eyes seeking landmarks, feeling a sense of connection and remembrance. She'd been barely more than a child when she'd been here last. But the city would always be a part of her.

She was grateful to Dominic for recognizing that. Now she took the hand he offered and met his eyes. "Thank you. It's good to be here." And as she said the words, she felt the tightness in her chest ease. She wasn't lying as she'd thought she would have to.

"Meet my baby girl," Dominic said, a father's deep quiet pride in his voice as he held out his daughter. "This is Lily."

"She's absolutely beautiful, Dominic," Carin said, and meant that, too.

Lily, who was probably four or five months old, looked a great deal like Lacey had at that age. She had lots of straight dark hair and deep-blue eyes just like her father's and uncle's. She studied Carin seriously.

"Hello, Lily," Carin said gravely and reached out a finger to stroke the little girl's hand. Lily's fingers wrapped around hers. She had a fierce grip.

"Can I carry her?" Lacey asked. "I've never had a cousin before."

Dominic grinned and, easing his daughter's grasp from around Carin's finger, he handed the little girl over to Lacey. "She wiggles. Hang on tight."

"I will." Lacey said the words as if they were a vow and took her little cousin from Dominic's arms.

Seeing the two together, Carin felt a pang of longing that caught her unprepared. The sight of another child like Lacey forced her to recall long-ago hopes and dreams of more children, of brothers and sisters, not only cousins, for Lacey to grow up with.

A quick look at Nathan told her that he was aware of how alike they were, as well. His eyes went from the girls to Carin. They challenged her with everything she'd once thought she wanted.

It was a relief when Dominic said, "Come on. Let's go. Sierra's home fixing supper. She'll be waiting."

Carin's worries about Sierra were unfounded. The younger woman welcomed them like long-lost friends.

"Oh, good! You're finally here!" She hugged Lacey and Carin exuberantly, then held Lacey out at arm's length and said, "You and Lily could be sisters." She sounded so pleased with the notion that Carin relaxed a bit more.

And when Sierra pushed her into an overstuffed chair overlooking Central Park, handed her a glass of wine and said, "Take it easy. You've still got an arm in a cast. You must be exhausted. You need to chill,'' Carin felt herself doing just that. She settled back, relaxed and actually found herself feeling at home.

Dominic and Sierra's Fifth Avenue apartment, which she had imagined would be a steel-and-glass palace, was far more comfortable and casual than Carin would have expected. It had to be worth millions, had at least ten rooms, four of them with huge windows overlooking Central Park. And yet it felt warm and welcoming with its red oak woodwork, overstuffed furniture and live foliage. Was that a real tree? By golly, it was!

Carin felt as if she were in a treehouse. And when she said so, Sierra laughed. ''Yes, the place is a holdover from Dominic's Tarzan days.''

''I like it,'' Carin said.

And Sierra nodded. ''I do, too. It's why I married him.''

Carin goggled, then realized that Sierra was kidding. It was hard to imagine anyone being able to joke about Dominic Wolfe. She certainly never could have. She was glad he had found Sierra.

She was amazed to find her own painting of Pelican Cay in the living room. She'd have expected abstract art, but instead the walls contained homely primitive paintings of the Wolfes' house in Pelican Cay and her own watercolor of the village from the custom house dock.

Now, catching Carin looking at her painting, Sierra grinned. ''It's my favorite,'' she said, ''because it captures the island so well. And because it reminds me of the day Dominic and I finally began to understand and trust each other—thanks to you.''

Her smile was so warm and friendly that Carin felt as if she were being praised for something she hadn't really done. She shrugged. ''I'm glad you like it.''

''Mariah does, too. I told her she needs to buy one of the island at your show.''

"I'll give her one. I wanted to give you and Dominic that one."

But Dominic had insisted on paying her—had, in fact, tried to give her more than she'd been asking, telling her she'd given him something worth far more than her painting.

Knowledge at last of why she'd jilted him, he'd meant. And when he'd come down in the spring he'd told her that meeting her and Lacey had opened communications between him and Sierra as well. Carin was delighted that they were so happy together. Watching him now, doting on his baby daughter, she couldn't help but smile.

The doorbell rang just then, and when Sierra opened the door more Wolfes spilled into the apartment.

Carin immediately identified Rhys, a slightly harder-edged, more muscular version of Nathan and Dominic. Rhys was a member of an elite corps of firefighters who traveled the globe putting out oil and industrial fires. With him was a stunning, dark-haired woman almost as tall as he was. Something about her eyes and her smile looked familiar. Then Carin remembered that she was Sierra's sister. She and Rhys were each carrying a child.

"Look, Mom. More cousins!" Lacey was beaming.

"Come meet the rest of the family," Nathan said and, snagging Carin's hand, drew her to her feet to introduce her to Rhys's wife and his twins, Stephen and Elizabeth.

Rhys gave her a hug, and Mariah did, too.

"Hugs," Elizabeth demanded. And Carin gave her one, too. And Stephen demanded a kiss, which he got.

"Lucky guy," Nathan said. "It's more than she'll give me."

"You gotta learn how to ask," Rhys said with a grin.

Carin had hoped she would be able to remain quietly aloof. There was no reason for her to get involved. It was fine for Lacey to be included. But this was Nathan's family, not hers.

Try telling the Wolfes that.

They didn't believe in aloof. Not even Nathan, the quietest of the brothers, was quiet tonight.

Put the three brothers together and the noise level rose exponentially. There was immediate talk of the Yankees and the Mets. Discussion of soccer and diving. Dominic and Rhys wanted Nathan to go to a ball game. Rhys and Nathan wanted Dominic to take time off to go fishing.

"You wouldn't think Nathan came to work," Sierra said.

"All they do is talk about fishing," Mariah agreed.

Sierra rolled her eyes. "Come on." She grabbed Carin and hauled her into the kitchen. "You can supervise me making a salad."

"Or a mess," Mariah said. "And we can warn you about getting involved with a Wolfe."

"I'm not involved with a Wolfe," Carin protested.

"Yeah, right." Mariah obviously didn't believe that for a minute. She put the lasagna she'd brought into the oven to heat it.

"You just keep thinking that and you won't know what hit you," Sierra agreed as she tore up lettuce and tossed it in a bowl. "They get what they want, those Wolfe boys."

"Nathan doesn't," Carin said firmly.

Both sisters looked at her, then at each other. "Maybe we're just pushovers," Mariah said to her sister. "Too easy. We should be tougher. Like Carin. After all Carin dumped your husband."

"I didn't—" Carin's face flamed. "I mean—"

"Jilted him, then," Sierra said, calling a spade a spade. "Sounds to me like he deserved it. And he didn't deserve you."

"Whereas," Mariah said dryly, "he definitely deserves Sierra!"

Sierra gave a wicked grin and chuckled in a way that made Carin laugh, too.

"The question is," Mariah said, "does Nathan deserve Carin?"

They both looked at her. "Does he?" Sierra asked.

"We're not—I don't—" Carin stopped, at a loss to explain.

"He has asked you to marry him, hasn't he?" Sierra stopped tearing lettuce and fixed Carin with a steady gaze.

"Yes, but—"

"You need to make him pay first," Mariah finished for her.

"I—"

"But then you need to marry him," Sierra said. "Because he's Lacey's father."

"I don't—"

"And you love him," Mariah said quietly.

Carin opened her mouth to deny it, but the words wouldn't come. They all looked at each other, the truth settling in.

Then suddenly Rhys appeared in the doorway with a twin in each arm. "They're starving. They're starting to chew on the furniture. When's dinner?"

"Coming right up," Sierra answered for her sister. "Go wash up. There's the bell again. Tell Dominic to answer the door," she added as the bell rang. "That'll be Douglas." Then when Rhys left, she turned her gaze on Carin again.

"Don't waste your love," she said. "It's too precious."

"Rhys almost blew it," Mariah added. "But finally he came around."

"And so did Dominic. You have to start somewhere," Sierra agreed.

"Ah, there they are!" Nathan's father, Douglas, appeared, beaming in the doorway. "The three most beautiful women in the world!"

He kissed each of his daughters-in-law, and then he kissed Carin, stepped back, paused and held her cheeks between his palms. "Ah, Carin. When are you going to make an honest man out of that son of mine?"

"Dad!" Nathan came up behind him and got a headlock on his old man. "Leave the poor woman alone."

"I was only asking," Douglas protested, slipping out of Nathan's grasp. "Just want her to know we're all for it. You do know that, don't you, Carin?"

Carin flushed. "Yes, Mr., er...yes, Douglas."

"Dad sounds better, don't you think?" He winked.

"I'm capable of doing my own proposing," Nathan said through his teeth.

Douglas turned his gaze on his son. "But are you capable of getting her to say yes?"

A tide of red washed above the collar of Nathan's shirt. "You'll just have to wait and see, won't you?"

"No fighting in my kitchen." Sierra advanced on them with a stirring spoon. "Out! Both of you." She thrust a handful of silverware at her father-in-law. "Make yourself useful. Set the table."

"Douglas has a subtle touch, doesn't he?" Mariah said with a grin.

"Oh, yes," Sierra agreed. They looked at each other and laughed. Then they grinned at Carin.

"He's very fond of you," Mariah told her.

"I jilted his son."

"But you gave him a granddaughter. That cancels things out."

Carin wasn't sure she believed that. But Douglas certainly did have a soft spot for Lacey. And, happily, he didn't say anything more during dinner about her getting together with Nathan.

Neither did anyone else. The talk was easy and general, and Carin let it wash over her as she listened to the various threads of conversation—the merits of a particular Yankee pitcher, the latest rock star Mariah had interviewed, the best fishing spots on the north shore of Long Island, whether or not Lily was teething—and enjoyed it all in spite of herself.

This was the sort of family she'd always dreamed of having.

An only child raised by a widowed father who had more time and interest for his business than he'd ever had for her, Carin had always dreamed of being a part of a family like this. When she'd agreed with her father's estimation of Dominic as a good potential husband, it had been in part because she knew he had brothers and she'd hoped to become part of his family circle.

Of course she'd ruined that herself. And since then she'd learned that families could be created by love and effort, that the same blood didn't have to run in people's veins to make them family.

She had her own "created family" on the island. Maurice and Estelle included her and Lacey in their holiday gatherings. And in the past few years she and Hugh and a few of the other young unattached people on Pelican Cay had created a family of sorts.

But those "families," wonderful though they were, didn't yet have much history—not like the Wolfe brothers, who were, even in the middle of a lovely dinner, reminiscing about baseball games of their youth and whose bike had popped a tire at an inopportune moment and which brother caught the biggest fish the last time they were all at Pelican Cay, and not like Mariah and Sierra, who shared a history, too.

How wonderful it would have been to have had a family who would share such memories.

Even as she thought it, Carin watched Lacey's expressions as she listened to her father and her uncles teasing and battling and arguing with each other. Her daughter's gaze went from one to the other, as if she was watching a tennis match. And all the while she was grinning so much her smile seemed to wrap two times around her face.

Carin tried to remember the last time Lacey had looked that happy.

It was the night she'd come back from Nathan's—the day he'd arrived—when she knew at last that her father loved her and that he'd come to Pelican Cay determined to make her part of his life.

Oh, Lacey.

"Tell me about your accident," Douglas requested, interrupting Carin's thoughts. "Nathan said he was terrified when you went over the handlebars. He thought you'd killed yourself."

She dragged her gaze away from Lacey's face. "I should have been going slower. I had to swerve when Zeno ran in front of me."

"Zeno?" Douglas's brows hiked. "You have a wolf on the island?"

"Not a wolf. A dog."

And so they talked about Zeno. And about her show. About her painting and who was handling the business while she was here.

Douglas said he was thrilled that she and Nathan were going to be part of this show together. But he didn't take advantage of the subject to ask her again when she was going to marry his son. He just talked about Nathan's photography, about how well Nathan was doing, about how proud he was of him.

Dominic poured more wine in everyone's glasses. Lacey took the twins out into the living room and built block towers with them. Rhys challenged Nathan to a game of pool.

Dominic tapped Carin on the shoulder. "The old man must be boring you by now. How about coming to talk to me while I clean up in the kitchen?"

"He wasn't—" Carin began to protest.

But Douglas stood up. "Yes, yes. You go on with Dominic. Don't let an old windbag waste your time."

"You didn't want to hear him sing Nathan's praises anyway, did you?" Dominic asked her.

Carin stammered, unsure how to answer that.

Dominic just laughed. "Come along."

If anyone had told her that she would ever stand in Dominic Wolfe's kitchen, talking to him while he loaded the dishwasher, she would have said they were insane. Not even when she had been going to marry Dominic had she considered that he would unbend that far. But he acted as if he was no stranger to dirty plates and pots and pans.

And while he did it, he talked about Pelican Cay, about going back there with Sierra. "I was scared to," he said.

"Scared?" Carin blinked, surprised at the confidence he was sharing.

Dominic shrugged. "It was sex at first, you know, between us. At least that's all we thought it was. But it wasn't just sex for long. It was Sierra. I cared a lot about her. I *loved* her. But I didn't know how she felt." There was still a raw aching sound in his voice when he spoke of those days.

"She loves you," Carin said quickly, trying to reassure him. Any fool could see that.

Dominic grinned. "I know that now."

"I'm glad," she told him sincerely. "I'm glad you're happy. I worried about it. About you. But I couldn't—"

"I know you couldn't marry me. It's a good thing you didn't. I just wish you could have told me why. I wish I'd *let* you tell me why." His mouth twisted wryly. But then he shrugged and smiled again, though his eyes grew serious. "I hope you and Nathan can be happy, too."

Carin wet her lips. What could she say to that? It wasn't the same as with him and Sierra.

"I hope so, too," she said at last.

It was close to midnight by the time they went home with Rhys and Mariah and the twins. Stephen and Lizzie were both asleep, and Lacey was yawning madly as Rhys flagged down two taxis and directed them to their brownstone across the park.

"I don't want to inconvenience you," Carin began.

"You won't," Rhys said flatly, "unless you make me take you down to midtown to some hotel."

Carin sighed and settled back against the seat, once more giving in to the inevitable, "I won't do that."

Rhys and Mariah owned the whole brownstone they lived in. They had two tenants on the upper floors, but the third-floor studio apartment that looked out onto the garden was vacant.

"We keep it for friends," Mariah said as she led Carin and Lacey up the stairs. Nathan had been deputized to help Rhys get the two sleeping children into their beds. "And brothers. And their families."

"I'm not family," Carin protested.

"I am," Lacey said firmly.

"Of course you are," Mariah said. "And Nathan is."

"*Nathan*?"

"Oh, dear. I just assumed... Would you rather Nathan slept downstairs with us."

"We stayed with him when Mom got hurt," Lacey said. "He slept on the couch right by her room. He carried her to the bathroom every day," she told her aunt Mariah.

After that revelation, Carin could hardly say she wanted him downstairs. "It's all right," Carin mumbled.

And then she discovered the sleeping arrangements.

It was a one-room apartment. The "sofa" was a trundle bed and there was a high built-in queen-size platform bed which was separated from the rest of the room by the two-foot high carpeted "wall" that enclosed two sides of it, giving only the illusion of privacy.

When Nathan finally came upstairs half an hour later, Carin had done the best she could.

Lacey, in pajamas, was tucked into the platform bed. The trundle was made up for Nathan.

"I'll just slip in alongside Lacey," Carin told him. At least they would have the two-foot wall between them.

"With your arm?"

Oh, hell. She hadn't even thought of that. She was so used to her cast by now that she barely gave it any thought. It was an inconvenience to her. But it would be more than that to Lacey, who was a restless sleeper. Lacey would be banging into her all night.

"I'll pull out the other trundle bed for you," Nathan offered with a grin.

He did—and lined it up right next to his. The room was now virtually a wall-to-wall bed—with Carin right next to Nathan.

"Isn't this cozy?" He grinned.

Carin gave him a hard look and didn't deign to reply.

"I think it's cool." Lacey shoved herself up on her pillow and peered over the little wall. "I know you said I was going to get a surprise," she said to her mother, eyes shining. "But this is so cool. All of us being here together like a real family." Lacey's gaze went from Carin to Nathan. "This is the best surprise ever."

CHAPTER NINE

OF ALL THE WOLFE BROTHERS, Nathan was the born fisherman.

Dominic and Rhys were fast-moving, take-charge, do-it-now men who gnashed their teeth if the fish weren't biting. They fished, but mostly they argued about where they ought to be fishing, what kind of bait to use, what time to go out, when to come in, and which one had caught the bigger fish.

The fact was, Nathan almost always caught the biggest fish because he was the one with the patience. He was the one who studied the currents, checked the depth, considered the temperature and the time of year and made his plans accordingly.

And then he sat. And sat. And sat.

He always knew what he was after, and he was always willing to wait. A guy didn't value something unless he worked for it, Nathan figured. And he valued it even more if he'd endured some hardship and frustration along the way.

What was true of fishing was also true of his photography and his books. They were products of much thought, long hours, vast patience and hard work.

So was courting Carin.

And if thought, long hours, vast patience and a fair amount of work had anything to do with it, the way Nathan figured it, he ought to value Carin more than anything or anyone on earth.

Talk about patience, endurance, frustration! God Almighty!

Here he was in bed lying mere inches from her— *inches!*—and she was sound asleep.

151

Carin wasn't frustrated. Not a bit! She had glared at him as if he'd manipulated the whole disastrous sleeping arrangements bit, then she'd brushed her teeth, kissed Lacey good-night, and climbed into the trundle bed right next to his as if she didn't even notice him.

So what else was new? Nathan thought, grinding his teeth.

He'd done his damnedest to make this evening a success, to make her enjoy herself, to encourage her to feel a part of the family—and what did he have to show for it?

Zip. Nada. Zilch. Not a damn thing.

Unless you counted the fact that she was now comfortable enough around him to fall asleep virtually in the same bed with him as if he weren't even there! Lots of comfort in that revelation, huh? Nathan practically snorted in disgust.

She'd spent the whole evening basically ignoring him. She'd seemed to enjoy his sisters-in-law. She'd played with his nieces and nephew. She'd chatted easily with his father and Rhys. She'd even gone off into the kitchen and, he hoped, had a heart-to-heart with Dominic. But had it done any good?

God knew.

Nathan certainly didn't. She was acting as if he wasn't even here.

Maybe he should have told her he was coming along. Oh, yeah, that would have done a lot of good. She'd have refused to come, point-blank. No, it was better he hadn't said anything. Better just to go on with events as planned— and hope that she eventually softened toward him, trusted him. Loved him.

But every time he hoped, every time he thought things would go his way, every time he thought he had come up with the perfect bait, Carin looked at it, swam lazily around, daring him to hope. And then…she turned away.

Nathan was a good fisherman. He was a determined fisherman. But a guy had his limits. He didn't remember Carin being so stubborn.

He didn't remember her being so beautiful! But then, she was only inches away, so close he could feel the heat of her body. A sigh shuddered through him.

He didn't know how long he could last.

"Dad?" Lacey's whisper cut into the silence, surprising him. She'd been so tired he thought she'd be asleep before they shut out the lights.

He rolled to a sitting position. "What?"

Her head appeared above the little wall. "Just checking." Her grin flashed in the moonlight. "I woke up and thought I'd dreamed it. But it's true. We're really here."

"Oh, yeah," Nathan muttered. "We're really here."

"Good." She sighed contentedly. Her head disappeared again and she settled back against the pillows. "G'night, Dad."

"G'night, Lace."

"Dad?"

"Hmm?"

"I hope it's always like this."

God help him, Nathan thought.

Carin wished it could always be like this.

Well, not the going-to-bed with Nathan just inches away. At least, not if she had to resist him. That was hard. And it didn't get any easier with each night that passed.

But the rest of the time was far more wonderful than she ever could have dreamed. She'd envisioned a happy little trip for herself and Lacey, a chance to sightsee, the possibility of visiting some of the places she'd known growing up, to show Lacey a little of her history.

But this was so much more.

And they owed it all to Nathan.

One more way in which she was beholden to Nathan.

The list went on and on. She didn't want to feel grateful. But on Lacey's behalf, she had to be.

Lacey was having a wonderful time. Sierra, with Lily in tow, took her up to see Uncle Dominic in his office the first day, while Nathan and Carin went to the gallery to talk to Stacia. From there, Lacey told her, they all—Dominic included—went sightseeing. They took a boat trip around Manhattan Island. They saw so many things Lacey couldn't remember them all. She was delighted—as much because she'd enjoyed the day with her uncle, aunt and cousin as because of where they went.

The next day Mariah and Rhys and Douglas took Lacey and the twins to the zoo and to Central Park. Lacey loved it—mostly loved *them*.

"I wish they would all come to Pelican Cay," she told Carin and Nathan that evening. "They can come soon, can't they?"

"Sure," Nathan said easily.

And Carin smiled, pained and pleased at the same time. "Of course."

Her own days had been as memorable as Lacey's—in a far different way. Stacia had asked her and Nathan to come down to the gallery to supervise the hanging of the paintings and photos and to meet with a couple of interviewers. She had been nervous, never having done anything on this scale before.

But Stacia made it easy. And Nathan made it an experience she would never forget. In the gallery she saw the professional Nathan Wolfe. She knew he had an eye for a good photo, but now she saw that he had an eye, too, for how those photos—and her paintings—ought to be displayed.

He countered Stacia's idea of just having their work in the same gallery and dealing with the same island with his own notion that the paintings and photos ought to work together, side by side, complementing and contrasting with each other, offering two perspectives on island life.

"Island Eyes, isn't that what you want?" he said to Stacia.

"But you don't know what paintings I've done," Carin said.

In fact, it seemed that he did. While she'd been laid up, he had helped Stacia pack and ship all her work. He'd taken photos of them. And then he'd gone out and shot pictures that would echo and complement her paintings.

As Stacia and the gallery personnel hung them, with Nathan's help, Carin sat back and stared. It was like seeing her vision amplified, developed, shaded, sharpened. Each of her paintings became a focal point, heightened by Nathan's work—and Lacey's—which surrounded it.

Carin was amazed at the quality of Lacey's work.

"She's good," Nathan said simply. He had picked half a dozen of their daughter's photos to use in the show and had matted and framed them himself.

"With Lacey's help," he told Carin. "That's what we were doing some of the mornings when we were gone."

"Does she know they're going to be up?" she asked.

He shook his head and smiled. "One more little surprise."

Lacey would be over the moon. Carin felt a lump grow in her throat.

One more thing they owed Nathan.

The third day—the day of the opening—Sierra came over and fixed both Carin's hair and Lacey's.

"Will you dye it blue?" Lacey begged. "Or purple? Like yours was."

Sierra's was a natural brown now. She'd stopped using dyes, she told Lacey, when she found out she was pregnant with Lily.

Now she wouldn't dye Lacey's hair, either. "It's too

beautiful a color the way it is," she said. "Like a beautiful sorrel. But I can add some beads."

Lacey's eyes widened. "Really? My friend Marisa has beads."

In minutes, so did Lacey. Sierra braided a few strands of multi-colored beads into Lacey's hair, giving it an unexpected flair, and making her niece grin and shake her head every time she came to a mirror.

"You look great," Sierra said. "And so do you," she told Carin.

Carin was pretty sure she was being kind. Of course her hair was fine, because Sierra had done it that afternoon. And her dress was lovely, because Mariah and Sierra had picked it out.

They'd taken her shopping last night, and while Carin had wanted to opt for a basic black conservative dress, they wouldn't hear of it.

"You want to look like you're going to an undertakers' convention?" Sierra demanded.

"Black is supposed to look arty," Carin said in a voice barely above a whisper.

"How much black do you normally wear?" Mariah asked.

"Not much."

"Well, there you are. Your dress should reflect who you are."

So she'd ended up with a casually sophisticated dress in a myriad of blues and greens, fitted at the bodice, nipped in at the waist, and flared so that it looked like the sea swirling around her knees when she walked.

"Island colors," Sierra said approvingly.

"And a style that shows off her tan," Mariah had agreed.

It showed way more tan than Carin thought appropriate. Only the thinnest straps held it up. And besides giving the world a look at Carin's tanned shoulders, it showed off most of her back. There was a good deal more to look at than the white plaster on her arm.

Nathan, who was waiting in Mariah and Rhys's apartment, goggled when she come downstairs wearing it.

"Turn around," Mariah commanded.

Carin did. And Nathan swallowed visibly when he saw the plunging back.

"That?" he said hoarsely. "You're wearing *that*?"

Nervous already, Carin managed, "Is it too...?"

But the fact was she could hardly speak for staring, too. She'd never seen Nathan dressed up before. He'd been appealing in scruffy shorts and T-shirts, but in a severe black suit, sharp white shirt and burgundy tie, Nathan Wolfe was a mind-boggling, lust-inducing sight.

They simply stood there staring at each other.

"Yes," Mariah said with satisfaction.

"Oh, my yes," Sierra agreed.

Nathan turned his glare on his smug sisters-in-law. "What are you trying to do to me?"

They grinned.

Then the door opened, and Dominic stuck his head in. "Car's waiting. Let's go."

Carin felt a shaft of pure panic, now that the moment had arrived. She was actually grateful when Nathan's hand closed around hers.

He gave her a wink and a grin. "Stick with me. You'll be fine. I'll take care of everything."

In fact he did. She didn't want to admit it, but by deflecting some of the attention and answering nosey questions with exactly the right mixture of nonsense, jargon and charm, Nathan made the whole experience far less of an ordeal than it would have been without his presence.

People—especially women—gravitated to him, talked to him, demanded his attention. And he gave it to them, but at the same time he kept a hand on Carin. He drew her into the conversation, introduced her to everyone, made sure they knew this was *her* show, not his.

"It's sort of a family affair," he said when they asked why his photos were being displayed with hers. "Some of our daughter's work is here, too."

Lacey had been amazed at the sight of her own work hung with her parents'. "I took that picture," she whispered to her grandfather when she caught sight of the first one—a shot of Zeno and Miss Saffron's cat, momentarily friends, curled up together in the shade of a palm.

She walked around the gallery wide-eyed, grinning from ear to ear. And when she found Carin and Nathan, she hugged them both, and Carin thought she saw tears in her daughter's eyes. More than once that night, watching Lacey, watching Nathan and his family—feeling the connections between them and wishing—Carin had felt tears of her own.

It would be so wonderful to be a part of this family. A real part. A beloved part—not just a duty.

"Lovely show." A woman's voice called her back to the present, and she turned to see Gabriela, Nathan's agent, smiling at her. "Looks like it all worked out."

Carin nodded. "Thanks to Nathan." She didn't hesitate to admit that.

"Oh, Nathan's a brick," Gabriela said dryly, then she turned to him. "I need to talk with you."

Nathan frowned. "Now?"

"Now. Sorry." She gave Carin a commiserating smile. "I'll return him in a moment. We have a bit of business. Then I have to catch a plane back to Santa Fe."

"Of course." Carin smiled at her. "I can manage," she assured Nathan, who looked as if he were going to argue with Gabriela.

Nathan's jaw worked for a moment. He hesitated, then shrugged. "Okay. One minute." He took Gabriela's arm and they moved to a corner of the room where Carin tried not to watch them talking. But whether she wanted to or not, her gaze kept drifting their way.

Gabriela was apparently determined to make the most of her minute. She was talking nonstop, gesturing, pointing, obviously feeling very strongly about something.

Nathan was leaning against the wall, hands tucked in his pockets, looking casual. But from the way his jaw tightened as he listened to her words, he didn't seem to be as nonchalant as his pose might suggest.

They were too far away for Carin to have any idea what they were saying. It wasn't her business anyway, she told herself severely. And she was glad when Stacia brought over a journalist to talk with her.

Carin mustered her own charm and wits and tried to answer his questions. All the while, though, her gaze went back to Nathan and Gaby. Gaby had her hand on his sleeve now, gesturing expansively with her other hand toward his photos, then spreading her palms and giving him an irritated look which wasn't hard to read.

And where are the rest of them? she seemed to ask.

Nathan's shoulders hunched. His spine stiffened. He said something, then shook his head fiercely.

Whatever he said, Gaby didn't agree with. That was obvious from her stance, from her stiff shoulders, from her waggling finger under his nose.

Nathan shoved her finger away and, clearly annoyed, pushed away from the wall and dipped his head toward where Lacey was standing with Mariah and Rhys. Then his gaze flickered briefly in Carin's direction. Gabriela's gaze followed his. She shook her head, then began arguing again. She looked annoyed, too, now. Whatever point she'd tried to make, Nathan had rejected.

He shook his head, then turned and walked away, leaving her alone as he headed back toward Carin.

Determinedly Gaby followed. "You're going to regret it, Nathan. It's a terrific opportunity."

Nathan ignored her. A muscle was ticking in his jaw. "You okay?" he asked Carin, as if she were the one under attack at the moment.

"Fine."

"See. She's fine," Gaby said. "She'd want—" Gaby began.

Nathan whirled on her. "Don't," he said fiercely. "Don't involve her."

Gaby's mouth was open. The words—whatever they were—were on the tip of her tongue. Carin could almost hear them. But Nathan had made his own point.

Gaby pressed her lips into a firm line. Her expression grew shuttered, and she turned to look at Nathan. "You're making it hard to be your agent."

He scowled. "So quit."

"I don't want to quit," Gaby said patiently. "I love your work. I love what you've done, what you *could* do!"

Nathan let out a harsh impatient breath. He shot back his cuff and looked at his watch. "You'll miss your plane, Gaby."

"Think about it."

"I've told you—"

"Think about it. And call me when you get back to the Bahamas." She smiled suddenly, then leaned forward and gave him a quick kiss. Then she turned her gaze on Carin. "It's been a great show," she said. "You two work well together." Her gaze flicked back to Nathan. "But there's only so much you can do on an island. *You* need to get back to work, Nathan."

And then with a waggling wave of her fingers, she was gone.

"Where does she want you to go?" Carin asked.

"Doesn't matter. I'm not going." He didn't even look at her. He was scanning the crowd. "There's Finn MacCauley and his wife. Finn's a terrific photographer— and a good friend of Rhys's. Come on. I'll introduce you."

And that was the end of whatever Gaby had in mind.

Finn MacCauley and his wife Izzy had a pair of twins who were just a bit younger than Lacey. Izzy promptly invited Lacey over to meet them the following afternoon.

"We're only here one more day," Carin said. "I thought we'd go somewhere."

"Drop her off," Izzy said. "You and Nathan go somewhere."

"We don't need—"

"Of course you do. Every couple with kids needs time alone together," Izzy said flatly. "I know. We have four. And when you come to pick her up we'll have a barbecue. I'll invite Gib and Chloe—they're here somewhere." She stood on tiptoe, looking around, and not seeing them, shrugged. "And Sam and Josie. They're in the city for a week. It'll be fun."

Steamrollered, all Carin could do was ask, "Who are Gib and Chloe and Sam and Josie?"

"Gib's a photographer. Finn's competition," Izzy added dryly. "He and Finn are always one-upping each other." Izzy laughed. "They're actually best friends, but the rivalry seems to spur them to greater achievements. And Sam's my ex-fiancé. Josie's his wife."

Carin blinked. She could just about swallow the "best friends/competitors" notion. But her mind balked at Izzy so cavalierly inviting her ex-fiancé to come to a barbecue. Something of her astonishment must have been evident on her face because Izzy laughed.

"We're good friends, Sam and I. We were *always* good friends. Unlike Finn and I." She shot a wry—and adoring—look at her husband who was deep in conversation with Nathan. Then she put a hand on Carin's arm. "Finn says I simply push people, and you don't have to agree. But it would be fun for the girls to meet Lacey. And who knows, maybe we'll get to the Bahamas again. Finn goes on shoots all over. Maybe sometime the kids and I could come."

"That would be fun," Carin agreed. She didn't want Izzy MacCauley to think her unfriendly. "And as for tomorrow, I—I'll talk to Nathan."

She didn't really want to be "alone together" with Nathan at all. But she did want to know what Gaby had talked to him about. Was Gaby pressuring him to take an assignment? It seemed likely.

Despite what he'd said about staying on Pelican Cay, they all knew he couldn't stay forever.

But there was no time to pursue the matter further. Not that night. They fell into bed exhausted as soon as they got home.

In the morning Douglas took all of them out to brunch to celebrate the success of the opening. He made a point of seating himself between Carin and Lacey, talking with Carin about her work, about her plans for the shop, about what she'd like to do next, and talking to Lacey about her photography.

That some of her photos had been in the show last night had delighted Lacey. But clearly what delighted her more was having a grandfather who doted on her, having uncles who teased her, an aunt who braided her hair, cousins who followed her around like ducklings.

Lacey was blossoming. She'd always been an outgoing child, but sometimes Carin thought Lacey tried too hard, displaying an almost overeager need to belong to whatever group she was in. Perhaps because she wasn't sure she did belong?

Carin hadn't considered that before. She didn't like considering it now.

Except she could see a difference here. With Douglas and his sons and their families, Lacey did belong. There was acceptance. No need to prove herself. She was part of this family.

Douglas turned his attention from his granddaughter to Nathan. "Heading back for the island now?"

"Yes."

"Still working on the book?"

Nathan nodded.

"So," Douglas said eagerly, "what's next?"

"Dunno." Nathan didn't look as if he cared, either. He cut another piece of pancake and swabbed it in the syrup on his plate.

Douglas looked surprised. He tapped his fingers on the table impatiently. "Surely you must have something lined up."

"Not at the moment." Nathan turned away from his father, looking at Rhys instead. "How about you and Mariah bringing the kids down this fall?"

"Yeah, sure. If you're going to be there."

"I'm going to be there," Nathan said almost fiercely.

Both Douglas and Rhys looked at him, surprised.

The subject of Nathan's work wasn't brought up again. It didn't stop Carin from thinking about it. And when Izzy called shortly after they got back to Mariah's and suggested coming by to pick Lacey up, Carin found herself saying yes.

As soon as Lacey left with the MacCauleys, Carin went in search of Nathan.

He was standing on the deck of their little studio apartment. He had his hands braced on the railing and was staring out over the gardens. But as she stood inside the screen door and watched him, she didn't think he was seeing any of them. His mind seemed a thousand miles away.

"Lacey left with Izzy," Carin said, opening the screen door.

Nathan whirled around, his expression betraying his surprise at the sight of her. Whatever else was going on in his head, though, she couldn't tell.

"They invited us to a barbecue at their place later to-night," she went on. "They're very nice."

"Yeah, they are."

She put her hands on the back of one of the deck chairs. It gave her something to hold on to. "Did Gaby have an offer for you?"

"What?" He scowled, then raked a hand through his hair. Shrugging, he turned away. "She's always got ideas."

"She thinks you need to get back to work."

He turned his head and glared at her. "I've been work-ing."

"Yes." She moved around the chair and went to stand alongside him, looking out over the tiny back gardens two stories below. "But you can't do that forever. What is Gaby's idea?"

"Another book about Zeno. The publisher wants me to go back, follow him some more. See if he's still out there. Shoot the sequel." Nathan's mouth twisted.

"That's a wonderful idea."

"Just dandy. But I'm not going."

"Why not? Lacey would be so impressed."

Nathan's knuckles whitened on the railing. He didn't say anything. He didn't look at her now. He stared out into the gardens.

"You don't have to stay just because you told me you were going to," Carin went on carefully in the face of his silence.

"Yes, I do," he said through his teeth. "I'm going to stay."

"Why?"

"Because," he said, turning now so that his blue gaze collided with hers, "I'm not leaving until you marry me. I told you that."

"But it's a good idea. And you can't—"

His jaw clenched. "I'm not going, Carin. You're not getting rid of me that way." He turned away and strode quickly back into the apartment. He banged out the door and clattered down the stairs without a backward glance.

The summer night was warm but not humid. The backyard barbecue at the MacCauleys was a resounding success.

Lacey and Finn and Izzy's daughters—"They used to be nieces," Lacey informed Carin, "but Finn and Izzy adopted them"—had become fast friends. They shared interests in photography and painting and a boy band that had a cute lead singer. Lacey was eager for them to come visit at Pelican Cay. And not just Tansy and Pansy, the twins, but Finn and Izzy and the little boys, too.

She thought the little boys, Rip and Crash—"Don't ask," said Izzy when she introduced Carin to the two dark-haired preschoolers—were so much fun.

"I wouldn't mind a brother," Lacey confided to Carin, "now that Dad's back."

The look Carin gave her must have precipitated second thoughts because Lacey said quickly, "Or, um, not." And seeing Izzy carrying a tray of lemonade out onto the patio, she hurried to help, leaving her mother by herself—to observe, to ponder, to reflect.

It was a lovely evening. A good time was had by all. And it was nearly eleven by the time they all got back to Rhys and Mariah's. Stephen and Lizzie fell asleep in the stroller. Lacey, who had bounced through the evening, began to slow down on the walk back uptown.

They had to get up early to catch a flight and so, when they got home, she fell into bed without a murmur and only one question.

"We can come back soon, can't we, Mom?"

Carin smiled and kissed her good-night. Then she took a shower while Nathan made up the beds. When she came out, the beds were made up, and he said gruffly, "My turn," and brushed past her into the bathroom.

Carin lay down on the bed and stared at the ceiling.

When she'd imagined coming to New York with Lacey, it hadn't been to a place like this. She'd imagined a hotel, not a home. She'd imagined strangers, not friends. She'd imagined herself and Lacey on their own.

It hadn't been anything like that.

But it had been good.

Even in her sleep, Lacey had had a smile on her face. She'd had a wonderful time in New York. She'd had a wonderful time with her family. With the Wolfes. She loved them, and they clearly loved her. They'd taken her into their hearts and their homes.

They had done much the same with Carin. Though Dominic had reason to dislike her, though they all had reason to resent her for what she'd done to Dominic and then for having kept Lacey's existence hidden for so long, they had actually welcomed her, too.

They had made her feel as if she was a part of their family. They had rekindled her longings, had reanimated her dreams. They had made her want things she had long ago told herself she would never have—not with Nathan.

The shower shut off. She heard him moving around in the bathroom. Seconds later the door opened and he appeared, lean and hard and beautiful, wearing only boxers, as he moved toward his bed.

She wanted him. Still. All the years and all the determination and all the heartache never managed to change that.

But what about Nathan? What did Nathan want? Really?

He pushed back the sheet and slid in, lying down flat on his back. If Carin looked at him out of the corner of her eye, she could see the rise and fall of his chest.

She knew what he would say he wanted—her. But that was duty speaking. And she didn't want him to marry her because of "duty". But she knew he wasn't going to turn his back on that duty. Obviously, he would turn his back on his career first.

In the silence she drew a breath. "Nathan?"

He jumped at the sound of her voice, then let out a harsh sigh, as if he'd hoped she was asleep and had suddenly discovered she was not. "What?"

She swallowed and stared at the ceiling, afraid to look at him, knowing her own duty. "I'm ready to get married."

CHAPTER TEN

NATHAN ROLLED onto his side and stared at her, unsure he'd heard right.

Carin didn't stare back. She didn't even look at him. She was staring straight at the ceiling, looking like one of those bodies carved on the tops of sarcophagi, hands folded below her breasts, eyes focused on the heavens.

He ran his tongue over his lips. "You're ready to get married?" He cleared his throat. "To who?"

Her head whipped around and she rolled to face him. Even in the near darkness he could see the outraged expression on her face. "Fine! Never mind. I just thought it made sense, but if you don't want to, that's perfectly okay with me." There was a high, tight tone in her voice that surprised him.

He held up a hand. "Whoa! Hang on. You just... surprised me. You're serious?"

"No, I'm joking. Of course, I'm serious."

"Why? Why now?" More to the point.

For that he got another glare. But damn it, he needed to ask. Dared to hope.

Carin pressed her lips together for a long moment, then she gave a little shrug. "It makes sense." She didn't sound annoyed now. She sounded distant, almost indifferent.

Nathan's hopes wavered. Hardly a declaration of her undying love. "Sense?"

She gave him an impatient scowl. "You're the one who thought so in the first place. Duty and responsibility and all that. Isn't that what you said?"

"Yeah, but—"

168

"Well, I've decided you're right. You're not the only one who can be dutiful and responsible." Her chin jutted.

Nathan felt a hollow ache begin. "So," he said slowly, "you're willing to get married out of duty?"

"Yes. It would be good for Lacey."

"I said that weeks ago."

"With just us, I couldn't see it. But now that I've seen her with your brothers and your father and your family...she's happy. I mean, she was happy before, but she didn't have a family. Lacey always wanted a family." The tightness was there in her voice again. Nathan wasn't sure what it meant.

So it all came back to Lacey?

"And that's all?" He shouldn't push. He couldn't make her say words that weren't true—even if he wanted desperately to hear them.

"I figure it's better for you, too. So you can go back to work. Do the assignment Gabriela wants you to do."

His teeth came together. "*That's* why you're marrying me? To get rid of me?"

"I'm trying to be sensible, Nathan. You'll hurt your career by insisting on staying, by being so stubborn. And if you don't know it, I do. I'm trying to tell you don't have to."

"Thanks very much," he said bitterly.

"Look," Carin said impatiently, "you wanted us to be a family. You came down insisting that I marry you so you could 'do the right thing'. Fine, I've agreed. Let's do it. We'll get married—and then you can get back to your life!"

His life. He didn't have a life anymore—not without Carin and Lacey.

But how the hell could he say that when she was wishing him gone? And how the hell could he pack up and leave without marrying her if she was finally agreeable?

It might be a marriage built on duty, but at least it would be a marriage—a starting point.

Given time, Nathan told himself, they could build something solid. They could find the love they'd lost—the love he'd killed. And yes, he might have to go away from time to time, but perhaps they would go with him. He'd have a right to ask them to if he and Carin were married. And even if she said no, if they were married he would always have the right to come back.

So he didn't get love in the bargain. At least he got the chance to earn it.

"Okay," he said. "Let's do it."

They did it.

Early the next morning Nathan canceled their flight home. "Got other plans," he told Rhys who was fixing toast fingers for Stephen. "We'll go tomorrow. Today we're getting married."

Rhys's jaw dropped. The knife clattered to the floor.

Nathan glared. "Don't act surprised. It's what everybody wanted."

"Well, yeah," Rhys said, then added carefully, "As long as it's what you want."

"It's what I want. Can Dominic pull some strings? Get us a license and a J.P.?"

"He did it for himself," Rhys said. "I don't see why he wouldn't do it for you." He paused. "Does Carin know about this?"

"Of course she knows. It was her damned idea!"

Rhys raised a brow. "And is she as happy about it as you are?"

"I don't think so, no," Nathan said honestly. He punched in Dominic's phone number. "Hey," he said when his brother answered. "Is this Weddings by Wolfe? Want to be my best man?"

Dominic, thank God, was enthusiastic. He didn't ask annoying questions like Rhys did. He said, "I'll take care of everything and call you back."

He called back in less than an hour with everything arranged. "Everything but a dress," he said. "Sierra said she and Mariah can help Carin with that." He rattled off an address downtown. "Be there by three-thirty." He paused. "Is Carin cool with this?"

"Why does everybody think I'm forcing her to marry me?"

"Just wondered. Anyway, speaking from experience," Dominic said dryly, "I'm sure if she doesn't want to, she just won't show up."

Lacey was thrilled when Carin told her the news. She gasped, grinned, then whooped and yelled and threw her arms around her mother.

"I knew it! I knew you still loved each other! Oh, this is perfect! Wait'll I tell Tansy and Pansy. Wait'll I tell Lorenzo." She jumped out of bed and began dancing around the room.

Carin took comfort in the fact that Lacey was delighted, because for her part, she was scared to death about what she'd done.

She'd caved in.

She'd rationalized it to Nathan—she'd babbled on about wanting Lacey to have a solid connection to her uncles and grandfather, about Lacey herself wanting to be part of a family. She'd brought up Nathan's career and what he owed to it.

All very true.

But she never said the truest thing of all—that she was marrying Nathan because she loved him, because she wanted to spend the rest of her life with him. And she simply couldn't fight it any longer. She could deny him the words because she didn't want to be pathetic, because she didn't want him feeling sorry for her.

But she couldn't deny it in her heart.

She had sworn she wouldn't marry unless her love was reciprocated. But that was selfish—and it was asking for the impossible. You couldn't make a person love you.

She wished Nathan loved her, but right now she would take what she could get. She was too weak to fight any longer.

It was the right thing to do for Lacey. It was the right thing to do for Nathan.

And if she knew the pain of loving without being loved—well, it couldn't be helped. At least she would have him in her life.

Maybe, given time…

But she wouldn't let herself go there.

First she would marry him. Then she would hope he would fall in love with her.

"You're *married*?" Fiona was astonished to hear the news.

"You got hitched?" Hugh didn't sound quite so surprised.

"'Bout time, that's what I say." Estelle put her hands on her hips and gave them a satisfied smile. "Didn't I tell you they were right for each other?" she asked her husband, Maurice.

Maurice bobbed his head. "You surely did."

"Well, if you're all done passing judgment," Nathan said, "maybe you could give me a hand putting the luggage in the Jeep. Carin and Lacey brought back presents for everyone on the island."

It was a calculated request, meant to make clear—in case Carin or Hugh or anyone else had other ideas—that Carin and Lacey were coming home with him. He shouldn't have had to worry.

But though she had smiled at the wedding and though she had let him hold her hand during the reception and put his arm around her when they left Rhys and Mariah's a day late, she had never unbent.

She hadn't bolted as she had when she'd been going to marry Dominic. She had shown up. She had said her vows. But the woman who had married him yesterday was definitely a woman fulfilling a duty. He had his work cut out for him.

"Can Zeno come?" Lacey asked.

Since Zeno had already jumped in the Jeep, and was even now panting happily at Nathan, there was only one answer. Nathan was inclined to say yes, anyway. "Sure. Why not?"

Lacey talked all the way home, making plans for tomorrow, who to go see, who to tell about her adventures, who to regale with the story of her parents' wedding.

Nathan let it all wash over him, making appropriate noises when required. It went with being a father, he'd discovered. He had no problem with it. So far fatherhood had come remarkably easily.

It was being a husband that was going to be tricky.

He wanted to be a good one. He wanted to be a real one.

So when Carin opened her mouth as he carried the bags upstairs, he said flatly, "We're married. We're sharing a bedroom."

Carin's expression grew shuttered and unreadable. But she closed her mouth and gave an almost imperceptible nod of her head.

So much for romance.

Of course she didn't expect it. She'd warned herself not to. They were married, but it was hardly a marriage of love.

Still, somehow she had hoped.

Fool, Carin derided herself. *You knew better.* But even so, it hurt that he was so abrupt, so harsh. He wanted her physically, that much was clear. He would share his body with her. But he wasn't going to give her his heart.

She wished she could refuse to sleep with him. She couldn't. Lacey would expect them to sleep together. But even acknowledging that, Carin knew it wasn't the whole truth—the truth was she wanted him. It was pathetic. *She* was pathetic.

But if this marriage was not going to be complete misery, they had to start somewhere.

They might as well start in bed. It was the place their relationship had begun to go wrong. Maybe now they could start to put it right.

They managed to be pleasant and polite, even teasing a bit, while Lacey was still up. But as soon as she'd gone to bed, the tension between them grew like a storm filling the sky. It wasn't terribly late, but all Carin could think about was her bag upstairs in Nathan's bedroom, about what it meant, about what the night would bring.

"Do you want a glass of wine?" Nathan asked. She was standing on the deck, staring out at the ocean, hoping that the evening breeze would cool her heated flesh.

Quickly she shook her head. "I'm fine. I…think I might like a bath."

When she'd finished she put on a thin silk nightgown—a gift from Mariah and Sierra and far more elegant than the T-shirt and gym shorts she'd worn in New York—and went into the bedroom.

Nathan was already there. He took one look at her, and something flared in his gaze. His jaw tightened and his whole body seemed to grow taut.

He'd already begun to undress. His shirt was unbuttoned, hanging loose and affording her a glimpse of his hard muscled chest. The glimpse only made her want more. She remembered the night she'd seen him coming up from the sea, remembered the sight of his naked body, and her breath caught and her pulse quickened as she anticipated seeing it again.

Nathan, hearing the catch of her breath, scowled. "Don't go all innocent virgin on me," he said, misinterpreting it.

"No fear," Carin retorted sharply, annoyed. "You already took care of that."

They glared at each other, electricity arcing between them.

"I damned well never forced you."

Carin's gaze slid away. "I know that," she muttered.

"And I don't want to force you now." Then he let his shirt fall to the floor and crossed the room to her. He put his hands on her arms, slid them down, then touched her waist, drew her close. His breath stirred tendrils of her hair. His stubbled jaw scraped lightly against her own.

And Carin trembled.

Nathan stilled, then stepped back. "Are you afraid of me?"

She shook her head resolutely. "N-no." It wasn't Nathan she was afraid of. It was her own traitorous heart.

"Then love me," Nathan said hoarsely. "Let me love you." And he drew her to the bed, and they lay down upon it.

Together, where they had longed to be, their bodies seemed unable to resist. Their limbs tangled, their mouths met, their tongues clashed. Carin felt his hands on her, stroking and teasing her breasts, her belly, her legs, the very center of her, finding her wet and waiting, making her writhe.

Determined to have her own way, Carin touched him, too. Her fingers sought his belt and unfastened it, tugged the zip and pulled it down. She pushed his khakis and boxers down his hips and, willingly, he kicked them away. Then he shoved her gown up and yanked it over her head and they faced each other, naked and hungry, eyes glittering, passions flaming.

It had been so long. So very very long. And yet, right

now, right this very moment, Carin knew that whatever had kept them apart, in this at least nothing had changed.

"Carin?"

She trembled, nodded. "Nathan."

And then he was kissing her and she was kissing him. He pressed her back onto the bed and slipped between her legs. He touched the liquid core of her and made her shiver, made her body open. And Carin touched the hard, hot length of his erection, ran her fingers over him lightly, saw him bite his lip and shut his eyes, felt him shudder and tense.

And then she drew him in.

It was a heat and a fullness she had never forgotten. It was a melding of bodies, a connection between souls. She had thought that once. She prayed it would happen again.

Love me, Nathan had said. *Let me love you.*

And as they began to move together, as their rhythms meshed and their bodies became one, Carin felt tears prick her eyelids as she prayed that he meant more than the pleasure their bodies were taking in each other.

He'd said her name. He'd asked. She'd answered.

It was a start.

If only he loved her and would let her love him...life would be beautiful.

It was a truce, Nathan supposed. A marriage built on duty and their daughter.

It was what he had asked for—and what he had got.

They were a family of sorts. They lived at Nathan's, all three of them and Zeno the dog. And during the days they settled into a routine. Lacey went to school, Nathan worked on his book, and Carin, once she got her arm out of the cast, went back to working in the shop and started painting again.

They were polite to each other—maybe more than polite. They smiled, they talked, and sometimes, tentatively, they teased. They were moving in the right direction, building connections.

But Nathan wanted so much more.

He wanted the casual contact he'd seen between Dominic and Sierra, between Rhys and Mariah. He wanted to be able to come up behind Carin while she was doing the dishes or working in the shop and slide his arms around her and pull her back against him and kiss the nape of her neck. He wanted to take her hand when they walked along the beach. He wanted to tell her that he loved her.

But he was afraid to push. He'd got this far, he told himself. He had her in his home. At night he had her in his bed. It was the one time that their inhibitions seemed to vanish. Their limbs tangled, their bodies merged. Physically they connected.

But they never spoke endearments. They never talked of love.

Someday they would, he told himself. But he had no idea when.

When Gaby called the first time, he said no. He wasn't ready. He was still on his honeymoon, he told her.

"It's been a month," Gaby said.

"I'm not ready," Nathan told her.

She called again a week later. And a week after that. He stalled her. Hedged. Put it off. Yes, he wanted to do what she wanted him to do—spend three months in the wilderness checking out the wolf Zeno or, if that didn't work, then a project of his own choosing.

He wanted to do it—but he wanted his marriage on solid ground first. Even better, he wanted Carin and Lacey to come with him. But he couldn't say so.

Gaby said it for him. "If you want to bring Carin and Lacey, do it," she'd said.

"I…can't," Nathan said awkwardly. "School, you know. And Carin's got her painting. Her business."

"She can get a lot of new material if she comes with you," Gaby said. "And think how educational it would be for Lacey."

"Mmm." Yes. Yes to all of the above. But he still couldn't ask.

He was afraid to. Afraid Carin would say no. Afraid he'd lose whatever advances he'd made over the past two months. Afraid if he left she would rejoice in his going and he would know she didn't love him—not really.

Afraid she wouldn't want him to come back.

"Well," Gaby said impatiently when he didn't answer.

"I'll think about it."

He thought about nothing else. He rehearsed a hundred ways to ask Carin—and Lacey—to come with him.

You could paint the north woods. You could paint wolves. Lacey would learn so much. Think of the educational opportunities. Not many kids ever get a chance to do something like that. I could show you my world. We could share it.

But that was getting dangerously close to personal. It was almost like saying *I love you,* and Nathan couldn't do that because he was afraid she didn't love him.

If he knew she did, it would be easy. If only he could figure that out without having to ask. He needed a sign, he thought, as he walked up to the house with Lacey three nights later, Zeno bouncing along ahead, darting after a lizard here and a frog there.

They had been out shooting in the twilight, and Nathan had talked a little about the light in the north woods. If Lacey said, "When are you going again?" he thought he would mention Gaby's offer.

But Lacey didn't ask. It didn't seem to occur to her that he would have to go again. Because he'd said he would stay forever, he reminded himself. Or take them with him.

Carin was in the kitchen when they came onto the deck. "Wash your hands. Supper's ready," she said. She didn't smile the way she usually did when they got home. She wasn't frowning exactly. She just seemed…remote.

"Something wrong?" Nathan asked.

"Wrong?" Blonde brows lifted. "What could be wrong?"

He didn't know. Still he felt an odd clutching in his gut at her words. A premonition?

He found out that night when they were going to bed.

"Gaby called," Carin said. She was brushing out her hair and she didn't turn around. But he could see her face in the mirror.

Nathan went very still. "Did she? What did she say?"

"She wanted to know what you'd decided about going up north." Carin's words were flat.

Nathan scrubbed a hand over his hair. The moment of truth. *Smile at me, damn it. Give me some encouragement,* he begged her.

But Carin just kept on brushing her hair. She didn't even look at him.

He paced around their bedroom. "I know I said I'd stay forever," he began.

"And we both know that's impossible," Carin said sharply.

"Well, I—"

"Gaby told me you need to go." Carin's tone was firm.

"I—" Hell. How could he just blurt out an invitation now? Damn Gaby, anyway! "I'll be back."

Carin's mouth pressed into a thin line. Her expression grew shuttered. "Lacey will be glad to know that," she said dully. Their eyes met in the mirror. And then her gaze dropped.

Nathan sighed. "I'll call Gaby in the morning."

"Good idea." Carin set the brush down, then got up and crossed the room. She slipped into bed and pulled the covers up.

Nathan shut off the light and came to slide in beside her.

Every night since their marriage they'd touched, they'd made love or they just wrapped their arms around each other and slept.

Tonight they lay inches apart. But neither reached across those few inches.

"Good night, Nathan," Carin said tonelessly. Then she rolled onto her side, turning away.

They went through the next three days like zombies. Polite, civil zombies who shared a bed and a daughter—and nothing else.

The rapport they'd built over the past weeks had vanished just as Nathan had feared it would. Carin shut him out and retreated into a shell. So much for wanting to take her with him.

Her indifference now was killing him. If he was going, he had to go now!

He called Gaby and told her, "Get me on the first flight you can."

She'd called last night. "Get to Miami in the morning. Your flight leaves at one."

Hugh agreed to take him. He had a cargo that needed to be delivered. "If you don't mind the seaplane," he said.

"Anything."

Even so, saying goodbye to his daughter nearly did him in. Lacey was distraught to learn that he was going away. She'd been sulking since he'd told her. "You could take us," she'd said.

But Nathan, seeing Carin's back stiffen at her words, had said, "No, I can't." He didn't say he wished he could.

Now Lacey wrapped her arms around him and gave him a fierce hug. "You'd better come back."

"Of course I will. Soon." It was the best he could do.

"You'll e-mail? You'll call?"

"Yes. And you will, too?"

"Of course," she said indignantly. "I love you."

Nathan's mouth twisted at the ease with which she spoke such words. He pressed his lips to the top of her head and held her close. "Likewise, kiddo."

"I'll come to the harbor to see you leave," she said.

"No, you won't," Carin said firmly. "You have to get to school."

"But—"

Carin looked at Nathan expectantly. He knew what she was waiting for.

"Go to school, Lace," he said heavily.

Their daughter sighed. She gave him one more fierce hug, then reluctantly she got on her bike and wobbled off down the road.

Then it was just him and Carin—and Carin wouldn't even look at him. She started cleaning the table, turning her back on him, washing up the breakfast dishes.

"Carin?" He came up behind her. One last chance. *Tell me you'll miss me. Tell me you love me.*

"Don't let me keep you," she said, and stepped away abruptly when he would have kissed her goodbye.

And just like that, he was gone.

There was a moment's hesitation when Carin thought he might have insisted on that kiss, when—God help her!—she wished he would.

But then wordlessly he'd turned, picked up his bag and walked out the door.

And there was none of the relief Carin had promised herself she would feel seeing him go. None of the satisfaction of knowing she'd been the one to turn away from him, that she had not let him have things his way, that she had never given in.

Instead she felt hollow, aching, desperate. It wasn't supposed to be like this!

She stood, rigid, soaked in pain and loneliness, and knew

the truth at last—that in denying him, she'd denied herself, as well.

She loved Nathan Wolfe. She would always love him.

And not admitting it didn't mean it wasn't so.

Not admitting it meant she was a coward, that she was afraid to take a risk. She'd refused to let herself hope. She'd tried every way she could to protect her heart, to deny her love. But it wasn't possible.

And it didn't hurt less for trying. If anything it hurt more.

She could have wrapped her arms around him. She could have held him. She could have had his kiss to remember, to savor. She could have said, "I love you."

And maybe…just maybe…he would have said it back.

Maybe it wasn't too late. If she could get to the harbor before they took off. She grabbed her tote bag and started to run.

She was almost to the village when she saw Hugh's seaplane circle above the bay.

She stopped, heart aching, and watched it go.

She made it to the shop before the tears began to fall. She sniffled and swiped at them, worried that someone would come in and see her. Please God, for a while at least, the tourists would stay well away.

But even as she thought the words, the door banged open.

She blew her nose, scrubbed at her eyes and pasted on a smile. "May I help— Estelle? What's wrong?"

"It's Nathan! Come quick." The whites of Estelle's eyes were enormous in her dark face. She turned and ran back out again.

Carin's bones turned to water. Her knees wobbled. Bile rose in her throat. Nathan! Ohmigod, Nathan! And Hugh, of course. But— *Nathan*!!!!

She ran after Estelle, out the door and down the steps, tripping, stumbling. "What happened? Did they crash?"

"Yes," Estelle said. "Yes!"

In the harbor? Were they still alive? Being rescued? Carin couldn't ask, could only run.

And then she saw him—limping up the road.

Limping up the road?

Carin stared. In the *road*? Not in the *harbor*?

But yes, it was Nathan, not fifty yards from her, with Estelle bearing down on him. She fluttered at him, but he brushed him off and soldiered on, scraped and battered, one arm looking wonky, an abrasion on his cheek—but *alive!*—and heading straight toward her.

Where was the plane? Where was Hugh? What in the world—?

They met in the middle of Pineapple Street, stopped an arm's length apart and stared at each other. Carin wanted to grab him and hold him, but could only shake her head.

"What—" she began.

"The plane?" she tried.

"You crashed?" she guessed.

"It was that bloody dog," Nathan said gruffly.

"The dog? *Zeno*?" Carin stared, astonished. Something dangerously close to a hysterical laugh threatened to bubble up. But it wasn't funny at all and yet—

"Zeno," Nathan confirmed, through gritted teeth.

Estelle was flapping at him, yammering about doctors and hospitals. They both ignored her.

"I thought…" Carin began. Her teeth beginning to chatter. It was shock, she thought. And joy. Pure joy at the sight of him. "What are you…? Didn't Hugh wait for you?"

She couldn't imagine Hugh leaving without him. Of course he had cargo, but surely he'd have waited if Nathan had been late. But Nathan hadn't been late. Had he?

"You better get yourself over to Doc Rasmussen's right now," Estelle said.

"Later," Nathan said firmly to Estelle. "Go away."

There was something in his tone that stopped all the fluttering and the yammering. Estelle looked at him, at the way he was looking only at Carin, then slowly she smiled and nodded her head. "I tell the doc you be along."

"Do that," Nathan said without glancing her way. He had eyes only for Carin. "I told Hugh to go without me."

"Because Zeno—"

"Zeno got me on my way back."

Carin stared. "What?"

"I didn't go with Hugh. I told him I wasn't ready. He brought me back to shore and I borrowed a bike. I was in a hurry. So was Zeno," he said dryly.

"But...but why?"

"Because I love you."

She stared at him. Words she'd almost given up hope on, words she'd feared never to hear were right there before her. More than that, though, there was the way Nathan was looking at her, intent, determined, and with a light in his eyes that she was sure met a matching one in her own.

Her jaw wobbled. Her eyes filled. "Oh, God, Nathan!"

"Don't cry, for heaven's sake!" he begged her, distraught. "I'm sorry. If you don't want to hear it, I'm sorry! I couldn't leave without saying—"

"I _want_ to hear it!" She would have flung her arms around him if she could have figured out how to do it without hurting him. "I love you! I love you, too!"

And then he wrapped his one good arm around her. And right there in the middle of Pineapple Street, right in front of the Win Pixie grocery store and the Pelican Cay school, Nathan was kissing her, hungrily, desperately.

And despite her fear of hurting him further, Carin was kissing him back.

"I love you," she said again. Her voice broke, but her spirit soared. The words, once spoken, were now easy to say. She smiled against his lips, tears threatening again. She dashed them away. "I ran after you to tell you. I didn't want you to go without knowing. I thought you'd gone.... And then I thought the plane..."

She started to cry in earnest now. And Nathan was hanging on to her, shaking his head. "Not gone. Not going. Not without you. I couldn't."

There were kids gathering at the windows of the school, watching, grinning. "Hey, Lace! Lookit! It's your mom and dad. They're kissin'."

But Carin barely heard them. She only looked at Nathan. "But you have to go. It's what you do. I don't expect you to stay for us."

"I'll go again," Nathan told her. He looked down at his arm which was probably broken and hurt like hell—but not as much as going without them had. "But only if you and Lacey come with me."

"Of course." Carin smiled up at him through her tears. "Of course we will."

Was it that simple? Nathan wondered, dazed. Would he wake up in Doc Rasmussen's and discover he'd dreamed it all.

But then Lacey was there, and all her classmates, whooping and cheering.

"We have to get you to the doctor," Carin said, easing an arm around his waist, trying to get him to walk with her.

"In a sec," Nathan said, reveling in the moment. He wasn't dreaming. There was no way he could have dreamed up an elementary school full of cheering kids. He kissed her again, and she kissed him back willingly. He needed this far more than he needed a doctor or X-rays or Band-Aids.

He needed Carin—and Lacey—more than he needed anything else on earth.

"Come on, Nathan," Carin urged him. "We need to get you to the doc and then home to bed."

"Bed?" Nathan said hopefully.

Carin looked up into his eyes and he looked down into hers. They looked at each other tenderly, laughingly, lovingly. "Oh, definitely," Carin said.

And then together, with her supporting him, they limped off up the street.

Zeno watched them, then looked at Lacey and wagged his tail.

Not bad, his eyes said, for a morning's work.

New York City, One Year Later

This time it was Nathan's show.

They all had a part again this year—Nathan, Carin and Lacey. It made sense, Gaby agreed, because they'd all gone on the expedition together. It had been a family affair.

With Nathan's arm broken and winter fast closing in, they couldn't leave until spring. But in May the three of them had flown up into the north woods. The temperatures had still been just south of frigid. The snow had been thick on the ground. It had been an education for Lacey, all right.

It had been a time to remember for all of them.

Now they were sharing the memories with the world at large. The book, *Not So Solo,* would be published just before Christmas. But the gallery show was opening in less than half an hour.

The highlights were Nathan's photos of Zeno the wolf and his pack. It had taken nearly a month for him to track the wolf down. He hadn't been in any of the places Nathan had expected to find him and, out of Lacey's hearing, he'd told Carin he was afraid Zeno, loner that he was, might have died.

In fact, he'd just been too busy to frequent his old stomping ground. The lone wolf was solo no longer. Four young wolf cubs—one who looked remarkably like the young Zeno—were obviously his. A pretty young gray-and-brindle female had made a family man out of him.

"There are some interesting parallels," Gaby said, smiling as she and Stacia hung the show.

"A few," Nathan agreed. He slipped an arm around his daughter and thought how much taller and grown-up she seemed now than last year. Lacey was a teenager, heaven help him. She was talking about boys! He might have to lock her up.

His gaze met his wife's. Everything they'd had the week they met they had again now—only better. They had love. They had trust. They had a future together. They were older, they were wiser. They knew to speak the words the other needed to hear.

"I love you," he mouthed now. "All of you."

All of them. Carin. Lacey. And Joshua, two-month-old Joshua, who—despite the commotion of the opening—was sound asleep in his mother's arms.

Nathan dropped a kiss on his daughter's brow, then leaned in to kiss his wife, a kiss that promised a lifetime of love to the woman he had so nearly lost, and then brushed his lips over his son's downy head.

"The littlest Wolfe cub," he murmured smiling into Carin's eyes.

She smiled back, loving this man now even more than she'd dreamed possible. Loving him for the past, for Lacey. For the present, for Joshua. For the future. Forever.

Their gazes locked.

"But hopefully," she said, "not the last."

D'ALESSANDRO'S CHILD

by

Catherine Spencer

Catherine Spencer, once an English teacher, fell into writing through eavesdropping on a conversation about romances. Within two months she changed careers and sold her first book to Mills & Boon in 1984. She moved to Canada from England thirty years ago and lives in Vancouver. She is married to a Canadian and has four grown children – two daughters and two sons (and now eight grandchildren) – plus three dogs. In her spare time she plays the piano, collects antiques, and grows tropical shrubs.

You can visit Catherine Spencer's website at www. catherinespencer.com

Don't miss Catherine Spencer's exciting new novel, *Sicilian Millionaire, Bought Bride*, available this month from Mills & Boon® Modern™.

CHAPTER ONE

INITIALLY, all Mike planned to do was observe the child.
From a distance. To establish, as well as he could, that all
was well in the boy's life. That done, he would pay a last
visit to his dying ex-wife, ease her tortured mind and heart,
then take the first flight out of San Francisco and head back
to Vancouver without disclosing to another living soul that,
more than four years earlier, she'd conceived a child. Mike
would even try to forget it.

It seemed the most decent thing to do; the most humane.
Because enough damage had already occurred, and what
right had he to plow into matters at this late stage and make
them worse?

But that was before. Before he could put a face to the
child. Before he heard the infectious belly laugh of delight,
or saw the dark hair so much like his own, or watched the
sturdy, sun-kissed legs pumping across the grassy slope to
the carousel at the other side of the park.

After that, *observing from a distance* just wasn't enough.
He wanted to touch. To speak, to listen. To learn everything
about the three and a half years since this child, this son
he hadn't known he'd sired, had come into the world—
little things like what foods he preferred, what his favorite
toy was, if he liked music, or model trains; whether or not
he could kick a ball, skate, swim.

A few yards from where he watched, the woman—the
"mother"—waved to the boy as he swirled past on a
painted pony. "Hold on tight, sweetheart," she called out,
her voice as musical as a genteel bell.

Hold on tight! The words held a bitter irony for Mike. Perhaps if he and Kay had held on tight to their marriage, he wouldn't be here now, trying to devise a way to strike up a conversation without raising suspicion.

Already he felt people were watching him, wondering about the stranger in their midst. In a town as small and seriously upscale as this, a guy in blue jeans stood out from the crowd as plainly as his midsize rental car looked out of place snugged up between the Mercedes and BMWs in the tree-shaded parking area.

The merry-go-round wound to a stop with the boy on the side farthest away from his mother. Standing on tiptoe, the skirt of her pretty mauve dress billowing slightly in the breeze, she waved to catch his attention. "Over here, Jeremy!"

Jeremy? He'd come across worse names, Mike supposed, but this one was a bit on the arty side for his taste. A boy needed a name that would sit easily on him when he grew to be a man. Something strong and indisputedly masculine. Like *Michael.* And a last name that reflected his heritage. Like *D'Alessandro.*

Slithering off his pony, the boy raced around the carousel and in his eagerness to get back to his mother, tripped and went sprawling practically at Mike's feet. Without stopping to consider the wisdom of such a move, Mike stooped to haul the little guy upright again.

There were grass stains on his knees. And the faint remains of baby dimples. The little body was sweetly solid, the eyes staring into his the same dark, fathomless brown as Kay's.

The feelings...sheesh, how to describe them! It was as if a hollow suddenly opened up inside Mike; a sense of loss so acute that he caught his breath at the pain of it. The child fearfully shying away from him was his own flesh and blood!

He ached to reassure him. To cup the smooth round cheek in his callused hand, to hug the innocent little body close and just once whisper, *You don't have to be afraid of me, son. I'm your daddy.*

Instead, he mumbled, "Hey, sport," then dribbled into awkward silence because, while he never had to think twice about what to say to his four-year-old twin nephews, with *this* child he had to watch his words.

A shadow slid across the grass, just wide enough to block out the sun. "Come here, Jeremy."

Even lightly coated with alarm, her voice remained musical and lovely. The hand which reached down to pluck her child out of a stranger's grasp was narrow and elegant, with long slender fingers and delicate oval nails painted pink.

Glancing up, Mike found himself pinned in a wary silver-blue gaze rimmed with feathery lashes. Straightening, he took a step backward and said casually, "He took quite a nosedive, but I don't think he's hurt."

She was too well-bred to tell him she no more gave a flying fig what he thought than she appreciated his touching her child, but the message came across clearly enough in her cool reply. "I'm sure he isn't, but thank you for being concerned. Jeremy, say thank you to the gentleman for being kind enough to help you."

"Thank you," Jeremy parroted, inspecting him with the uninhibited curiosity of any normal three-year-old now that he had the safety of his mother's leg to cling to.

Mike wished he dared ruffle that thick mop of black hair—just once experience the pleasure of its texture slipping through his fingers. But it was out of the question. *She* was watching him too intently, her protective instincts on full alert. So hooking his thumbs in the back pockets of his jeans and hoping his grin didn't look too manufactured, he settled for, "Any time, kiddo."

"Well...." The mother folded the boy's hand protectively in her own and turned away. "We must be going. Thank you again."

"Sure thing."

He watched them leave, her with the erect carriage of a duchess, and his boy with the agile enthusiasm that only the very young and innocent could know. *You've accomplished what you came to do,* Mike's rational mind informed him. *The child's well-dressed, well-fed, and well-mannered, and even a fool can see the mother dotes on him. Convey the news to Kay, then stick to your original idea and forget this afternoon ever happened.*

"Fat chance," he murmured, his gaze trained on the pair as they joined the lineup at the buffet tables set out under striped, open-sided tents.

The scene, perfect down to the last detail, might have been lifted from a painting. Too bad it couldn't erase the picture indelibly imprinted on his mind of the room in St. Mary's Hospital in San Francisco, and Kay's face, already pared by illness to skeletal proportions, rendered even more pitiful by her mental anguish.

"I gave him away," she'd whispered, her sunken eyes filling with tears and her fingers, so bony they resembled claws, worrying the hospital sheet stretched across her painfully thin body. "Finding I was pregnant, just when I was starting out afresh...with such ambitions. I was so close to achieving my dream...I could smell the success. I couldn't handle a baby, Mike. Not then."

But I could have, he thought bitterly. The brief taste he'd just enjoyed told him that, and he was ravenous suddenly, not for the food people were heaping on their plates, but for closer acquaintance with a child who should have belonged to him.

He could no more walk away and forget the boy existed than a starving man could refuse nourishment.

"Who's your secret admirer, Camille?"

Though lightly phrased and threaded with amusement, the question brought a flush to Camille's cheeks which completely undercut her offhand, "I haven't the foggiest idea what you mean."

"Oh, come off it! This is *me* you're talking to!"

She should have known better than to try fooling the woman who'd been her best friend since kindergarten. Frances Knowlton hadn't shared her secret passion for Mortimer Griffin at nine, helped her dye her naturally blond hair a horrific ruby red at fifteen, supported her at twenty through a wedding involving four hundred guests, and kept her together when her marriage fell apart the year she turned twenty-eight, without learning a thing or two along the way.

"If you're referring to the man at the table over there," she said, refusing to glance his way even though her eyes would have been happy to feast on him indefinitely if she'd allowed it, "we met very casually over by the carousel. He was kind to Jeremy."

"Which no doubt explains why you're practically drooling at the mere mention of him now. Not that I blame you." Fran, never one to care too much about social protocol, lowered her sunglasses and subjected the stranger to a frank inspection before fondling her husband's knee under the table. "If I weren't already happily married to the sexiest man on earth, I'd be sticking a Sold sign on Mr. Blue Eyes' forehead before anyone else, including you, Camille, beat me to it."

He did have the most gorgeous eyes, Camille was forced to admit. Not the pale blue-gray she'd been cursed with, but a deep, tropical indigo that blazed with an almost electric energy from his tanned face. And he did keep switching that gaze to her. She could feel it pulsing across the distance between them, a magnet persistently drawing her attention away from Jeremy who was up to his elbows in crabmeat salad.

"Isn't it a shame that, like you, he's here alone?" Fran observed, flinging down her paper napkin and swinging her long legs over the picnic bench. "In the spirit of small town hospitality, I think I should do something about that."

Heat rushed into Camille's face again. "Please don't, Fran! For a start, I'm not alone, I'm with Jeremy, and...."

But she might as well have saved her breath. Fran had already descended with single-minded determination on the man seated two tables away. He was acknowledging whatever she said to him, his initial look of inquiry giving way to a dazzling smile.

A moment later, he'd scooped up his plate and was loping behind her as she wove her way back to where Camille sat stony-faced with embarrassment.

"If I were you, I'd try to keep my wife under better control," she informed Adam Knowlton.

Adam grinned. "Short of keeping her on a very short leash and muzzling her, there's not much I can do. She's her own woman, always has been, and I wouldn't have her any other way." Then, as Fran made a beeline for a seat next to her husband, thereby leaving the stranger with no choice but to sit beside Camille, Adam leaned forward and muttered, "Better take the scowl off your face and smile, sweet thing. You're about to be introduced."

His name was Michael D'Alessandro. He was, he said, on a working vacation. He lived north of the border, in

Vancouver, and owned a construction company and was chiefly interested in building town houses. Back home, the Californian style of architecture was very popular, and he'd come south in part to solicit bids for designs on a gated community he hoped to develop on a tract of land he'd recently acquired.

He said a lot of other things, too: that he couldn't believe his luck in running into Adam who was an architect specializing in earthquake-proof residential construction; that he'd discovered Calder by chance and found it very picturesque.

He answered Fran's not-so-subtle questions with forthright charm. Married? Not anymore. Traveling alone? Yes. Just passing through or planning to stay in town awhile? No fixed time frame; he was his own boss and could pretty much do as he pleased.

He even found time to pay attention to Jeremy, drawing him out with the ease of someone used to being around small children. Jeremy responded like a starving plant to water, bursting into infectious giggles and showing off with three-year-old pride. ''I can swim,'' he announced. ''And I've got a football and I got my hair cut,'' all of which information Michael D'Alessandro received with absorbed attention.

But the only thing that really registered with Camille was the instinctive feeling that everything about the man spelled trouble, from his mesmerizing, take-no-prisoners eyes, to his stunning smile and his sexy, come-hither voice.

Sexy? She almost fell off the bench in astonishment. How had *sexy* managed to sneak into her thoughts? She must have a touch of sunstroke! ''Sexy'' was no more a part of her vocabulary these days than ''romance.'' She'd renounced both and concentrated all her love and passion on Jeremy ever since the day her marriage fell apart and Todd walked out not just on her, but on their child as well.

"So what's this public picnic all about, or do people in Calder always get together for a crabfest on summer weekends?"

Fran kicked her under the table, alerting Camille to the fact that the sexy voice had finally got around to addressing a direct question at her. Flustered, she avoided meeting his gaze and stared instead at his hands.

He had a working man's hands, big and tanned and capable. Like his arms and, no doubt, all the rest of him so snugly encased in white T-shirt and blue jeans softened to doeskin by numerous washings. Nothing like Todd, who turned a fiery red if he stayed out in the sun very long, and who thought muscle sat best on those who didn't have much in the brain department.

"Tell Michael about the women's shelter, Camille," Fran prompted, in much the same tone of voice one might use with a social incompetent suddenly turned loose in public.

"Women's shelter?" As he shifted to look at her more fully, Michael D'Alessandro's arm brushed against Camille's. If finding herself the focus of those arresting blue eyes wasn't disturbing enough, the shock of his actually touching her ran clean past her shoulder and settled somewhere in the vicinity of her throat, temporarily impairing her vocal cords—not to mention her mental faculties.

"I...." she croaked, shredding a corner of her paper napkin. "We—a group of us, that is...it's a project we thought was...um, worthwhile."

"As usual, she's being too modest," Fran chimed in, rolling her eyes in exasperation when Camille stumbled into silence. "She's chair of the fund-raising committee—

is the one who started the ball rolling in the first place, come to that, and it's mostly thanks to her efforts that it's been so successful.''

Camille swallowed, and vowed she'd throttle Fran the very first chance she got.

''Is that so?'' Laugh lines creased the corners of his eyes as he let loose with a smile that could have melted the polar ice cap. ''I wouldn't have expected there'd be a need for such a place in a town like this.''

''There isn't. It's in San Francisco,'' she said baldly.

''I see.'' A shadow of sadness seemed to cross his face and he lowered his eyes briefly. He had ridiculously long lashes. And sleek level brows as black as his hair which needed a trim. An inch longer and the ends would touch the crew neck of his T-shirt.

Aware she was staring, Camille turned her attention to Jeremy on her other side, glad that the conversation seemed to have petered out.

Fran, though, wasn't about to let that happen. ''If you're interested in supporting the cause, you're welcome to buy a ticket to our annual gala next Saturday,'' she informed the man breezily. ''You'll get a fabulous evening's entertainment in return—gourmet catering, live dance music, fabulous door prizes—and the really good part is, it's all tax deductible.''

''Not for Mr. D'Alessandro,'' Camille put in quickly. ''He's not a U.S. resident. In any case, I doubt he'd be interested in attending a function where he doesn't know anyone.''

''I know you,'' Michael D'Alessandro said, bathing her in another sultry smile. ''Not well, perhaps, but enough that I'd like to know you better.''

Fran jumped on that faster than a flea on a well-fed dog. ''Well, isn't it amazing how things work out sometimes!

Would you believe that, less than an hour ago, Camille told me she hasn't yet lined herself up with an escort? You'd be doing her a double favor if you bought a ticket and offered your services.''

"Fran, honestly!" Truly annoyed, Camille turned a scathing glare on her friend. "I don't need you to set me up with a man, and I'm quite sure Mr. D'Alessandro doesn't appreciate being pressured like this. Drop the subject, please.''

"I don't feel pressured," he said mildly. "Surprised, perhaps. I'd have thought your husband would be your date.''

"I don't have a husband. My marriage broke up two years ago.''

For some reason, the news rendered him temporarily speechless. She couldn't imagine why. People got divorced all the time, as he should know. She was hardly unique.

He soon recovered, though. "In that case," he said, "I'd be honored to act as your escort.''

"I can't allow it. For a start, you're on vacation and might have other plans for next Saturday.''

"As a matter of fact, I don't, at least not in the evening. So unless you're afraid I'll step all over your feet—''

"It's not that!''

He regarded her quizzically. "Then what is it?''

"Everything!" She shook her head, bewildered by her agitation. "Even discounting the fact that we've barely met, I haven't been part of the singles scene in over ten years.''

"Perhaps," he suggested gravely, "it's time you got used to the idea again.''

Just seconds before, she'd have sworn nothing would persuade her to go along with such a notion. But the warmth in his tone of voice, the sympathy she saw in his eyes, had her suddenly thinking, *Why not?*

It had been months since she'd known any real excitement; longer still since she'd met a man as attractive as he was. And it wasn't as if they'd be alone. Fran and Adam would be there, and so would her parents, along with just about everyone else in town. If it turned out that she and Michael D'Alessandro had nothing to say to each other after the first half hour, there'd be plenty of other people willing to carry the conversational ball for the rest of the evening.

"Perhaps it is," she agreed. "All right. If you're still here and of the same mind next week at this time, I'll be glad of your company."

He subjected her to another of those long, intense looks. "You can count on it, Camille," he said. "I'm not going anywhere, any time soon."

She hadn't expected to see him again before the night of the gala, but avoiding anyone in a town as small as Calder was near to impossible, especially when that person was as eye-catching as Michael D'Alessandro. Over the next three days, she ran into him on three different occasions.

The first time they met was at Dolly's Coffee House. Camille and Jeremy were sitting at one of the outside tables, he with an ice cream cone and she with an iced cappuccino, when her Saturday night escort suddenly showed up. He stopped just long enough to say hello, let his glance linger a moment on Jeremy, and observe, "He's a fine-looking boy, Camille. You must be very proud."

"I am," she said. "And very lucky, too." Then, fearing her reply sounded unnecessarily clipped, felt obliged to add, "Would you care to join us?"

"Wish I could," he said with what seemed to be sincere regret, "but I'm meeting Adam Knowlton and a couple of his associates in a few minutes."

Later that morning, they ran into him again in the delicatessen. "Thought I'd put together a picnic lunch and eat down by the river," he said. "I'm told there's a swimming hole just outside town that's well worth a visit on a day like this." Then, seeing the way Jeremy's face lit up, added, "Don't suppose I can talk *you* into joining *me* this time?"

"Afraid not," she said. "We're due at the dentist in an hour for our six-month checkups."

Then, early on Tuesday afternoon, he drove into the service station on the highway right after she did, and pulled up to the gas pump behind hers.

"I'm on my way into San Francisco," he told her, coming to her car and bending almost double to look in the window while the attendant checked under the hood. "Thought I'd better fuel up here, rather than risk running short in the tunnel or on the Bay Bridge."

If it hadn't been preposterous, she'd have thought he was deliberately seeking her out, but after this opening comment, he seemed more interested in Jeremy than her, joking about his being the back-seat navigator for mom and a lot of other nonsense.

Again, Jeremy flowered under the attention. Apropos of nothing, he announced, "I've got teeth!" and bared them in all their pearly infant glory.

Michael D'Alessandro had teeth, too, and promptly showed them off in a smile that, annoyingly, set Camille's heart to fluttering. "You sure have, pal," he said. "Bet your dentist gave you a gold star for looking after them so well." He swung his glance back to her with obvious reluctance. "I guess I should get going."

"Yes. Do you have friends in the city?"

As it had the day they'd met, a brief cloud of sorrow dimmed his smile. "I...wouldn't say that, exactly. Just getting to know the area better, that's all."

She'd asked purely to be polite, and wondered why such a straightforward question made him uncomfortable. From the little she'd seen, he didn't strike her as a man easily put offstride.

Seeming to recognize that his hesitancy was out of character, he said, "I found Golden Gate Park the other day and thought I'd explore it further. It's huge."

She nodded. "Over a thousand acres, I believe. Just don't get caught in the rush hour traffic on the way back to Calder. It's a dreadful commute."

"So I've discovered. I plan to stay downtown well into the evening."

The attendant slammed down her car hood, wiped his hands on a rag, and gave her the thumbs-up sign. "Everything looks good, Ms. Whitfield."

"Well...!" She offered Michael D'Alessandro a cool smile. "See you on Saturday, if not before."

"It'll be before," he told her. "The Knowltons invited me to dinner the day after tomorrow, and I understand you'll be there, as well."

"Really?" It was her turn to be caught offguard. "We usually do get together on Thursdays but I hadn't realized Fran had asked you to join us."

"I think she feels sorry for me wandering around on my own, so she's taken me under her wing."

Camille thought Fran's motives were more devious than that, but she wasn't about to put ideas in his head by saying so.

Fran poured the last of the Chardonnay into their glasses, dropped into the chair next to Camille's, and kicked off her shoes. "Well, was the evening as bad as you thought it'd be?"

"Bad?" Camille sipped her wine thoughtfully. "I

wouldn't say 'bad' so much as 'pointless.' Why go to all this trouble to cultivate an acquaintance with a man who's only passing through town? It might be different if he were moving here permanently.''

''Because he's a nice man, and it looks as if he and Adam are going to be doing business together, and it's my wifely duty to entertain a client.''

''But why include me?''

Fran, who tended to favor forthrightness over tact, took an unusually long time to answer. Finally she said, ''When was the last time you felt any kind of excitement about life?''

''I don't need excitement. I had enough of that trying to keep my marriage intact. These days, I'm happy to settle for peaceful and uneventful.''

''You're too young and beautiful to settle for anything, least of all that.''

''I'm thirty years old, Fran.''

''Exactly! And most of the time, you talk and act as if you're pushing ninety!'' Fran leaned forward emphatically. ''But you came alive tonight, Camille. The old sparkle was back in your eye. And we both know why.''

''If you're suggesting Michael D'Alessandro's the reason—''

''He's the reason, all right! He flirted with you—in an entirely gentlemanly way, I might add—and you flirted right back. He made you laugh, and he made you blush almost as much as you're blushing now.''

''For heaven's sake, I did not *flirt!*''

''You didn't hoist up your skirt and fling yourself in his lap, perhaps, but I saw you giving him the old eyeball treatment.''

''He was my bridge partner. I was trying to warn him not to overbid.''

Openly snickering, Fran said, "I see. And I suppose when you were ogling him during dinner, you were trying to warn him there might be caterpillars in his salad?"

Camille slammed down her wineglass with rather more force than was good for it. "I'm not up for this discussion tonight. I'm going home."

"Just because I'm pointing out truths you'd prefer not to hear is no reason to take it out on my good Steuben crystal," Fran said equably. "Nor do I understand why you're getting so hot about this. There's absolutely nothing wrong with your finding a man attractive. Nowhere is it written that a divorced woman has to shut herself off from the opposite sex and act as if she's taken holy orders."

"But I don't know this particular man! How often do I have to repeat that before it sinks in with you, Fran?"

"Most adult relationships start out that way, my dear. It's what comes of *getting to know* someone that counts."

"Michael D'Alessandro isn't going to be around long enough for me to get to know him—at least, not in any meaningful fashion."

"So forget 'meaningful' and just have a fling. Heaven knows, you're ripe for one, and the opportunity's staring you in the face. Lighten up and have some fun for a change. You might find you like it."

Was it possible Fran was right, and she *was* ripe for a fling? Did that explain the heady feeling that had begun during dinner and lasted throughout the short drive from the Knowltons' house to her own—as if she were a little giddy from too much champagne, even though she'd had only two and half glasses of wine all night? And if so, might she not be better off experimenting with a man who just happened to be passing through, rather than someone she'd known all her life? At least that way, if the whole thing turned out to be a disaster, he wouldn't always be around to remind her of it.

The idea percolated at the back of Camille's mind all the time she was arming her home security system for the night, sending Nori, her Japanese nanny, off to bed, and making a last check on Jeremy. By the time she, too, was ready to turn in, she'd half convinced herself Fran was right, and the prospect of being escorted to the gala by Michael D'Alessandro didn't seem such a bad idea, after all. In fact, it had assumed intriguing new possibilities.

Kay's condition seemed to have deteriorated by the Friday. After leaving her, Michael drove along the western rim of Golden Gate Park, found his usual bench overlooking the water, and sat there, elbows on his knees, fingers steepled in front of his mouth.

A light mist had drifted in earlier, turning the June evening cool and leaving that particular stretch of park almost deserted. Just as well. If he was going to start bawling, he didn't need an audience.

"How much longer?" he'd asked the nurse, before he left the hospital.

She'd shaken her head. "Maybe weeks, maybe days. It's hard to tell."

He'd asked his next question before and already knew the answer. Chemotherapy had failed, radiation had failed. Still, he'd had to ask again, "Is there nothing that can be done for her?"

"We're keeping her comfortable, Mr. D'Alessandro. I'm afraid that's the most we can offer. If she'd seen a doctor and been diagnosed sooner...."

His sense of helplessness had spilled over into anger. "Why the devil didn't she? She had medical insurance."

The nurse shrugged sympathetically. "Perhaps she was

afraid of what she'd find out. A lot of people are. By the time she did come for help, it was too late."

Too late in more ways than one!

Just before he left her, Kay had pinned him in a haunted, pleading gaze. "I'd like to see my baby, Mike…just once…just for a minute. Couldn't you find a way… please…?"

But she didn't know how she looked now; had no idea how terrifying a three-and-a-half-year old would find her. Once again, she'd left it too late. And even if she hadn't, there was no way he could have arranged a visit without telling Camille the whole story—which opened up another can of worms he wished didn't exist.

As a woman, Camille Whitfield was off limits to him. He knew that with utter certainty and to behave as he had last night would bring nothing but disaster. Yet she pulled him like a magnet.

He tried to justify his response by telling himself he had to cozy up to her if he wanted to get closer to his son. The woman was no longer married, after all, nor, as far as he could determine, involved with another man, so what was wrong with cultivating a bit of a relationship? He'd even gone the route of thinking that the reason he found her so attractive lay in the fact that, physically, she was the antithesis of Kay: clear-eyed, sweetly fleshed, golden.

There was no doubt that seeing his ex-wife in her present condition affected him more deeply than he'd ever expected. Each time he left her in that narrow, sterile hospital room, every instinct cried out for him to hold on to a warm, healthy body and let it drive away the specter of the woman he used to know.

Maybe that was natural enough. But if so, it shouldn't be Camille Whitfield's body he reached for! Bad enough he was already using her. To compound the sin by encouraging anything that might fan the flames of sexual attraction between them was out of the question and he simply couldn't allow it to happen.

It couldn't be Jeremy he held on to either, even though he'd have given ten years of his life to be able to wrap his arms around that little boy and hug him close to his heart. The same blood might run in their veins, but circumstance had relegated him to the role of friendly stranger in his son's life. He couldn't do anything which might jeopardize strengthening so fragile a link.

Hell, what a mess!

Lifting his head, he stared out at the blurred lights pricking the darkness—and knew it wasn't mist obscuring his vision, it was tears. How many times had he come to this spot to get himself back together after visiting Kay? How often had he wound up sniveling like a kid? And how many more times, before it was over for her?

Damn! He hadn't been a tenth as broken up when their marriage went bad. Been glad to see the back of her, in fact. So why all this emotion now when it was too late to do either of them any good?

Swiping an impatient hand over his eyes, he hauled himself off the bench and started back to where he'd left the car. Enough of the brooding and self-pity. He'd promised Kay he'd find a way to photograph the child and bring her a copy.

Sitting there asking questions no one could answer wasn't going to get the job done. He'd be better off thinking up ways to wheedle his way further into Camille Whitfield's good graces without compromising his integrity any more than he already had—and hope to high heaven he wouldn't give in to temptation along the way.

CHAPTER TWO

THANKFULLY, the madness passed and she was able to withstand Fran's suggestion that being seen on the arm of a "hunk" warranted buying a new dress for the gala. When Saturday came, Camille didn't even haul out the family diamonds, even though she knew her mother would comment on their non-appearance.

Instead she picked out a black chiffon creation she'd worn several times before, and teamed it with black silk pumps and the black pearl choker and earrings her father had brought back for her from one of his overseas business trips.

"Good grief, who died?" Fran exclaimed, when she and Camille met for pre-dinner drinks on the terrace of the country club that night. "Don't tell me you offed your date?"

"No," Camille said sweetly. "If I were bent on murder, old friend, you'd be my choice of victim. Michael's in the lobby, buying raffle tickets."

"Well, at least he's graduated to being called 'Michael' instead of 'that man' or worse! Is he in funereal garb as well?"

"He's wearing a very nice dinner suit."

"And looks delicious in it, I'm sure."

Camille pressed her lips together, but the smile crept through anyway. "As a matter of fact, he does. And unlike you, he sees nothing wrong with *my* outfit, either."

Actually, what he'd said when he came to pick her up at the house was, "Holy cow!" but the way his eyes had swept her from head to toe told her he very much liked what he saw.

"Well, that's what matters." Fran tipped her head to one side and inspected Camille again. "And on second thought, maybe there is something to be said for the contradictory way you've done yourself up—all that demure black giving out a touch-me-not message, while the neckline begs 'Take a peek!' It's enough to drive any red-blooded man off the rails."

"What?"

"You heard!" Fran glanced over her shoulder to the doors leading into the clubhouse. "Please close your mouth and stop hyperventilating, Camille. Your escort and my husband are about to descend on us bearing gifts, and you're wasting all the trouble you've gone to to look alluring by gaping like a landed fish." Then, without missing a beat, she sang out blithely, "Hello, Michael! So nice to see you again. I was just admiring Camille's dress. Lovely, isn't it?"

"Very nice indeed."

An acceptable enough response, Camille supposed, but definitely lacking his earlier moment of spontaneous approval. In fact, when she came to think about it, apart from that initial burst of enthusiasm, his manner toward her had tended to be as formal as his attire.

He handed her a glass of champagne without quite touching her fingers, then stood a respectable distance away and showed no inclination at all to look down the front of her dress, or at any other part of her, come to that! For all the interest he showed, she might as well have been just another potted plant. What confounded her the most, though, was that she felt so let down about it!

He showed no such reticence with the Knowltons, laughing and chatting with them as comfortably as if they'd all grown up playing in the same sandbox, so she was glad when her mother and father eventually showed up. At least she could count on *them* not to ignore her.

"Come and meet Michael D'Alessandro, Camille's date for the evening," Fran caroled, after the obligatory round of air kisses and greetings. "Michael, this is Glenda and David Younge, Camille's parents."

"D'Alessandro? I'm not familiar with the name," her mother said, offering the tips of her fingers in a handshake. "You're not from around here, are you, Mr. D'Alessandro?"

"No, ma'am," he replied. "I'm Canadian."

"Visiting, are you?" Glenda eyed him up and down, her faintly raised brows denoting some serious doubts about a man who, dinner suit and flawless manners notwithstanding, could have used a haircut and had calluses on his hands.

Her father's tactics were even worse. He inspected Michael over the top of his rimless glasses, and made no bones about quizzing him. "What do you do, young man?"

"I'm a building contractor, Mr. Younge."

"Commercial or industrial?"

"Residential."

"Humph! High end?"

"Very." He didn't try to hide his amusement.

"Any partners?"

"None."

"Except the bank, I imagine."

"Not even the bank, although I did have to call on them during a pretty thin period a few years back. But I'm out of the red now."

Her father digested that for a moment. "Must be a very small operation."

"I prefer to call it exclusive. My houses are custom designed, and I use only the best materials and trades."

"What makes you so sure that's what you're getting?"

"I know quality when I see it and I pay top dollar to acquire it. There's nothing shabby about the way I do business."

"I admire your confidence," her father said, but his tone suggested "arrogance" might better fit the description. He wasn't used to having a man thirty years his junior speak to him as if they were equals.

But Michael didn't seem at all put out at being cross-examined, Camille thought resentfully, so why did he continue giving her the cold shoulder all through dinner and make no effort to engage her in a private tête-à-tête—no effort to *flirt* with her, as he had on the Thursday evening?

It wasn't until the live music started and everyone else at their table was on the dance floor that, left with little option other than deserting her altogether, he said, "Well, Camille, are you happy with the evening's turnout?"

"Yes. Raising funds for the shelter is a project very dear to my heart, and I think we'll make a lot of money tonight. I couldn't be more pleased."

His sudden smile washed over her like warm honey. "Should I take that to mean you're not finding it too embarrassing having me as your escort, after all?"

"I'd be enjoying it more if you asked me to dance," she said boldly. "You've been so distant, I'm beginning to think you're the one who's embarrassed."

"Then either I'm sending out the wrong message, or you're not reading me correctly." He pushed back his chair, and offered her his hand. "On your feet, madam. Let's go show 'em how it's done."

Given that she'd practically forced him into dancing with her, she half expected he'd be more the one-two-three-four box step sort of partner than one who'd lead a woman through a foxtrot without missing a beat, *and* manage to hold a conversation at the same time—which just went to show it wasn't wise to make assumptions about people one barely knew.

"So tell me," he began, weaving a deft path between the couples packed on the floor, "how long have you been sponsoring this women's shelter?"

"Almost four years. This is our third fund-raising gala."

He executed a sweeping turn and cut a swath through the crowd. "And what prompted you to take on such a project in the first place?"

"My son's birth mother," she said, then let out a tiny yelp as his shoe ground down on her foot.

"Sorry," he muttered, placing his hand more firmly in the small of her back. "It was step on you or the fat lady behind you, and she's bigger than I am! Your son's...*birth mother,* you say?"

"Jeremy's adopted," she told him. "I'd forgotten you wouldn't know that. We brought him home right before Christmas, when he was just five days old."

"Did you indeed."

"Yes." She smiled, that memory, at least, untarnished by what came after. Within months of Jeremy's birth, Todd had started drinking again and dabbling in drugs. She'd dreaded the unpredictability that came with his addiction: the rages, followed by undignified displays of remorse; the abandonment of personal and professional responsibility. "Jeremy was the best Christmas gift I ever received."

"I'm sure he was," Michael said, rather grimly she thought, "but I don't see the connection between that and your deciding to finance a women's shelter."

"If you'd known his birth mother, you would. She was in such dire straits, poor thing."

"At having to give up her child?"

"To some extent, yes. But mostly at having no other choice."

"I'm not sure I follow you. No one held a gun to her head, surely?"

"Not literally, perhaps, but he might as well have."

"He?"

"Her husband."

"You make him sound like a monster."

"He was." Her dance partner didn't know his own strength. She winced at the sudden crushing grip of his hand around hers as he swung her into another reverse turn. "He abandoned her with no means of support. If we hadn't met her when we did, I hate to think what might have become of her and her baby."

Michael made a sort of choking noise and she looked up to find him staring at her with eyes blazing such an electric shade of blue that they put to shame the spotlights reflecting off the twirling crystal ball overhead.

"I know," she said, giving the satin lapel of his dinner jacket a consoling pat. "It's hard to believe a man could be so wickedly unfeeling."

"Isn't it, though!"

"On the other hand, if he hadn't behaved so badly, I wouldn't be a mother today."

Michael stretched his neck, as if his shirt collar were a size too small. "Did it ever occur to you there might be another side to this story—one which doesn't paint the guy in quite such a bad light?"

"When a pregnant woman's practically living on the street, Michael, there *is* no other side to the story!"

The music ended just then which was a good thing because he seemed to be on the verge of an asthma attack, or something. Looking rather flushed, he walked her back to their table but when her mother suggested he take her in a turn around the floor, he abruptly refused. "I need some fresh air," he said. "Excuse me, please."

"He doesn't look very well," Fran said, staring after him as he fairly bolted for the door. "I hope he's all right."

"Might be something he ate," Camille's father said. "I thought the shrimp seemed a bit off."

Mightily offended at being rejected by someone she'd ordinarily have dismissed as being unworthy of notice, her mother was not nearly so disposed to be charitable. "Or else his rented suit's a shade too tight. I don't think it was designed to accommodate a man of his proportions."

"What's that supposed to mean, Mother?" Although puzzled herself by his behavior, Camille felt obligated to spring to his defense.

Glenda Younge gave a dismissive shrug. "The man's got the build of a laborer. He belongs in dungarees."

"If I'd known you'd take such exception to his appearance, I'd have arranged for us to sit at another table."

"Why, dear!" Her mother reared back, one hand splayed across the emeralds at her throat. "I had no idea you felt so strongly about him!"

Until that moment, nor had Camille. Feeling the need to champion a man manifestly able to look after himself surprised her as much as it did her mother. "It isn't him personally," she said. "I'd feel the same about any guest of mine being subjected to insult, especially by a member of my family."

"I made sure he was well out of earshot before I spoke my mind and I hardly think anyone else here will feel the need to repeat what I said." Glenda, never one to concede an argument if she could possibly avoid it, attacked from another angle. "As for his being your guest, Camille, I was of the impression he'd bought his own way in here. He made a big enough point about contributing to a worthy cause.''

"Let it rest, Glenda," her husband warned. "He's a bit too full of himself, I admit, but there's nothing wrong with a man working for a living."

"Oh, David, please don't you start defending him, too! We all know he's not *one of us*. What's so terrible about stating out the obvious?''

"I'm not sure I know what being *one of us* really amounts to," Fran put in, "but for what my opinion's worth, I happen to like Michael."

Again, Camille surprised herself. "So do I. Very much. And while you might find him not quite upper-class enough for your refined tastes, Mother, I'm willing to bet he'd never make a public fool of himself the way Todd did the first time we held this gala. I doubt my father and Adam are going to have to pick him up, dead drunk, off the floor and carry him to the car before the evening's half over."

Her mother let out a forbearing sigh. "Camille, this isn't about Todd's appalling behavior, it's about your sudden fascination for—''

"You're right, Mother, it isn't about Todd. It's about a man who's done nothing to deserve your contempt, so if you'll all excuse me, I'm going to go after him and make sure he knows he's welcome to join us again when he feels up to it."

She found him down near the man-made lake below the terrace, staring at the sweep of the fairway. He stood so unnervingly still, it was as if the essence of the man had flown away to some other place and left behind just the shell of his body.

Tentatively, she touched his arm. "Michael? Is something wrong?''

"Yes."

She waited for him to elaborate, and when it became obvious he wasn't going to, said, "Can you tell me about it?"

When at last he turned to her, his eyes were so empty she might have been looking at a dead man. She had no idea whether he was angry, or ill, or just very tired. She did know the way he was acting frightened her. "No. You're the last person I can talk to," he said.

"Why?"

He inhaled so deeply, the starch in his shirt crackled. "I have no business being here with you tonight—no right at all cultivating an acquaintance with you."

"Because we come from different worlds?"

He let out a bark of laughter. "More than you can begin to imagine!"

"If you're talking about money—"

"I wasn't, but since you mentioned it, we're hardly in the same tax bracket. I bet the closest you've ever come to a man like me before is the last time you had to call in a plumber. Small wonder your mother just about swallowed her emeralds when she laid eyes on me. She probably thinks you've lost your mind."

"What if I don't care what my mother thinks?" She slid her fingers down the sleeve of his jacket and found his hand. "I took charge of my life a long time ago, Michael. I choose who I want to spend time with, and tonight I want to be with you."

"And exactly who do you think I am, Camille?"

"The man who, two days ago, made eyes at me across the Knowltons' dinner table. The same man whose smile reminded me I'm more than a mother, I'm a woman, too."

"Don't go down that road, Camille! It's a dead end."

He tried to withdraw his hand, but she wouldn't let him.

She caught it in both of hers and turning it over, traced her fingertips over the calluses on his palm. "Why? What's changed since Thursday, Michael? If it's something about me—something I said or did—please give me the chance to put things right again."

"It isn't you," he muttered. "You're…lovely."

"But no longer desirable?" She moved closer. Enough to detect the faint scent of soap on his skin. Enough that the warmth of his body feathered over her bare arms and reached inside the low neckline of her dress. "Is that what you're really saying, Michael?"

A tremor ran through him. "No."

"Then why are you keeping me at such a distance?"

"Because we're not a couple of high school kids looking for any chance we can find to grope each other!"

"But we *are* consenting adults," she said, trying to smother the pleading tone creeping into her voice. "And rolling around in the bushes is a far cry from treating someone as if you're afraid, if you get too close, they might infect you with the plague."

"Sorry if you feel I've short-changed you," he sneered. "Maybe this'll make you feel better."

He yanked her against him and bent to pin her mouth beneath his, his manner so far removed from tender that she might as well have been kissed by a brick wall. At least, that's the way things started out. But no sooner had their lips made contact than the spark he'd tried to deny ignited as brilliantly as a burst of fireworks across the night sky.

If it scorched her, it seemed almost to destroy him. A groan escaped him, torn reluctantly from some deep well of pain inside. The unyielding pressure of his mouth softened to a caress. His hands let go their iron grip of her waist and smoothed a hypnotic path up her spine. She felt his fingers steal through her hair, the brush of his eyelashes against her brow, the heavy, uneven beat of his heart against her breast.

She was scarcely a novice where lovemaking was concerned. For at least seven of the eight years she and Todd had been married, they'd tried every means known to man and science to conceive a child. Ovulation charts, fertility thermometers, candlelight, body oils, seductive music, chocolate, oysters, massages—*atmosphere* by the bushel, not to mention plain old-fashioned intercourse, they'd tried them all.

But not once in all those times had she experienced the wild blossoming of pleasure she found in Michael D'Alessandro's arms—as if she'd faint if he didn't stop. As if she'd die if he did.

She wound her arms around his neck and clung to him. Scarcely waited for the questing nudge of his lips against hers before she opened to admit him. As to what followed...how was it possible that his probing exploration of her mouth could effect such far-reaching results? How could the pulsing rhythm of his tongue engaging hers find an echoing spasm between her legs—as if a direct line of contact were hot-wired between the two zones? When had her pelvis taken it upon itself to undulate against his and revel in the painful pressure of his arousal?

Sweet heaven, where were her scruples that when he began inching her dress up past her knees, she parted her thighs in wanton surrender?

He must have asked himself the same question and not liked the answer. "Cripes!" he exclaimed, wrenching his mouth away from hers and releasing her so suddenly she almost fell over. "You really are willing to roll around in the bushes, aren't you?"

If half the town had caught her having sex stark naked

in the middle of Calder's main street, she couldn't have been more humiliated. Face burning, hand scrubbing at her mouth, feet stumbling over themselves, she struggled to recoup her dignity. To fell him with a few well-chosen words so pithy he'd be left speechless.

Instead, she heard disgust in his voice, saw it in his expression, and was struck dumb herself. Because he was right: she *would* have rolled in the bushes with him, if he'd allowed it. She'd have guided his hand inside her panties and let him touch her until she was ready to scream for him to fill her with his big, vibrant masculine strength.

She must be mad!

He buttoned his dinner jacket, and shot his shirt cuffs into place. "If you don't want people asking awkward questions, you'd better pay a visit to the powder room before you go back to your table. You look a bit disheveled."

"If anyone asks questions," she shot back, "I'll refer them to you."

"Not a chance! I've had all the country club hoo-ha I can take for one night. I'm out of here, sweetheart. I'd offer to drive you home, but under the circumstances—"

"Oh, please! Don't do me any more favors!"

He shrugged and, without another word, loped up the steps to the terrace. By the time she found her way there, he'd already disappeared around the side of the clubhouse. And a good thing, too. If he'd hung around another moment, he'd have seen she was crying and that was one satisfaction she wouldn't afford him.

Face averted, she scuttled through the foyer to the ladies' room and locked herself in the nearest stall. The evening, which had started out so full of promise, had ended in a shambles. This was one fund-raising gala she couldn't wait to forget.

* * *

Of course, he was an utter jerk. But she had to share some of the blame, coming on to him like that and practically begging him to do her! Sheesh, what did she think? That he was dead from the waist down? That he was as blind as he must be stupid, not to have noticed she outshone every woman in the room when it came to sheer sex appeal?

But trying to excuse his behavior as he hurled the car around the narrow curves of the road back to Calder did nothing to erase the image of her wide-eyed hurt, and even less to diminish the lingering ache of desire which had damn near crippled him.

His B and B lay on the far side of town, right on the river. He parked on the graveled area reserved for guest cars, but instead of letting himself into the house, followed a path running under a flower-draped trellis to the water. No point in trying to sleep. He needed to get her out of his system first. Wash away the taste of her with a blast of night air. Rid himself of the scent of her. Forget the texture of her skin, her hair, her mouth.

"If I hadn't been around to take that phone call a couple of weeks back, I wouldn't be in this mess now," he complained to the night at large.

The river rolled on by, scarcely breaking a ripple. *Too late, buddy!*

True enough. It had been too late the minute the woman on the other end of the line had opened her mouth.

"My name's Diana Moon," she'd said. "I'm a volunteer at St. Mary's Hospital in San Francisco and I'm calling on behalf of Rita Osborne, a patient in our oncology unit."

It had taken him a minute to clue in because although Kay had been born Rita Kay Osborne, she'd always gone by her middle name, and had taken D'Alessandro as her surname after their marriage. By the time he'd made the connection, the ominous connotation behind *oncology unit* had sunk home, and the die was cast. Divorced or not, he couldn't turn his back on her, knowing she was dying. Probably couldn't have, even if she'd been a stranger. To learn she was asking for him merely added extra poignancy to the whole sorry business.

He'd left Doug Russell, his chief foreman, in charge, and flown down to San Francisco the next day, braced to cope with the physical devastation of Kay's illness and willing to do whatever he could to help ease her final days. But the sight of her poor ravaged body—emaciated, bloodless, her once glorious auburn hair reduced to a few pale wisps, her milky skin turned bilious yellow—did not hit home quite as hard as the bombshell she handed him when he arrived at her bedside.

We had a baby, Mike...a son. I gave him away....

That he hadn't been able to think straight since was his only excuse for the way he'd acted tonight. Because if he'd stopped to use his brains, he'd have realized that alienating Camille accomplished nothing. She was his passport to Jeremy. He needed her in ways she couldn't begin to imagine.

Stooping, he sent a rock skipping over the moonlit surface of the water and watched the ripples spread toward the far bank in a complex, glimmering chain. Sort of like his life, right now, he mused.

Two weeks ago, he'd been single, unattached, and successful. The lean years were behind him, the money rolling in, his life, like his financial records, an open book in perfect order.

Today he was an undercover father lusting after a woman he couldn't have; a liar, a sneak, and now, as the final icing on the cake, supposedly an abusive ex-husband.

He could hardly wait to find out what tomorrow would bring!

CHAPTER THREE

IF SHE'D known who it was ringing her bell at eleven o'clock the next morning, she'd have slipped into something less revealing before answering. Better yet, she wouldn't have answered at all. But expecting it was Fran, whom she knew must be eaten up with curiosity about what had gone awry the night before, Camille left Jeremy splashing in the pool under Nori's watchful eye and flung open the front door without a second thought.

Fran, though, didn't top six feet by at least three inches, or sport the kind of shoulders associated with beefcake movie stars in their prime. She didn't wear khaki shorts that showed off a pair of tanned athletic legs dusted with fine black hair. And she did not, as a rule, look as if she were about to have a seizure at the sight of Camille in a bathing suit.

"I know," Michael D'Alessandro began, eyeing all the skin she was showing with undisguised interest and not the least bit deterred by what she hoped was the icy glare she offered him in return. "I'm probably the last person you want to see."

"That's putting it mildly."

"I'm a jackass."

"Yes."

"Your mother would probably like to see me strung up by the thumbs."

"Leave my mother out of this," she shot back. "It's what *I*'d like to see happen that you need to worry about."

"I wish I could explain."

37

Explain reducing her to molten lava with his expert seduction, then tossing her aside and leaving her to return to
the gala alone to face her family and friends? ''Don't even
try. There's no excusing the way you behaved. I've never
been so embarrassed in my life.''

''I kinda figured that might be the case.''

''Then it should come as no surprise that you're not welcome in my house. I'm giving you exactly thirty seconds
to vacate the premises.''

''At least let me apologize before you turn the rotweilers
loose on me.''

The man had the audacity to smile as he said that and
she, dolt that she was, had a hard time not smiling back.
''I don't keep rotweilers. Until I met you, there was never
any need.''

''Until *I* met *you*,'' he said, his voice as smooth as warm
satin against her skin, ''I never behaved like a maniac on
the loose. But then, I've never met a woman like you before, either, so I'm a bit at sea on the proper protocol.''

Oh, the nerve of the man, trying to look angelic and
remorseful all the time his insolent gaze roamed over her
without a shred of shame! ''It's no great mystery,'' she said
tartly. ''In the kind of social situation we shared last night,
it's customary for a gentleman to treat his dinner partner
with the same courtesy and respect that she extends to
him.''

''I know.'' He tried to look suitably humble, but the
devil lurking in his eyes was laughing. ''However, when
the lady in question persists in turning the social situation
into a romantic tryst beneath the stars, a gentleman's better
instincts tend to get lost in more…earthy concerns.''

''Are you suggesting that I deliberately set out
to…to…well, to…?''

''Get me so hot I couldn't see straight?''

Shocked by such a blunt assessment, she backed away. "I had no such intention!"

"Didn't you?" he said, losing no time getting his foot in the door and stalking her across the foyer. "Wasn't that why you followed me outside?"

"Certainly not!" She had never sounded more definite in her life. Neither had she ever blushed so furiously that even her ankles turned pink!

"Mmm-hmm." He gave her a pitying smile, the kind which said, *Come off it, Camille! I wasn't born yesterday and neither were you!*

"I thought you weren't feeling well and came after you to see if there was anything I could do."

"You came after me because you thought I no longer found you attractive and you wanted to know why."

She opened her mouth to deny it, but giving voice to such a barefaced lie put a stranglehold on her vocal cords and rendered her mute. Was there to be no end to her humiliation?

He touched his forefinger to the underside of her lower lip and pushed it back where it belonged. "In case I left you in any doubt, I find you damn near irresistible, Camille."

He sounded as if he really meant it; as if, in having hurt her, he'd hurt himself. It had been so long since a man had spoken to her like that, with his voice cloaked in tender regret—as if she mattered, as if he *cared!*—that her eyes filled and her chin quivered.

Noticing, he hooked his finger in the strap of her bathing suit and tugged her toward him. "If you thought my behavior was out of line last night," he said, his mouth inching dangerously close to hers, "you should know that I'm fighting a serious urge to kiss you again now, and if you start crying, I don't hold out any guarantee that I'll be able to control myself.''

''I'm not sure that I want you to,'' she whimpered.

''Oh, brother!'' He closed his eyes and exhaled, his breath ruffling sweetly over her face. ''I'm in trouble!''

''Not necessarily.''

The back of his finger slid from her shoulder to graze the upper slope of her breast. ''Are you sure you know what you're saying? I'm not made of stone, Camille, and you're not exactly dressed to receive company. Do you really want to run the risk of Jeremy walking in on us?''

''Heavens, no!'' She pulled away and slapped her crossed arms over her breasts before he noticed how animated they'd become at the prospect of a little morning seduction. ''Thank goodness one of us has some sense!''

He shot her a cajoling glance. ''Does that mean I'm forgiven for last night?''

She'd never been much good at holding a grudge. An optimist herself, she looked for the best in other people; wanted to believe that their motives were pure, their intentions good. And the more she saw of Michael D'Alessandro, the more she sensed that his was a strength drawn as much on integrity as physical power.

''I think we should forgive each other and move on,'' she said, stepping well out of the reach of temptation before she weakened and begged him to throw caution to the winds and follow his instincts. She'd wound up in enough trouble last night when she was fully clothed. Playing fast and loose with fire when she had barely a stitch on was asking to be burned.

''In that case, I have something in my car I'd like to give to Jeremy—with your permission, of course. Come and tell me what you think.''

Slinging an arm around her shoulders, he steered her

outside to his car and lifted the hatchback. "What do you think of that?" he said, nodding at the fire-engine-red car inside.

She recognized it at once. It had been donated by a local businessman with a passion for vintage cars, and was a scaled-down working reproduction of a 1920 roadster, perfect to every last detail. "I know it's one of the items raffled off last night and that half the fathers in this town hoped they'd be taking it home with them. How did you come by it?"

"Someone phoned me at the B and B this morning to tell me I'd won it." He stroked an admiring hand over the gleaming chrome rear fender. "It's a beauty, and I hoped, since I've missed out on so many—" He stopped suddenly, his expression startled, as if he'd caught himself about to say something untoward. It took him a moment before he recovered enough to continue, "Well, I hoped you'd let me give it to Jeremy."

"Michael!" she protested. "I'm the one who solicited donations for the raffle. I know what that toy's worth and I can't possibly let you give it to a child you barely know."

"Why not? There's no one else I'd sooner see have it, and as for how much it cost...." He shrugged. "I got it for the price of a couple of tickets. A pretty cheap way to give a boy pleasure, wouldn't you say?"

"But isn't there someone at home you'd rather save it for?"

"I don't have children waiting there for me, if that's what you're asking."

Well, she *had* wondered about that, given that he'd mentioned he'd been married at one time, but she hadn't expected touching on the subject would trigger quite such a vehement reaction in him.

As if realizing he'd been abrupt, he said lightly, "My

cousin Dante and his wife have four-year-old twins, but those boys already have enough toys to fill a barn. They don't need any more." He gestured at the roadster. "In any case, I'll be flying home, and there's no way this is going to fit in my carry-on bag."

"Jeremy isn't exactly lacking when it comes to playthings either, you know."

"I'm not suggesting he is."

"I know. I just feel I'm taking advantage of your generosity. Wouldn't you rather give the car to charity—maybe to a children's hospice, or even to our shelter? Many of the women we help are mothers with small children and a toy like this—"

"Jeremy will have a blast with it and I'd like to see it go to him." His tone was edging toward sharp again, and he made a conscious effort to moderate it. "Look, I'll make a deal with you. Let him have it for now, and when he outgrows it in a year or two, you have my permission to donate it wherever you think it will do the most good."

My, the man was stubborn! But he was also right. Jeremy *would* be in seventh heaven. "Well…okay! You've convinced me. I'll go get him out of the pool and into some dry clothes."

His face broke into the smile she couldn't resist. Was there a woman alive who could? "Terrific! While you're doing that, I'll unload the car."

The mixture of awe and delight reflected on Jeremy's face when he saw his gift left Camille midway between laughter and tears. It was impossible not to enjoy his pleasure—and equally impossible not to be aware yet again of how much he missed not having a father around to share such moments with him.

After his initial shriek of delight and wide-eyed, "Wow, Mommy, look!" she was relegated to the role of spectator as he and Michael got down to the serious man-to-man business of examining the car and figuring out how it worked.

"The thing is, buddy," Michael said, hunkering down beside him and flipping open the trunk, "your engine runs on these batteries in here."

"Cool!"

"Yeah, but it won't be so cool if they get drained. So when you're finished playing for the day, you have to take them out like this, see?"

"But not 'til I park, right?"

Michael buried a grin. "Right. When you've parked, they need to be plugged into an electrical outlet to recharge so that you're ready to roll again the next day. Think you can sweet-talk your mom into doing that for you?"

"I can do it myself." Jeremy puffed out his chest with pride. "I do it for my remote control truck. Mom showed me how."

"No kidding." Michael looked appropriately impressed. "I guess you're more grown up than I realized."

"I'm *three!*"

"That's pretty grown up, all right."

"Can I drive now?"

"Sure, as long as you remember to steer straight and brake when you want to slow down, otherwise you'll be plowing through your mom's flower beds and I'll be for the high jump." He held open the door while Jeremy climbed into the driver's seat, then stood back and gave him the thumbs-up. "Hit the road, Jack!"

Camille held her breath, all at once unsure she'd made the right decision. "How fast can that thing go, Michael?"

"About as fast as this," he assured her, his long-legged stride keeping easy pace as Jeremy took off around the circular turn-around at the foot of the steps. "Don't worry,

I'll stay with him until he's got the hang of things, and as long as you keep the driveway gates closed so he can't wander out into traffic, he'll be fine.''

He really was a nice man, she thought; patient, kind, and generous not just with material things, but with his time and the attention he paid to her little boy. ''I've got my camera in the car,'' he said to her, at one point. ''Do you mind if I take a couple of shots to record the moment, before the novelty wears off?''

''Of course not. I should have thought of it myself.''

He snapped a picture of Jeremy beaming behind the wheel, and another of him polishing the hood of the car with the tail of his T-shirt, then caught her offguard and took one of her, as well. Later, when Jeremy asked him to play football, Michael made a big production of trying to wrestle the ball away from him and not succeeding.

Jeremy was in seventh heaven and would happily have kept him hopping all afternoon if Nori hadn't come out to say that lunch was ready.

Michael seemed genuinely sorry to see him leave. ''He's a real gem, Camille.''

''I know. And you were wonderful with him.''

''Yeah, well, he's easy to…like.'' He stuffed his hands in the pockets of his shorts, seeming almost uncomfortable with the compliment. ''Thanks for hearing me out—and for letting me unload my winnings on him.''

He gave a little salute and turned away with no mention of seeing her again. The possibility that their association had come to an end, that he might leave Calder and head home without so much as a goodbye, all at once struck her as unthinkable. ''You don't have to go just yet if you don't want to,'' she called out, seconds before he climbed into his car. ''You could stay for lunch—unless you have other plans, that is?''

"No plans," he said, loping back and coming to a stop so close to her that she could see her reflection in the pupils of his eyes. "At least, not until later this afternoon."

"Then please say you'll stay. I know Jeremy would like it."

"Just Jeremy?" His mouth twitched with amusement.

She flushed. "All right, I'd like it, too."

"You just talked me into it."

Her heart beat a little tattoo against her ribs. "It won't be anything fancy."

"It doesn't have to be," he said. "Just seeing you blush like that could turn dry bread and water into a feast."

Her idea of fancy didn't coincide with his. Although a member of two of Vancouver's most revered clubs, when he was on the job he usually brown-bagged it for lunch, which meant something simple like a sandwich and fruit. He'd hang out with his employees, using the time to listen to their beefs and iron out any problems. Or, if the weather was really lousy, he'd take the whole crew down to the nearest hamburger joint.

Sushi on a sun-dappled terrace might be considered a "nothing fancy" lunch in Camille's world, but it was a "special occasion" treat in his.

What really stunned him, though, was the way Jeremy dug right in, wielding chopsticks better than most kids his age used a fork. Tuna, abalone, eel, pickled ginger—the whole lot went down the little red lane with equal relish.

"Quite the cosmopolitan little gourmet you've got there," Mike remarked.

"He loves Japanese food, and I have Nori to thank for it." Camille exchanged smiles with the tiny woman hovering over Jeremy, then lowered her voice to add, "She's been with me from the day we brought him home from the hospital. I don't know how I'd have managed without her, especially since the divorce. She's been a second mother to him—not that that makes up for his not having his father around, of course.''

His father's around, sweetheart. You're sitting right next to him!

Hard-pressed not to spit out the truth and have done with, Mike turned his attention to a plate of California rolls and selected one. But either he needed more practice with chopsticks, or he was too preoccupied with his private dilemmas because the roll took on a life of its own, flipped loose and splattered on the table.

Jeremy burst into the same infectious giggle which had captured Mike's heart the first time he laid eyes on the boy. ''You made a mess, Michael. You've got *gohan* all over your shirt.''

''Gohan?''

''Rice,'' Camille said. ''He's picked up quite a bit of Japanese from Nori. Do you care for more tea?''

''No, thanks. I should be going. I've taken up enough of your time.''

He might be mouthing words he didn't mean, but she wasn't when she replied, ''Oh, please! We've hardly had any chance to visit privately.''

''Quit tempting me! I might wear out my welcome.''

''Don't be silly. Jeremy goes down for a half-hour nap once he's finished eating, so unless you really do have to rush off, do stay a little longer.''

He knew he ought to refuse and get out of there. The more time he spent with her, the more he liked what he saw—and so far that day, he'd seen a lot! Before they sat down to eat, she'd put on a long print shirt over her swimsuit, but she was still showing plenty of leg. On the other hand, there was a lot he still didn't know about his boy's life, so why pass up a heaven-sent chance to fill in some of the gaps—particularly those relating to the absent "father"?

"We can take our tea by the pool. It's cooler down by the water," she said, apparently mistaking his silence for reluctance.

As if he needed bribing!

Not only was the pool Olympic size, with a bridge and a mini-waterfall at one end, and a children's wading area off to one side, there was at least an acre of lawns surrounded by massed flower beds beyond the brick-paved deck.

"How do you manage the upkeep on all this?" he asked, joining her on a long cushioned swing shaded by a striped canvas awning. "Do you have a gardener, or does your ex-husband help out?"

Dumb question, of course. Any fool could see the grounds were professionally maintained, but he had to start somewhere, and if she thought he was a dim bulb for asking, she was too polite to let it show. "I have gardeners come in twice a week. My ex-husband hasn't been near the property since our divorce."

Interesting! "Is that your choice, or his?"

"Both. We stay out of each other's way. Our breakup wasn't exactly amicable." She toed the swing into motion and looked at him over the rim of her teacup. "What about you? Were you and your ex-wife able to remain friends?"

"We're...not enemies." But they would be, if Kay wasn't in such sorry shape that he couldn't bring himself to ream her out for the mischief she'd wrought!

"So why couldn't you make it work between you?"

You're more married to that company of yours than you are to me, Mike D'Alessandro, and I'm tired of it. I have ambitions, too, and they amount to something more exciting

*than reading a set of blueprints. My talent's being wasted
in this backwater. You could still build award winning
houses if we moved to L.A.....*

*My work is here, Kay. You knew that when you married
me.*

And you knew I wanted a career in show business!

"We were looking for different things and ended up going in different directions to find them."

"It doesn't sound like much of a reason to end a marriage. Couldn't you have worked out a compromise?"

"Could you, when you saw your marriage going down
the tubes?" he snapped, irked by the implicit censure in
her question.

She held his gaze a moment. "I had more compelling
reasons to file for divorce which involved more than just
me and Todd. I had a baby to think about."

"Most people consider that a good reason to fight to save
a marriage."

"I did fight. For over five years. But it was a battle I
couldn't win."

"*Five years*? You mean to say, you and your ex were
having trouble before you adopted Jeremy?"

"Yes."

"Then what the hell right did you have to bring an innocent baby into the middle of it?"

His anger caught them both by surprise. He bellowed,
and she flinched. But the pink flush staining her cheeks told
him she'd asked herself the same question and suffered
agonies of guilt over the answer, which made it easier for
him to swallow his outrage and say, "Sorry, Camille. I
didn't mean to shout like that and I've got no business
judging you. I'm sure you thought you were acting in
everyone's best interests at the time."

She stared across the lawns to the sun-baked hills in the

distance. "I thought having a baby would improve things. I called him my miracle child. But he wasn't able to fix what had gone wrong. I suppose, when I realized that, I should have given him the chance to be adopted into a better home, with two parents who wanted him, instead of just one. But it would have broken my heart." She bit her lips, clamping down on them until they flattened into a thin line of misery. She closed her eyes, but not before he caught the sheen of tears. "I loved him so much—too much, some people might say. He's my whole life."

"I don't think a child can ever be loved too much," Mike said, feeling lower than dirt for raking up memories which caused her such obvious pain—but not enough that he could ignore the growing list of questions gnawing at his mind worse than an aching tooth. Damn it, if his boy had been bought to plug the holes in a leaking marriage, Kay wasn't the only one with a lot to answer for! He'd seen the agreement she'd signed and he didn't need to be a lawyer to know she'd been dazzled more by the money she stood to gain than any thought of what would be best for her baby. "And it's not as if he doesn't still have two parents."

"But he doesn't have two parents, Michael, that's the pity of it."

"Why not? Your ex isn't dead, is he?"

"No," she cried, "though, God forgive me, I sometimes wish he was!"

He'd slumped back into a corner of the swing, feigning the sort of mild interest a stranger might find in her story, but this latest turn in the conversation had him jackknifing to attention again. "Why?"

"Oh, it's a long, pathetic story, and not one you want to hear."

Wrong, sweetheart!

But it wouldn't do to appear too eager, so he forced himself to remark as casually as he knew how, "Why don't you let me be the judge of that?"

She made a face. "Todd has what's politely called 'a substance abuse problem.'"

"You mean, he's a lush?"

"To say the least."

Uh-oh! He didn't like where this was leading. "Are you saying he's into more than just booze?"

"Yes."

"Drugs?"

"I'm afraid so."

And you allow him unsupervised visits with my son?

How he didn't yell the words aloud, he hardly knew. He wanted to hit something. *Something?* Hell, he wanted to break every bone in Todd Whitfield's body! As for his son's adoptive mother…!

Bitterness welled up in him, so strong he could taste it, and this time it was directed at her. Did she have *any* brains behind that pretty face, any backbone at all? Afraid of what he might say, of the recriminations he was tempted to fling at her but which would blow his cover if he did, he lunged off the swing and strode up and down the length of the pool deck until he'd recovered enough control that he trusted himself to phrase his next question with a semblance of detachment. "I gather we're talking about more than the occasional aspirin for his hangovers? That he's into the illegal stuff?"

"Yes."

"And that doesn't worry you?"

"No. It's no longer my business or my concern." She wiped her fingers across her face and pushed her hair out of her eyes. "I'm not his baby-sitter. Not anymore."

But you're my son's, damn it!

He took a calming breath. "How the blazes do you leave a helpless child with a man like that and sleep at night, Camille? Or isn't that any of your concern, either?"

"Don't be ridiculous," she said. "I wouldn't let him within a mile of my son. Jeremy hasn't seen Todd since the day we went our separate ways. I doubt he even remembers he ever had a father."

The weight inside Mike's chest eased a little. "What if Todd suddenly decides he wants visitation rights?"

"I'd move heaven and earth to prevent it. But it won't happen. He relinquished all claim to Jeremy at the time of the divorce. I have his written promise that he'll never try to interfere in my son's life."

And if it was anything like the adoption agreement he'd drawn up, it wasn't worth the paper it was written on! "What guarantee do you have that he'll abide by such a promise?"

"We've been apart over two years, Michael, and he hasn't even phoned, let alone tried to come to my house. He no longer lives in California. I think that spells out pretty clearly that he's not interested in resuming any sort of relationship with his son. I can see from your face that you're having a hard time believing this, but if you'd lived with one, you'd know that addicts don't care about anything except their addictions."

"I know they can kick the habit and resume useful, productive lives if they put their minds to it. And it would seem to me that having a son I wasn't allowed to see would be incentive enough to stay clean."

"You're assuming Todd cares about Jeremy, but he doesn't."

"Then why the devil did he agree to the adoption?"

"Because he wanted me, and he thought, if he found a way to give me the baby I longed for, that he'd be able to keep me. He knew I was ready to leave him and he was desperate to give me a reason to make me stay.''

"So he bribed you by buying you a child?" Try as he might, Mike couldn't keep the sneer out of his voice. "Gee, what a novel concept! But I guess when a woman's got more money than she knows what to do with and a man wants to impress her, a string of pearls or a diamond ring don't cut much ice.''

"Is that the kind of person you think I am? Do you really believe I'm so selfish, so…*capricious* that I'd use *anyone,* let alone a helpless baby, like that?''

The stricken look she turned on him left him feeling as if he'd kicked a puppy, but the facts as she'd related them were pretty incriminating. "If I'm missing something here," he said, hardening his heart against the misery she couldn't hide, "clue me in. Because unless I've misunderstood, you knowingly stayed in a bad marriage just so you could get your hands on a child.''

Neither of them noticed they were no longer alone until her mother's voice cut across the conversation. "I'm not sure by what right you feel justified in badgering my daughter like this, Mr. D'Alessandro, but since she's obviously too distressed to point out the obvious, I'll do it for her. Nothing about her life is any of your business. She owes you no explanations for the choices she's made, and if you had half the brains that you have brawn, you'd have arrived at that conclusion without my having to spell it out for you.''

"We're having a private conversation, Mrs. Younge," he snapped, in no mood to tolerate her insults on top of everything else. "Take a hike!''

Vibrating with outrage, she scoffed, "Private? I could hear every word coming out of your mouth the minute I stepped from my car. I imagine half the town could.''

"Oh, Mother, please!" Spots of color on her cheekbones heightened the pallor on Camille's face. She really did look about ready to keel over. "Stop exaggerating and don't interfere. Michael and I are having a perfectly harmless conversation."

"Really? Try telling that to Jeremy. He might be only three, Camille, but his hearing and eyesight are every bit as good as mine, and it might interest you to know that when I arrived, I found him watching you from the terrace."

Camille looked up at the house, her expression horrified. "I expected he'd still be napping. How long had he been there, do you think?"

"Long enough to ask me why Mr. D'Alessandro was making you cry."

"Damn!" Much though he hated to admit it, the old bat had a point. Judging from the little Camille had revealed, Mike guessed the boy had lived through enough emotional turmoil already, without his adding to it. "Camille, it might be best if I left."

"But we haven't finished—!"

"For once, I must agree with your guest." Her mother, bristling like a guard dog about to attack, stepped between him and Camille. Behind her, the pool glimmered turquoise in the sunlight. "You can find your own way out, I'm sure, Mr. D'Alessandro."

Oh, yeah! And one wrong step on my part, you over-bleached string bean, and you'd be in the water with your high-priced silk skirt floating up around your ears, and wouldn't that be something to see!

Grinning at the image he'd conjured up, he nodded at Camille. "I'm out of here. Thanks for the lunch."

"Will I see you again, Michael?"

"Not if your mother sees me first," he said. *"Sayonara!"*

CHAPTER FOUR

SOME twenty yards from Maddox Lodge, the guest house where Michael was staying, she found a place to park. A slight hollow only, it sloped away from the paved surface of the road at such a steep angle that when she backed into it, she feared for a moment that the car might flip over.

It served the purpose though. A bend in the lane behind hid her from anyone watching from the house. A stand of trees immediately ahead shielded her from an approaching vehicle yet allowed her to see the warning sweep of headlights turning off the main highway. Killing the engine, she settled down to wait.

It was almost nine-thirty, well over seven hours since she'd sent her mother packing, and almost eight since Michael had left. But it had taken most of the intervening time for Camille to find the courage to follow her instincts and go after him. She'd left Nori in charge at home, and driven to the guest house with her heart knocking against her ribs in nervous anticipation.

But, "He's not here," Susan Maddox had said, when she came to the door. "I haven't seen him since he left this morning."

"Left? You mean, he checked out?" The panic came out of nowhere, leaving Camille fighting for breath.

"No, all his stuff's still in his room. I just meant he's not here right now, which isn't unusual. He's gone most days and seldom gets back before dark." Susan had regarded her curiously. "You look a bit frazzled, Camille. Do you want me to have him call you when he gets in?"

She'd have said yes, if she'd thought he'd comply, but although the anger in his voice when he left her house that afternoon had been directed mostly at her mother, the disgust in his eyes he'd reserved solely for Camille. She thought it unlikely he'd initiate further contact.

"No, thanks," she'd said. "I'll wait and catch him later."

How much later, though, was the critical question. Whether it was instinct or fear she couldn't say, but something told her that his time in Calder was coming to an end, and the thought of his leaving filled her with inexplicable desolation.

Her mother would tell her she was crazy, and no doubt she must be, lurking in the dark like some third-rate private investigator on a stakeout, but she couldn't let him go, not yet, and certainly not with the way they'd left things that afternoon. Too many things remained unsaid between them, too much...emotion unexplored.

What kind of emotion, Camille? her rational self mocked. *And please don't tell me you're so far gone that you're deluding yourself into thinking you're in love with the man. If you're determined to make a fool of yourself, at least act your age and recognize lust when it's staring you in the face!*

Was that really what tonight's escapade boiled down to? Instead of being snug at home where she belonged, was she sitting in the dark waiting to accost a man who might well laugh at her—or worse, reject her outright—all because she was starving for a little male attention?

No, there was more at risk than that. Her integrity was on the line. Jeremy had seen and heard too much of that afternoon's exchange between her and Michael, and the conversation resulting from it hadn't been easy, not for Camille or for her son.

Why don't I have a daddy, Mommy?

Well, darling, some little boys just don't, that's all.

But Andrew has a daddy. He sleeps at their house all the time. Why can't I have one, too?

She'd tried to satisfy his curiosity by steering a middle road between outright lies and complete disclosure of a truth too sordid and complex for a child to grasp. But the task, coming so soon after Michael's probing interrogation, had left her with an urgent need to make the man, as well as the child, understand that she'd tried to act in everyone's best interests.

Michael D'Alessandro might be nothing more than a stranger passing through her life, but they shared something special and she would not soon forget him. The impressions he took away with him mattered to her a very great deal. She couldn't let him leave believing she was a selfish, unfit mother. She had to clarify to him, face-to-face, all the reasons why she'd felt justified in going ahead with the adoption. She only hoped he'd show more inclination to listen than he had when he'd stormed out of her house that afternoon.

And if he refused?

Her car, a roomy BMW 750, felt too close and confining suddenly. She opened the sunroof, lowered the seat to a full reclining position, then lay back and took deep breaths of the flower-scented air.

Of course he'd listen!

Night noises—the chirp of crickets, an owl's eerie call, a dog barking in the distance—competed with the nervous thud of her heart. Overhead, stars blanketed the sky and reflected pinpricks of light on the slack surface of the river. A lover's moon rose behind the trees.

And she, holed up in her car on the side of the road, sat waiting for a man who probably hadn't spared her a second thought since he'd marched out of her house that afternoon. If her mother knew what she was up to, she'd have her committed!

Folly on top of folly had been how Glenda Younge described Camille's behavior, during their confrontation earlier. "Explain to me, if you will, your fascination for a man about whom you know absolutely nothing but the most superficial details," she'd demanded, as the sound of Michael's car faded away. "What sort of hold does he have over you that you'd share with him confidential information about your marriage?"

At a loss, Camille had turned away. How could she explain something she didn't herself understand? To try, especially to someone of her mother's skeptical nature, was to invite nothing but ridicule.

As though regretting having spoken so bluntly, her mother had touched her shoulder. "Not that I care one iota what the man thinks of you, dear, but you must know that, to an outsider, your reasons for bringing Jeremy into your home appear self-serving, if not downright immoral! You've said yourself, often enough, that if you'd had the slightest inkling of the extent of Todd's problems, you'd never have gone ahead with the adoption."

"If Michael's so unimportant, why are you making such an issue of my associating with him?"

"Because both your father and I feel there's more to his being here than meets the eye, and we're worried by your willingness to let him into your life. Think about it, Camille! The man claims he's here on vacation, but even the most dedicated tourist can see everything Calder has to offer inside two days. So why do you suppose he's still hanging around over a week after he first showed up? More to the point, what's his real interest in you?"

"Maybe he likes my company."

"Or maybe he has a more devious agenda. It doesn't take a genius to see you're a wealthy woman. One look around at everything you have here…!" Graceful hands fluttering like doves, she'd gestured at the gardens, the pool, the house.

If she hadn't still been too close to tears, Camille might have laughed. "Is it so inconceivable to you that a man might want me for myself?"

"Of course not! But why this man? What does he hope to gain in making such a play for you when, by his own admission, he's just passing through the area? I know you think I'm overly critical and suspicious—"

"You're a snob, and we both know it."

"Perhaps so. But I'm also a mother who's afraid her daughter is being used and will end up being badly hurt— again! Whether or not you're willing to admit it, the divorce *did* leave you very vulnerable, Camille."

"At the time, yes. But it's been over two years now and I've recovered. Enough that I'm ready to resume a normal life."

"Normal's one thing!" Her mother's well-modulated voice had risen dramatically. "But stepping out with a man like Michael D'Alessandro, just because he's making himself available, is pure madness."

Oh, Mother, she thought, closing her eyes to the beauty of the night, *how would you react if I'd confessed that I'm in too deep to simply walk away? What would you say if I told you I'm already half in love with his smile, that his voice stirs my blood, and that with one kiss he melted the cold protective wall I'd built around my heart?*

The owl hooted again, a sleepy, hypnotic sound. The stars swam in the sky, their bright edges less sharply defined than they'd been a moment ago. A wisp of cloud hung over the moon. She found, if she stared at it long enough, that she could make out Michael's face in its shape.

Yes, there was the strong line of his jaw, the sweep of his cheekbones, the curve of his mouth....

He'd had enough for one day.

When he arrived at St. Mary's, Kay had barely known he was there. She'd opened her eyes once, smiled at him, and reached for his hand before sinking back into a sleep so closely imitating death that, if it hadn't been for the rhythmic leap of the pulse at her throat, he'd have thought she'd slipped away.

He'd remained with her well into the evening, the questions, the *accusations* he'd wanted to fling at her, vying with the pity he couldn't suppress. So he'd kept everything bottled up inside, along with the anger he'd brought with him from Camille's.

It was a deadly mix that stayed with him during the drive back to Calder, and he was in no mood to play good Samaritan when he saw the other car pulled so far over on the soft shoulder of the road that it was in imminent danger of sliding into the ditch.

He drove as far as the B and B, parked in his usual spot, grabbed the flashlight from the glove compartment, and headed back to investigate. If a couple were making out in the back seat, it was probably expecting too much to hope they still had their clothes on. But given the way his luck had been running lately, it was more likely he'd come across a body—some poor slob who'd maybe lost everything on the stock market and decided to end it all on a quiet country lane.

The moon cast just enough light for him to make out a top-of-the-line BMW with the sunroof open. To prevent the windows from steaming up? He didn't think so! The silence emanating from within the car was too deep. If there were occupants inside, they weren't moving around.

He approached the driver's door, aimed the flashlight's beam at the window, and let it play over the face of the woman stretched out behind the wheel. He hadn't known he'd been holding his breath until it blasted out of his lungs in shock.

What the hell...!

She wasn't moving. She lay flat on her back. One arm dangled between the front seats, the other was tucked out of sight beneath her body. But apart from the fact that her being there made absolutely no sense, what scared the living daylights out of him was that her legs were sprawled slackly apart in a way that would have had Mother Younge reaching for the smelling salts.

Something was very wrong. In fact, it looked to him as if she was unconscious.

Stepping closer, he rapped sharply on the window.

At first, she didn't know where she was. Was aware only of a chill on her skin, pins and needles in her hands and feet. And light, relentless and brilliant, scoring at her sleep-dazed eyes.

Then, in a rush, memory returned, and with it sudden stark fear. Beyond the aura of light outside her car, a figure loomed; a murky silhouette imprinted darkly against the fitful glow of the night sky.

She let out a shriek and scooted across to the passenger seat, one hand shielding her eyes, and the other searching for the door handle. But if there was no recognizing the face of the man peering in at her, nor was there any mistaking his voice.

"Camille? What the devil are you doing out here at this hour?"

"Waiting for you," she wheezed, clutching one fist to her racing heart. "What the devil are *you* doing spying on me like that? And will you please point that blasted light somewhere else before I go blind?"

He stepped back and directed the beam over her car. "I don't know who you paid to teach you to park," he said conversationally, "but either you should ask for a refund or else negotiate a few free lessons."

Oh, how like a man! "If you think I've been sitting here half the night for the pleasure of listening to you lecture me on my driving skills, think again! I had something a bit more important in mind."

"I'm sure you had, and heaven forbid I should be handing out unwanted advice." He was laughing at her, not outright perhaps, but it was there in his voice. "However, at the risk of being told it's none of my concern, your car appears to be listing dangerously to starboard. I suggest you drive up onto the road before we take this conversation any further—unless, of course, you prefer to conduct it from the bottom of the ditch?"

It occurred to her then that the car was sitting at an even steeper angle than it had been before, and as if to verify the fact, it gave a little lurch to the right. She braced her arm against the door and tried to sound nonchalant. "I think I might've left it too late."

He climbed back onto the road and took stock. She couldn't be certain, but she thought he was openly grinning. "Not if I give you a boost from behind," he decided. "Quit cowering over there and get back behind the wheel."

"And do what?"

No doubt about the grin this time; he was definitely having a good time at her expense. "Start the engine, honey child, what else? Then shift into low gear and step on the gas. Gently."

"It sounds too dangerous. What if I slide backward?"

He practically cackled aloud at that. "Then you'll have to scrape up my remains and your mother'll declare a national holiday to celebrate my early demise."

The car sighed gently and settled further into the unstable shoulder of the lane like a weary body sinking into a mattress. Through the open sunroof she heard gravel slithering out from under the wheels. "This is no time for jokes!" she said, her voice splintering with fright.

"And you're in no position to be giving me orders, Camille," he said calmly. "Trust me, together we can do this."

And together they did, though not before she felt the car skidding out of control and, in an effort to correct it, pressed her foot down hard on the accelerator.

A rooster tail of dirt spurted out from under the rear wheels. She heard a yell, felt pinpricks of sweat break out down her spine, and almost sheared off one of the trees ahead as the car shot out of the hollow and onto the pavement.

Legs shaking, blood pumping, she set the parking brake and climbed out. "Michael?"

But all the moon showed was an empty strip of road and, off to one side, the dark shape of a prostrate body.

"Michael!" She had no recollection of covering the distance between them. Felt no pain as she fell to her knees beside him. All her awareness was focused on her fingers sliding over the warm skin of his neck in search of a pulse, and the relief that flooded through her when she found it to be steady and strong.

He moved then, heaving himself onto all fours and hunching over with a muffled groan that lapsed into something which sounded suspiciously like retching.

"Are you throwing up?" she cried, envisioning all manner of internal injuries.

His eyes gleamed malevolently in the moonlight. "No, sweetheart. I'm trying to spit out the mouthful of dirt *your car* threw up when you stepped on the gas. I thought I made it clear that gunning the motor isn't a good idea when you're up to your hubcaps in sand and loose gravel?"

"I panicked," she said. "I thought the car was going to roll. I'm so sorry."

He ran an experimental finger over his mouth. "I guess I should be glad I still have all my teeth."

"Let me look at you."

They were kneeling so close that his shirt brushed the front of her blouse. Cupping his jaw, she turned his head from side to side. He hadn't shaved since that morning. Except for the silky line of an old scar just below his right ear, his skin had the texture of fine pumice against her fingertips. His eyelashes threw inky crescents of shadow over his cheekbones. And his mouth.... Oh, better not to dwell too long on his mouth!

"I don't see any blood," she said, "but you do have a scratch on your chin."

"No kidding!" His voice slid a husky octave lower than usual and his fingers closed around her wrist to imprison her hand against his cheek. "And what do you propose to do about it?"

The way he managed to infuse the question with outright invitation left her in no doubt about what he had in mind. His mouth was so close to hers, his words vibrated against her lips.

Sounding as if she'd been winded from a blow to the solar plexus, she said, "You want me to kiss it better?"

"Isn't that what mothers do best?"

"Not to grown men."

If she'd tried, she couldn't have found a more effective way to ruin the mood or the moment. "You're quite right," he said, hauling her upright and putting a safe six feet of space between them. "In that case, why don't we stop playing games, and you tell me why you were lying in wait for me to get back?"

She'd been so sure he was going to take her up on her first offer, so *ready* to throw caution and propriety to the winds and kiss him, that she could barely swallow her disappointment. "Oh…it's nothing really. I just thought, what with it's being such a lovely evening…so mild and all—"

"Camille, by your own admission you've been waiting half the night to speak to me, which leads me to expect it must be a matter of some importance to you and perhaps even to me, right?"

She nodded, miserably aware that she was making an utter fool of herself.

"Then don't expect me to buy the lame excuse that you wanted to chat about the weather." His gaze scoured her face in the moonlight. "What's really going on here?"

"I feel I owe you an apology. Not only was my mother very rude to you this afternoon but she interrupted us before I had the chance to explain—about my marriage to Todd and the reasons we adopted Jeremy. But it's a long, sordid story which you probably don't want to hear."

"Wrong. I've got nothing but time on my hands and I don't subscribe to the catchphrase 'never apologize and never explain.' I happen to believe confession is good for the soul."

"But it's all rather…personal."

"In my experience, anything to do with marriage generally is."

She sighed. "You're not going to let me off the hook, are you?"

"Not a chance." He took her elbow and steered her across the lane. "We'll walk down by the river. You might find it easier to talk if I'm not staring you in the face the whole time."

She thought it unlikely. Dredging up those painful memories was never easy. But doing so with the trees casting deep pools of shadow over the moon-splashed path at least made her feel less exposed.

"I guess," she began, "to put you fully in the picture, I should mention that Todd and I grew up in Calder. Our parents were good friends, belonged to the same clubs, supported the same charities, attended the same church. They were thrilled when we told them we wanted to get married and went out of their way to give us a fairy-tale wedding."

"Why don't we skip ahead to the reason you decided to adopt a child?" Michael said, with more than a touch of impatience. "I'm not a great fan of fairy tales."

"The point I'm trying to make is that we—Todd and I— thought we had it all. We were the golden children of golden parents—families with old money and social prestige to spare. We were rich, educated, socially aware, and beautiful in the sense that we were young and fit, with perfect teeth and shining hair and clear bright eyes."

"And then you found out that money couldn't buy love? You disappoint me, Camille. I expected you to come up with something more earth-shaking than that old cliché to explain your failed marriage. Is that why good old Todd started hitting the bottle?"

She glanced at him sharply, surprised by the bitterness in his tone. "No. That came much later, after years of trying to conceive a child."

"Uh-oh! Golden boy couldn't deal with a wife who couldn't lay the golden egg?"

"You know, Michael," she said, his sneering attitude

beginning to grate on her nerves, "I don't *owe* you this explanation, but since you insisted on hearing it anyway, the least you can do is keep the editorializing to yourself until I'm finished."

He stuffed his hands in his pockets and looked suitably chastened. "Point taken."

"I couldn't conceive. At least, that was the assumption for the first three years of our marriage. Finally, though, we went to a fertility specialist who diagnosed Todd as having...um...." She paused, searching for a delicate way to phrase the diagnosis. "The...*problem*."

Michael shared none of her diffidence. "Low sperm count, huh?" he said bluntly.

"Um...yes." She stared across the river to hide her discomfiture. "For the next two years, we tried without success every invention known to science in our desperate efforts to have a baby. Although I was disappointed, I believe Todd suffered more. You've never had children, Michael, so you might not think it all that important—"

He inhaled sharply and she tensed, expecting another derisive comment. But whatever he might have been inclined to interject, he thought better of it and said simply, "Go on."

"His inability to produce a son to carry on the family name took a terrible toll on his pride and self-esteem. Our relationship deteriorated. He changed. Closed himself off from me. Perhaps when a man is told he can't fertilize a woman's egg, he feels less like a man. Or perhaps what others viewed as unfortunate, Todd saw as shameful."

Afraid her voice would break as the memories came rushing back to haunt her, she lapsed into silence. "Take your time," Michael said, watching her. "I've got all night."

They strolled perhaps another hundred yards along the

riverbank before she felt able to pick up the thread of her story. "I don't pretend to have all the answers. I only know that he grew increasingly sullen and resentful, refused to seek help, refused to consider adoption, and refused to discuss ways of dealing with this crushing disappointment."

"Cripes, talk about spineless!"

Force of habit had her defending Todd, even after all this time. "Until you've tried to father a child yourself, Michael, you're hardly in a position to pass judgment!"

The breath hissed between his lips as though it was all he could do to hold on to his temper. "I don't have to be in his place to recognize the man was missing a few neurons if he couldn't figure out you were in as much pain as he was!"

"I don't know why you're getting yourself into such a state," she said. "I'm the one who had to live with him."

"Which prompts me to ask the obvious. Why the devil didn't you leave him?"

"When things reached the point where I was afraid of him, I did."

"If you're saying you waited until he started smacking you around before you took action, Camille, don't expect me to smile and slobber sympathy all over you. He might have made you his victim, but you're the one who let him get away with it."

"He never laid a hand on me. He took out his frustrations in other ways, drinking too much, driving too fast, being verbally aggressive with other people. He channeled all his energy into a controlled rage which was eating us both alive and I'd finally had enough. I told him I wanted a separation."

"And?"

"It did what no amount of pleading or persuading had managed to do. It seemed to be the shock that brought him to his senses. He begged for another chance, promised he'd clean up his act. And for a while, he did. Some of his old sweetness returned. I believed we were back on track, especially when, for the first time ever, he agreed to look into adopting and made good on the promise within weeks by finding a child for us.''

''And you weren't made the least bit suspicious by the speed with which he managed to do that? Where I come from, adoptions take months, sometimes years.''

''I was surprised at how quickly a baby became available, but Todd's a lawyer and he had connections. He put out the word and because we had the money to pay for a private adoption, I guess we were able to cut a few corners.''

''More than you can possibly know,'' Michael muttered, glaring ahead and striding along at a furious pace.

She raced to keep up with him. ''What's that supposed to mean?''

''Damned lawyers thinking they can bend the rules to suit their own ends, that's what it means!''

''We didn't do anything illegal, if that's what you're implying.''

''Are you sure? Did you read the fine print before you signed the adoption papers?''

''There was no fine print. We had a straightforward agreement drawn up which we and the birth mother signed, with Todd's two law partners acting as witness.''

''Didn't it strike you as odd that an important part of the equation was missing?''

''The natural father, you mean? He forfeited any rights he might have had when he walked out on his pregnant wife and left her to fend for herself.''

''Even if he were as delinquent as you seem to think, I

suspect you needed his signed permission for the agreement to hold up in court.''

''There's no 'even if' about it, Michael,'' she snapped. ''The man was a louse and there isn't a court in this land who'd uphold his bid to contest the adoption, especially not after all this time.''

''There might be,'' he countered. ''Given the fact that your husband opted out of the parental responsibilities he voluntarily undertook and then abandoned, a court might look very favorably on the natural father's claim to his blood child.''

''He'd have to get by me first and if you think I'd hand Jeremy over without a fight, you greatly underestimate the power of a mother's love! And whose side are you on, anyway?''

''I wasn't aware I was being asked to take anyone's side but if I had to choose, I'd say Jeremy's. Shouldn't the best interests of a child always take precedence over everything else?''

''Of course they should! Do you think I'm not aware, with every passing day, that Jeremy deserves two parents, that he *needs* a father? Don't you think, if I could, I'd give him one?'' She didn't know she'd begun to cry until her words choked on a sob. ''But what do you expect me to do, Michael? Run out and shanghai the first man who slows down long enough for me to catch him, and force him to be a daddy to my boy?''

''No.'' He caught her hands and tried to pull her into his arms. ''And I didn't mean to make you cry, either.''

''Don't you touch me!'' she cried, slapping his hands away. ''You've left it a bit too late to play the sympathetic friend. I must have been mad to think I could confide in you or expect that you'd understand.''

"Hey," he said urgently, pinioning her wrists against his chest, "I'm not the enemy here, Camille."

But the reassurance came too late. His questions had raised specters she couldn't ignore.

How do we know the father won't show up one day, Todd? What if he decides he wants his baby, after all?

He won't.

How can you be sure?

Because I know what I'm doing. That agreement is watertight.

But you're the one who's always said there's no such thing as a contract which can't be broken.

I'm the legal expert, Camille, not you, so instead of harping on about things you know nothing about, why don't you stick to what you do best and look after the kid?

She'd let herself be convinced, in part because she had bigger things to worry about. Her husband's growing indifference toward their new son suggested that acquiring a baby had mattered more to Todd than being a father. Then the drinking started again, and with it the rages and the accusations.

What the natural father might or might not do had paled beside the very real risk to which she was exposing her son by remaining in such a marriage, and by the time she'd finally put her house in order again, her other fears lay so far in the past that she'd grown complacent.

Until Michael D'Alessandro came on the scene, that was, and unearthed them again!

"You might not be my enemy, but you're not my friend, either," she said, too overwrought to care that she was thrashing around in his arms like a wild thing. "If you were, you wouldn't be trying to undermine my confidence like this. I'm a good mother and I love my son."

"I know, I know! For Pete's sake, Camille, no one who's

seen you with Jeremy could ever doubt that and I never meant to suggest otherwise. Please stop crying, sweetheart.''

''I really don't know why I started.'' She leaned her head against his chest, all the fight suddenly seeping out of her. ''It's just that I sometimes feel I let Rita down and if she knew, she'd regret having trusted me with her baby. I promised her we'd give Jeremy what she couldn't give him—two parents and a loving, stable home. Yet within months of his birth, I'd filed for divorce and Todd had walked out of our lives for good.''

''You did what any mother would have done in the same situation. You protected your child the only way you could. Don't beat yourself up because Todd didn't hold up his end of the bargain. That was his choice, not yours.''

His voice flowed over her, deep and smoky, blunting all the rough edges of her distress. His arms closed around her, warm and strong. She had never felt so safe and protected.

''If I'd been married to a man like you to begin with,'' she said, lifting her face to his, ''things would have turned out differently.''

''Oh, yes,'' he said thickly. ''That much I can safely guarantee.''

She thought, from the way he spoke, that there might be a hidden message in his words. She thought, from the way he looked at her, that something was troubling him. She opened her mouth to ask him. But before she could voice the question, he bent his head and kissed her. And once again, everything fled her mind but the sheer magic of his lips on hers.

CHAPTER FIVE

HE TASTED of grass and the wildflowers that grew along the side of the road; of the river-scented air and the cool star-filled night. A dizzy, intoxicating mixture that left her so light-headed she sank against him with a whimper.

She wound her arms around his waist. Pressed herself so close that his belt buckle gouged the thin fabric of her dress. Driven by a raging hunger to know him ever more intimately, she let her hand slip down to caress his buttocks. Tilted her hips to meet the thrust of his.

He tore his mouth free and shoved her away so abruptly she'd have stumbled if he hadn't caught her. "This is madness! Get back in your car and go home."

"Why?" she asked him. "What are you afraid of?"

"Me," he said unsteadily.

"I'm not." She dared to touch him again, tracking the thin line of his scar with her forefinger. "I trust you."

"Never trust a stranger, Camille. You're asking for trouble if you do."

"Then let me rephrase it. I trust myself, and my instincts tell me you're a good and decent man."

"We both know your instincts aren't always on target. If they were, you'd never have married Todd."

She let her hand skim to the pulse throbbing at the base of his throat. "What's happening between us has nothing to do with Todd, Michael, and we both know it."

"It has nothing to do with anything!" he said savagely. "That's why, if you're a tenth as smart as you like to think you are, you'll get the hell out of here as fast as you can."

"I'll do that just as soon as you tell me you don't want to kiss me again."

"I don't want to kiss you again."

"Really?" She moved close enough that their bodies brushed against each other, and lifted her face to his. And waited.

The air whistled past his lips. "*Damn* you!"

The curse caressed her like a benediction, fraught with pent-up longing. It was all the encouragement she needed to continue along a course already so far beyond her usual diffidence that she wondered where she'd found the courage to set out on it in the first place. "Yes," she whispered, her lips feathering over his. "Damn me."

He hauled her into his arms. His body slammed against hers, powerful, unyielding, primitive. But his mouth…oh, his mouth wooed her with refined genius! She dissolved beneath its seduction. The moon could have fallen into the river and she wouldn't have cared. He held her spellbound.

"You're driving me crazy," he rumbled, the tip of his tongue teasing the outer shell of her ear, then plunging deep into the tightly furled inner coil—in and out, in and out, in bold imitation of sexual intimacy.

"Me, too," she said on a dying breath.

He threaded his fingers through her hair and cradled the back of her head in the palm of his hand. "The first time we kissed," he said, his gaze devouring her face, "I promised myself it would be the last."

"Why, when we do it so well?"

"Because I knew it would never be enough. And I was right. I want to make love to you, Camille." He slid his hand down her spine and splayed his fingers over the curve of her hip. His thumb stole into the crease of her groin, teasing, tantalizing. Swept a fleeting caress across the top of her thigh and circled that part of her already weeping for his touch, marking it his to possess.

A spasm of pleasure, so acute and unexpected that she gasped aloud, quivered through her. Shamelessly, she imprisoned his hand between her thighs. "I wish you would!"

"No, you don't, not if you stop to think about it," he said hoarsely. "We're neither of us the one-night-stand type. Allowing ourselves to get carried away only serves to make everything more complicated between us."

He might be refuting her assertion verbally, but the sinuous pressure of his hand against her susceptible flesh conveyed quite a different message. He could easily have broken the contact and left her wilting with disappointment, but he didn't.

"You're making all the right noises, Michael," she said, "but if you really believed what you're saying, you'd push me away, just as you did the other night. You'd belittle me, tell me I'm a tramp...."

His fingers curved to fit the shape of her more snugly. "If I were to say that, would you make me stop what I'm doing?"

He was stealing her soul, her mind, her sensibility. "No...! Please, Michael...make love to me...."

He lifted his head and scanned the area, his breathing as tortured as hers. "Not here. There's a place farther along the river...." He stopped and pinned her in one last searching gaze. His mouth skimmed the planes of her face. "If you're going to change your mind, Camille, now's the time to say so."

Without hesitation, she placed her hand in his.

His fingers closed around hers, strong and dependable. He led the way down the embankment and along the grassy strip running beside the water to a stretch of sand half hidden by an overhanging willow. A shaft of moonlight pierced the branches, just enough to show his heaving chest. Just enough to reveal the pale line of his scar against the darker shadow of his jaw. Just enough that she could see the swollen profile of his virility straining against the fly of his jeans.

She placed her hand flat against his waist, then drew it down in provocative slow motion until her palm covered him. He smothered a moan, but apart from the slow droop of his eyelashes, he remained perfectly still.

She slid her hand again to his waist, tugged free the hem of his T-shirt, and lifted it to bare his midriff. Although ridged with underlying muscle, his skin felt smooth; warm and pulsing with hidden energy.

She raised the hem higher. Moonlight played over the contours of his chest, creating a subtle patchwork of copper and bronze and mahogany. Too mesmerized by the symmetrical beauty of him to care what he might think of her daring, she leaned forward and swirled her tongue first over one flat nipple, and then the other.

Another strangled moan escaped him. Yet still, he didn't move.

She stroked her hands down the line of his ribs. Dropped to her knees and dipped her tongue into the hollow of his navel.

She had gone too far. The sky tilted, the willow tree swung at a crazy angle. With a soft thump, the ground tumbled up to meet her. Cool grainy sand clung to the back of her legs and speckled her hair. His body covered hers. The tough, male weight of him flattened the breath from her lungs. The feel of him, hard and pulsing with life, left her body aching and her mind spinning.

"Enough!" he muttered roughly.

But the hand pinning her wrists above her head was gentle; the knee inching her legs apart questing rather than encroaching.

For the space of a heartbeat or two, he scrutinized her, feature by feature. Then reining in a breath, he said, "Don't push me to the brink too soon, Camille. If we're going to do this, let me show you at leisure what loving's all about."

She squirmed beneath him, her blood churning at the promise she heard in his voice. Todd had never spoken to her in words charged with such impassioned restraint; never made her tremble with a single telling glance. From the earliest days of their marriage, their coming together had been all about reproduction. A matter of timing and technique.

"Your dress is lovely," Michael said, releasing her hands and pulling himself up to kneel astride her. "Fine, just like you." He slipped the top button loose, then the next and the next, until only the gauzy half-cups of her bra covered her breasts. "Fine and feminine," he said, pushing the dress down her arms and sliding the bra straps from her shoulders, "just like you."

A breath of river air drafted over her exposed skin and left goose bumps in its wake. He seared them into oblivion with his tongue, then fastened his mouth over the aching bud of her nipple.

A live wire of electricity raced from the point of contact to her pelvis, swift, sharp and exquisitely painful. She clutched at him, her nails gouging the smooth muscle of his shoulders. Her legs jerked spasmodically. "Michael...." she whimpered.

He reared back, peeled off his T-shirt, and tossed it behind him. It floated in the night, a white ghostly object drifting aimlessly a moment before dropping with a sigh into the long sweet grass at the foot of the willow.

Rising up to meet him, she fumbled with his belt. He

caught her hand and drew her to her feet. "No," he said, stepping back the better to watch her as she stood there, half undressed, with grains of sand sliding over her skin and trickling from the ends of her hair. "Get rid of the dress and the underwear, instead."

Hypnotized by his dark unblinking stare, she obeyed, moving as if she were in a trance. She kicked off her shoes and he, her partner in the surrealistic mating ritual, did the same with his. He shed his jeans at the exact moment that her dress puddled around her ankles; shucked off his briefs as she shed her panties.

Realizing she was staring, she half turned away. "If you can't even bring yourself to look at me," he said, "then you're not ready to have me make love to you, either."

Shyly, she ventured a glance at him. He stood naked before her, carved in moonlight and dusted with shadow; powerful and magnificent in his masculinity.

She had no recollection of how they came to be standing only a few inches apart. Did he move first? Did she? Or did involuntary strands of magnetism draw them together until his breathing mingled with hers and she could taste him deep in her lungs?

He touched his forefinger to her chin. Traced a thin line down her throat. Wove a tormenting figure eight around her breasts without actually touching them. Paused and said, "I knew you would be beautiful," then meandered down to draw a convoluted pattern from her ribs to her waist.

The shivering anticipation he left behind puckered her skin in a thousand places, tightening each pore until it shrieked for relief. "Ahh!" she cried helplessly, struggling to tame his elusive seduction, to halt his slow destruction of her soul.

He framed her hips in his hands. Steered her an inch

closer, just enough that the heated tip of him nudged at her belly. She teetered toward him, felt his kiss feather along her cheek and over her mouth, teasing, tempting. Felt his palm drift to the small of her back, and over the slope of her hip. His finger slipped between her thighs and pressed against her once. Just once.

A tiny scream tore loose from her throat. A tiny flood pooled where he'd touched. And a need measureless as the universe took hold of her, driving away whatever timidity she had left. She looped a frantic arm around his neck and reached down to touch him; to delight in the virile satin-smooth dimensions that made him a man.

He inhaled sharply and bore her to the sand once again. Covered her breasts with his big powerful hands. Left the damp imprint of his kisses down her rib cage and kept on going...lower and lower still.

A sliver of doubt clouded her mind. *Nice girls don't do this!*

But she'd left girlhood behind years before, and her thighs had a mind of their own. They parted willingly to accept him because they knew what she was only just coming to understand: that there was no reason to refuse him when all he wanted was to give her pleasure.

And give he did, with dedicated, exquisite finesse, inciting her to such delirium that she thought she'd splinter apart.

Finally, though, even his formidable self-discipline reached breaking point. Aligning his body with hers, he slipped his hands beneath her hips to forge an intimacy of flesh which allowed for no secrets between them, and with one masterful stroke invaded her. Driven by a pagan hunger, he rocked within her, awakening a deep, dark center that nothing and no one had touched before.

Caught in the ever more urgent rhythm of his loving, she

relinquished herself to its cadence. She heard him call out her name on an agonized breath, a warning in itself that he was losing his grip on sanity. His heart hammered next to hers, fierce and frantic. Obedient to every nuance of his loving, the tension spring coiling through her blood tightened in response. For one eternal second, every last inch of her—from her toes, to the backs of her knees, to her scalp—hung in the balance.

Then, with one last mighty thrust, he let his seed run free inside her, hot and robust. At that the earth dropped away, a sneaky trapdoor hurling her into a primeval free fall which would surely have destroyed her had his arms not held her safe. Battered by wave upon wave of sensation, she clung to him, the passion sweeping over her with a vengeance so completely foreign that she cried aloud in shock, a reedy, needy wailing that hung in the night like a banshee's call.

When its last echo faded away and the silence covered them again, Michael rolled to his side and tucked her into the curve of his body. He stroked his hand over her hair and down her arm.

So this, she thought dazedly, *is how it feels to be desired by a man for no reason other than the simple joy of giving his partner pleasure!*

"I can hear your mind buzzing. What are you thinking about?" he asked, his voice vibrating against her forehead.

"Nothing," she said, for how did a woman describe the wonder of her first orgasm, especially to a man who wasn't her husband? How did she begin to do justice to the purity of the experience, to the absolute sense of connection she'd felt with him, and not send him running for the hills by straying into the dangerous language of love?

"No regrets?"

"None."

His chest heaved in a silent sigh.

Disquieted, she said, "Are *you* having second thoughts, Michael?"

"About lying here in the buff where anyone might find us, and keeping you up long past your bedtime?" He attempted a laugh and disengaged himself from her. "Yes. You need to get home."

"Oh...!" Brimming with dismay, the exclamation was out before she could contain it. "You wish we hadn't...done it."

He wouldn't look at her and he didn't speak. Instead, he climbed into his clothes with unflattering speed and went to retrieve the flashlight which had rolled down by the water. Embarrassed, she took advantage of the momentary privacy to step into her panties and pull her dress over her head. Miserably aware of the damp sand sticking to her skin, of her utter dishevelment, she struggled to hang on to her dignity and not give way to the humiliation and disappointment threatening to burst free.

How could he so easily dismiss something she'd found beautiful beyond compare?

The answer hammered at her without a shred of remorse. *Because, stupid, it didn't mean anything at all to him!*

"If you're worried that I'm going to make a nuisance of myself and start stalking your every move, don't be," she said, striving to sound blasé. "I might not be the one-night-stand kind, as you so charmingly phrased it, but that doesn't mean I'm planning to boil your pet rabbit, either! There are no strings attached to what happened between us tonight."

He rotated the flashlight between his hands and expelled another sigh. "That's not what's worrying me."

But it was. Why else would he be in such a hurry to get rid of her?

"Well, you were very *good,* if that's what you're wondering."

He didn't need to tell her he found the remark both uncalled-for and distasteful. Even in the semidark, the reproach on his face was unmistakable. "I'll walk you to your car, Camille."

"No need." She stuffed her feet into her sandals and fumbled with the buttons on her dress. But she was trembling so hard, she couldn't coordinate her fingers.

"I said, I'll walk you to your car."

"And then what? Kiss me good-night and tell me you'll give me a call one of these days, when we both know you've no intention of doing any such thing? I'll pass, thanks!"

He ran his hand back and forth over the flashlight as though he hoped, if he rubbed it hard enough, a genie might appear and vaporize her in a puff of smoke. "Are you always like this after you've—?"

"Had sex with a stranger?" She pushed distraught fingers through her hair, scarcely aware of what she was saying. "I really don't know. It's not something I've done before and I'm beginning to understand why. It's not worth the humiliation that follows."

"I gave you every chance to back out before things went too far."

"So you did. Chalk it up to inexperience that I didn't have the good sense to take you up on the offer, and rest assured I've learned my lesson. I made a mistake and I'm very sorry that you have to bear the brunt of my regret."

He studied his feet, the overhanging branches of the willow tree, and finally, with marked reluctance, her face. "I'm the guilty party here, Camille, not you. I hold myself entirely responsible for what happened tonight."

Teeth clenched against the pain spearing her, she said,

"Spare me your charity, please! My pride's taken enough of a beating."

"The last thing I ever wanted was to hurt you."

"Perhaps," she said, furious to find her voice water-logged with tears. "But it happened anyway, which just goes to show that the road to hell really is paved with other people's good intentions."

He made a move toward her, hands outstretched, though whether in irritation or remorse she couldn't tell. All she knew was she couldn't bear to have him touch her again, not if she wanted to hang on to the crumbling edges of her composure—and hang on to it she must, if she was ever to look herself in the mirror again and not blush with shame at what she saw staring back.

Clutching the top of her dress closed, she stumbled away, up the bank and back along the lane to where her car sat ready to go at the turn of a key. Having to ask Michael D'Alessandro for help getting it back on the road—or worse, being forced to accept a ride home from him—would have been the last straw.

Where he was concerned, she'd made fool enough of herself to last a lifetime. She never wanted to see him again.

The squeal of tires split the silence. The smell of burning rubber chased away the scent of her still teasing his senses, and filled his mind with horror pictures.

Her car was powerful, designed for speed. She was angry and hurt and probably crying. And she was driving much too fast. If she ended up wrapped around a tree, or flew off the bridge a mile up the road and nose-dived into the river, it would be his fault.

Congratulations, jackass! You've really screwed up this time!

Furious with himself, he aimed a vicious kick at the willow tree. Pain exploded in his ankle and swept in jarring waves up his leg.

Too bad you didn't nail your head instead—or the other place you left your brains tonight!

Hopping around on his good foot, he cursed the day he'd agreed to Kay's request. Ignorance *was* bliss, and never mind what the pundits decreed. He'd been better off not knowing. Trouble was, now that he did, there was no going back. From the minute he'd learned he had a son, his life had been divided into two separate eras. Before. And after.

Something wrapped itself around his shoe, almost tripping him. When he bent to investigate, he found her bra tangled in the laces of his runner. "Well, why the hell not?" he muttered bitterly, shaking sand out of the flimsy half-cups and looping the straps over his fingers. "I've stamped all over her pride already. Might as well grind a little dirt into her clothes as well, while I'm at it."

But the only real dirt was that sticking to his conscience. He'd used her, pure and simple, to satisfy his own raging desire, and the worst of it was, he couldn't bring himself to regret it. She was lovely, and innocent in a way that had caught him so thoroughly off guard that he'd found himself dangerously moved. He'd known he should stop; that he couldn't afford to muddy his own agenda by losing his objectivity. And he'd known she would be incapable of maintaining hers.

It would have been different if she'd been cut from the same cloth as her mother. Then, he might have been able to tell himself that, sometimes, a man had to do what a man had to do—and believe it. But if Glenda Younge was as tough as old rope, Camille was delicate as a butterfly.

She'd been badly scarred by her marriage. He suspected that, until tonight, she'd never been with any other man but her husband. He was afraid the only way she'd forgive

herself for what she'd done with him was to invest the
incident with more meaning than it merited.

He'd heard it in her voice, in the quivering disappointment she hadn't been able to disguise. He'd seen it in the
way she'd bitten her lip and scrunched her eyes closed to
stop herself from bursting into tears when he hadn't told
her what she'd hoped to hear. But what scared him the most
was how badly he'd wanted to chase after her and restore
her illusions; to give her the fairy-tale ending she was looking for.

"Get a grip!" he admonished himself scornfully, stuffing
the bra into his back pocket and heading up the bank to the
road. "This isn't high school and she's not the cheerleader
who let you get into her pants because you're too full of
raging hormones to control yourself! She's the mother of
your child. If you really care about her, do the decent thing
and get the hell out of her life now, before you cause any
more damage."

Trouble was, he couldn't do that. He was in too deep to
walk away. And that was the real reason he practically
gagged on the bitter aftertaste of guilt souring his tongue.

The morning after, she'd told Fran, *Don't bother playing
matchmaker anymore. The Michael D'Alessandro experi-
ment was a disaster. I never want to see him again.*

She'd told herself it was true, that he was a louse who'd
wormed his way into her affections by being kind to
Jeremy, that she was a dreadful judge of character to have
been so easily taken in by a pair of broad shoulders and a
charming smile, and that she was lucky she'd found out
early what sort of man he really was: a bounder who preyed
on a woman's susceptibility to clever seduction.

So it made not a scrap of sense that when, five days after
it had happened, he showed up on her doorstep again and

started out with, "I'm probably the last person you want to see, but—"

He looked a little drawn, as if he, too, had had trouble sleeping. But the shadows under his eyes did nothing to detract from his beauty. He was gorgeous in navy linen pants and a pale blue shirt topped with a lightweight beige jacket. It wasn't fair that he should catch her looking so pale and uninteresting!

Curbing the urge to fling herself into his arms and thank him for coming back, she said coolly, "Correct me if I'm wrong, but didn't we already play this scene last week?"

At least he had the grace to look sheepish. "I'm too embarrassed to come up with a more creative opening, Camille. The fact is, you've been on my mind ever since the other night. I never should have let things go so far."

"It's a bit too much after-the-fact for regrets, don't you think? The damage has been done."

"Perhaps, but that doesn't mean I can just dismiss it. I need to know that you're all right."

"And it took you this long to figure that out?" She'd promised herself she wouldn't betray how devastated she'd been by his neglect, but the hurt came tumbling out the minute she opened her mouth. "It's been nearly a week, Michael. If you really cared about me, you wouldn't have waited this long to try to make amends."

"I'd have been in touch sooner, but other…business came up."

"Of course. And business always comes before pleasure." She didn't care that she sounded like a fishwife. He was lucky she didn't rake her nails down his handsome face!

"The point is, it *was* a pleasure."

"For you, perhaps."

"I thought, at the time, for both of us."

She cringed before his unflinching honesty. Whatever else his omissions, he'd given her a gift she'd always cherish and she did them both an injustice by pretending otherwise.

The truth was, all those times she and Todd had tried so hard to make a baby, a part of her had remained aloof and refused to abdicate control. She'd never had an orgasm in her life, but she'd read enough to convince herself she knew what they were all about—until the other night when reality had made a mockery of her attempts to fool anyone, least of all herself.

"Was I wrong, Camille?"

She wished she could lie, and knew she never could. Not to him. "No."

Some of the tension went out of his shoulders. "Then can we start over and this time try to remain nothing more than friends?"

Could they? Would friendship be enough, after what they'd shared? On the other hand, could anything be worse than the terrible emptiness she'd known when she thought she'd lost him forever? "I don't know," she said. "But it's a chance I'm willing to take."

CHAPTER SIX

His sudden smile washed away all the hurt and anger she'd nourished over the last few days. "Thank you. That's more than I dared hope for and a lot more than I deserve."

"Not really. What happened between us the other night...." Her mouth went dry but she held his gaze. "We both know I was a willing accomplice, Michael, if not the downright aggressor. If I didn't like the outcome, I've got only myself to blame."

"Let's leave blame out of it," he said, mesmerizing her all over again with the way his lips shaped the words. As if it had happened only minutes before, the memory of how he'd used that mouth to drive her wild flashed to the forefront of her mind, evoking a jolt of sensation that left her trembling inside. "I've got enough on my conscience without adding blame to the list. Let's settle for 'memorable', instead."

Amazed at how quickly the right man saying the right words could make the world lose all its ugliness and restore a woman's faith in herself, Camille opened the door wider. "Would you like to come in? It's a bit early for lunch, but we can have coffee. Nori's taken Jeremy to the park so it's nice and peaceful around here for a change."

"Thanks, but I can't. I have a pressing appointment in the city, and I'm already running late."

Another one? Good grief, with the amount of time he spent in San Francisco, why didn't he just stay there as well and save himself a lot of unnecessary driving? Unreasonably disappointed, she said, "You shouldn't have bothered to stop by then. You could just as easily have phoned.''

''And take the coward's way out?'' He shook his head. ''I might not always do the right thing, but I hope I'm man enough to apologize face-to-face when I've made a mistake. In any case, I had to return this.''

Reaching into his jacket pocket, he pulled out a small plastic bag bearing the Maddox Lodge logo and dropped it in her hand. Weighing no more than an ounce or two, it rustled lightly against her palm.

''Oh!'' She realized at once what it was, and hardly knew where to look. ''My bra. How embarrassing! Imagine if someone else had found it.''

''No one else did, Camille. I made sure of that. And if I'd known I was going to make you blush like this, I just might have mailed it to you, instead of presenting it in person.''

He was teasing her, beguiling her all over again with his smile and the laughter in his eyes. She covered her burning cheeks with her hands. ''I'm being ridiculous, aren't I?''

''Not a bit. 'Ridiculous' is the last word I'd apply to you.'' As quickly as it had arisen, his amusement died. ''Unless you have other plans, will you have dinner with me tomorrow night?''

''If you like.'' Her answer, embarrassingly overeager, was out almost before he'd finished the question.

''I'd like,'' he said. ''When shall I pick you up?''

''It's better for me if we make it later—say half past eight? That way, I'll have time to give Jeremy his bath and read him a bedtime story before I leave.''

''Eight-thirty it is. See you then.''

For a second, he sort of hovered on the doorstep, as though uncertain how to take his leave. With a hug? A peck on the cheek?

She wouldn't have minded either one. He'd gone a long way toward redeeming himself by coming to her house and being so frank. In the end, though, she was left wanting. He stepped away, gave a little salute, then took off down the steps to his car without a backward glance.

She told herself not to read more into his visit than he'd intended. He'd made it clear where they stood, that the most he could offer was friendship, and probably the only reason he'd asked her to dinner at all was that he felt he owed it to her to make up for their last meeting. She'd be a half-wit to imagine for one second that he harbored any romantic intentions toward her.

"Maybe so," she said, watching until he was lost to sight by the shrubbery lining the driveway, "but just in case, I'll spring for a new dress this time."

"For someone who said she never wanted to see the man again, you're going to extraordinary lengths to impress him," Fran remarked, lounging on the little sofa reserved for guests in *Hyacinthe,* Calder's most upscale ladies' boutique. "That must be the tenth outfit you've modeled, which suggests to me that, for you at least, there's a lot more riding on this dinner date than a decent meal and a good-night handshake."

"I asked you to come shopping with me because I value your fashion judgment, not to listen to you playing pop psychologist," Camille said, adjusting the scarf of the silk crepe two-piece she'd tried on. "What do you think of this?"

"Get rid of it. You look like the mother of the bride with a slingshot hanging around her neck." Shuddering, Fran got up and rifled through a rack of newly-arrived designer creations which Camille had dismissed as being dressier than the occasion called for. "Ah, *yes!*" she crowed, holding up a shimmery beaded number with a plunging neckline and a thigh-high slit up the front of the narrow skirt. "This, on the other hand, was tailor-made for you."

"Fran, it's indecent!"

"On me, maybe. On you, it'll merely look decadent. Come on, Camille, at least try it on. What've you got to lose?"

"Common sense, that's what—something I don't seem to have much of where Michael's concerned! Wearing a dress like that is just asking for trouble."

Fran shook the thing like a matador trying to goad a reluctant bull to action with his cape. "You've got the legs to carry it off, dearie, and Michael strikes me as a very civilized man. I doubt he's going to attack you between the soup and salad course just because you're showing a bit of skin."

"*No!* It's too…formal. We're having dinner, not attending the governor's ball."

But the more she looked, the more she weakened, and Fran knew it. "Let's see how it looks on you before we decide."

Why fight the inevitable, especially since nothing else had caught her fancy? "All right, but I'm telling you now, it's a waste of time."

It wasn't, though. It was a dream come true. The silk lining shimmied over her body like a caress. The silver-blue beading echoed the color of her eyes. The lightly-boned bodice meant she could dispense with a bra and wouldn't have to worry about straps showing. The slit in the skirt tempted a little, without revealing too much. In short, the dress was perfect.

"You'll knock his socks off," Fran decreed, when Camille appeared for inspection. "Get out your credit card and prepare to blow your budget, girlfriend. We've found the killer dress for the occasion.''

Although he managed to keep his socks on when she opened the door to Michael at thirty-two minutes past eight that evening, he *did* look as if someone had knocked the wind out of him. ''Holy cow!'' he wheezed, his gaze skating past the daring neckline to the slit in her skirt. ''That is some outfit!''

''Should I take that to mean you approve?''

He blinked and ventured another hurried glance at the way the fabric barely managed to drape her breasts. ''Oh yeah! I just wish I did you credit as your date, is all! As it is, you're stuck with what you see.''

What she saw was so delectable, her mouth watered. He wore a silver-gray jacket over a white dress shirt whose French cuffs were held closed by discreet silver links. His dark gray tie gleamed with the subtle sheen of fine Italian silk. The knife-edge crease in his black dress pants bisected the top of hand-made black leather shoes. In her book, he easily topped the list of best-dressed men-about-town, and there wasn't a thing about him she wanted to change.

Curbing her enthusiasm for fear it might send him running for the hills, she said primly, ''You look very nice.''

He gave a wry laugh. ''Kind of you to say so. Now that we've got all that out of the way, let's go.''

''Would you like to come in for a drink, first?''

''No, thanks.'' He reared back as if she'd made an indecent proposition. ''I managed to get us in at the Quail Lodge which I'm told is a good half hour's drive from here, and whoever took the booking made it pretty clear they won't hold our table if we're late.''

''I'm surprised you were able to get a reservation at all,'' she said, but it was a lie. He could charm apples off trees without even trying, and there wasn't a woman alive who wouldn't succumb to the sexy timbre of his voice sliding down the phone.

"How's Jeremy?" he asked, once they'd cleared the town limits and were headed east. "Still thrilled with his car?"

"More than you can begin to know. He'd take it to bed with him, if I'd let him. You're his hero."

His hands tightened on the steering wheel. "Somebody should be, and your ex obviously doesn't want the job."

"Just as well. He's hardly the kind of role model I want for my son."

"I still wonder why fatherhood wasn't enough to keep the guy on the straight and narrow."

"I hoped it would, but the novelty of having a son soon wore off and he became worse than ever. It was as if he saw the baby as a daily reminder of his personal failure to father a child of his own. He began finding excuses to work late every night, then started disappearing for days at a stretch."

"Sounds like a real hands-on kind of dad, all right!"

"It was the old pattern repeating itself. When he did finally come home, his behavior was so unpredictable, I never knew what to expect. The awful thing was, Jeremy picked up on the tension and cried the whole time his father was around, which just made matters worse. Todd was resentful, I was exhausted and at my wit's end with worry, and my poor baby was miserable."

"Small wonder!" Michael let out an exclamation of disgust and took a corner so sharply, the tires squealed in protest. Alarmed, Camille braced her hand against the dashboard.

Realizing he'd frightened her, he eased his foot off the accelerator and said calmly, "Relax, Camille. I haven't killed a dinner date yet. I'll get us there and back in one piece, I promise."

"I'm sure you will, but there's no great hurry, you know. We're making very good time."

"I realize that. I just got so riled up with what you were telling me, I let my attention wander. Not a good idea, I know, especially in unfamiliar territory, but it won't happen again."

He inhaled deeply and pointedly changed the subject. "Pretty countryside," he said, surveying the passing scenery. "Too bad it's getting dark already. I wouldn't mind coming back during the day and seeing more of it."

"I'll be happy to act as tour guide, if you do."

A second of silence spun by before he said, "Unfortunately, I doubt I'll have the time."

What shocked her the most about his answer was not the reminder that he wouldn't be around much longer, but that the news should leave her so utterly desolate.

What was the matter with her? She'd always known he'd go, sooner or later. She'd encouraged their relationship precisely *because* she knew it would be short term: a fling, a brief encounter, no strings attached—and any number of other tired clichés on which she'd hung her decision to become involved with him.

But hearing him give voice to the inevitable cut through her smug delusions and laid bare the truth hidden underneath. *She did not want to lose him, not now, not ever!*

"I see," she said, dismay casting such a long shadow over the evening that she didn't know how she'd survive it. "You'll be leaving shortly, then?"

She had to ask. Not knowing—living with the fear that she'd wake up one morning and discover the reason she hadn't heard from him in days was that he'd left without saying goodbye—was more than she could face.

"I'll be leaving, yes. How soon I really can't say. I have a few...loose ends to tie up before I go and no idea how long that will take." His gaze lingered on her intently a moment before swinging back to the road, and although his words had been neutral enough, she thought she saw longing in his eyes, and a strange ambivalence.

It was all the encouragement needed for a tidal wave of hope to rush through her. Those loose ends he was referring to meant him and her. She knew it as surely as she knew her own name. All his talk about friendship was a front, just as his offhand dismissal of what had happened the other night had been. If he really didn't care about her, he'd never have bothered to contact her again. He wasn't ready to admit his real feelings, that was all, because he was a man, and men were more cautious than women when it came to love.

Love, Camille? When did "love" enter the picture?

"Camille? Am I right?"

He was applying the brakes. Almost bringing the car to a stop. Pinning her in his gaze, his expression inquiring. Hedgerows on either side cloaked the quiet back road in darkness, made it a private, intimate place. Her heart fluttered up into her throat. "...Right?"

"We turn at this intersection?"

"Oh," she said faintly, pressing a hand to her chest as her heart fell back where it belonged. "Oh, yes, right...I mean, left. You turn left."

His soft, sexy laughter flowed over her. "I've known dinner dates to fall asleep on the way home, but you're the first to pass out on me before you've been fed. I must be losing my touch."

Not you, Michael! You couldn't if you tried. "I wasn't sleeping," she said. "Just daydreaming."

Not long after, they reached the lodge, as famous for its

chateau style of architecture and acres of gardens as it was for its food. He'd secured a table in a quiet corner next to a window on the lower, fireplace level of the dining room.

"I'm glad I found out about this place," he said, once the wine-tasting ritual was out of the way and their oyster Rockefeller appetizer had been served. "I wanted to bring you someplace special tonight, and I'd say this fills the bill."

A man didn't bring a woman to a special place to give her the brush-off. He didn't need sterling and bone china and crystal set on table linen starched to a fare-thee-well to prove he was her friend. He didn't order champagne to toast the end of an affair. Steeling herself not to read too much into his every word and gesture, she said, "It is lovely, isn't it?"

He fixed her in another sober, heart-melting stare. "Not quite as lovely as you, Camille. The way you look tonight is something I'll remember long after I leave here."

As quickly as her hopes had soared, they sank again. Premonition, cool as midnight in February, stole over her. "I don't want to talk about your leaving," she said, shivering. "I want to learn more about *you*—about the kind of life you've lived. Who are you, Michael, when you're not playing tourist? What kind of hopes and dreams shaped you into the man you are today? Where do you see yourself, a year from now, and if you could have just one wish, what would it be?"

It had taken him a full five days to come to grips with what he knew he must, in all conscience, do. Their relationship had run off the main track and was headed down a dangerous side road built on a shifting foundation of deceit. Regardless of the cost to him, he had to put a stop to it.

He'd see her one last time, tell her the truth, and that would be it.

Once he'd made up his mind, he promised himself two things: he wouldn't lay a hand on her, no matter what the provocation, and he wouldn't let *anything* get in the way of his coming clean.

The first was easy. There'd be no dancing, no getting cozy beside a roaring fire, no playing footsies under the table, and definitely no fooling around in the car on the way back or accepting an invitation to come in for a night-cap.

The second he'd known would be difficult. He could hardly blurt out of the blue, "By the way, I've been mean-ing to tell you I'm your son's natural father."

But her spate of questions had handed him the perfect lead-in. All he had to do was answer her, and the truth would come out. Only a fool would turn away from such a heaven-sent chance to make a clean breast of everything.

He was a fool! Raising his glass in a silent toast, he said, "Not until you finish telling me your story."

She gave a little shrug, just enough to draw his eye to the low-cut front of her dress and the lovely honey-gold skin it revealed. "There's nothing else to tell."

"Sure there is," he said, gulping down a healthy swig of the champagne. He should have ordered something with more bite—something raw and bitter that would burn down a man's throat and bolster his courage—instead of a wine synonymous with the prelude to seduction. "When did you reach the end of your rope with Todd? Was it something specific or just battle fatigue in general?"

She shrugged again. *Damn!* "A bit of both, I suppose. His behavior was destroying him and everyone around him, and he didn't care enough to want to change. Perhaps if it had still been just the two of us, I might have tried harder to keep the marriage alive, but clearly it was no kind of environment for a child, so I took Jeremy and moved out and filed for divorce.''

''You mean, the place you're living in now isn't the one—?''

She shuddered, which was almost as distracting as if she'd shrugged. The top of her dress, what little there was of it, slithered over her breasts like a jealous lover. ''No! I wanted a completely fresh start, away from all the bad memories.''

Even though he cleared his throat, he still sounded like a choirboy in the midst of exchanging his soprano for a tenor. ''And he didn't fight you on it?''

''He was glad to see the back of us.''

Gad, Mike D'Alessandro wasn't the only fool walking around! ''The man must be a moron. Couldn't he see what he was giving up?''

She leaned forward so that even more of her cleavage showed. ''He had other priorities, Michael. People with addictive personalities are driven in ways you and I can't begin to understand. All that matters to them is catering to their obsession—whether it be power or money or mountain climbing. In Todd's case, it happened to be alcohol and eventually cocaine.''

''I can understand being driven,'' he said, forcing himself to concentrate on what she was saying, instead of what she was almost wearing. ''We've all got things—people, principles—that matter to us enough that we'll do just about anything to honor them. But I can't imagine anyone being willing to sacrifice a child.''

What the hell was he saying? Hadn't Kay jettisoned their marriage and their son because dancing in a chorus line and playing bit parts in a third rate Hollywood movie had mattered more?

"But that's how addicts are," Camille said earnestly. "They can't help themselves. Half the time, I don't think Todd was even aware of the effects his actions had on me or the baby."

"Uh-huh." He ran his finger inside the collar of his shirt and unbuttoned his jacket. Anything to take his mind off what he wanted, which was to touch her. She was so fine, so elegant.

"You're staring," she said, a smile lurking at the corners of her mouth. "Do I have spinach caught in my teeth?"

Awareness caught him off guard, triggering a soft implosion that almost had him groaning aloud. He shouldn't be looking at her; shouldn't be admiring her smooth complexion, the scalloped curve of her upper lip, the dimple in her chin.

Hers were not the features he should be committing to memory. He hadn't assumed a false identity and all the lies which went with it to make an ass of himself over a woman who, once she knew his true history, would plant her dainty foot in the seat of his pants and boot him out the door.

He'd done it for the too brief pleasure of sharing a few stolen days of his son's life. *Those* were the memories he should be hoarding against a future which of late had lost so much luster that he could barely bring himself to think about it.

"Let's order our main course," he said, grabbing the leather-bound menu and disappearing behind it before he did or said something really asinine. "You've been here before. What do you recommend?"

"The rack of lamb, the crab cakes.... Is something wrong, Michael? You seem upset."

"Yes, something's wrong!" he practically barked, slapping the menu closed. "The man you married made your life a living hell, not to mention your child's, yet you keep defending him.''

''I'm not defending him,'' she said, her eyes wide with dismay.

''You sure aren't condemning him!''

''I divorced him, Michael. What else should I have done, hired a hit man and had him shot?''

''Sounds like a pretty good idea to me.''

Before he realized what she intended, she slid her hand across the table and folded her fingers around his. ''He gave me my baby. I'll always be grateful to him for that.''

The remark cut him to the quick. *Wrong, sweetheart!* he wanted to bellow. *I'm the one who did the giving!* Instead, he marshaled his vanishing control and avenged himself the only way he knew how. ''Exactly how did he do that, Camille?''

She pulled her hand away and stared at him, surprised, he suspected, as much by the bitterness in his tone as by a question whose answer should have been evident to a congenital idiot. ''How do you think, Michael?''

''Well, let's see.'' He leaned back in his chair and counted off his reply on his fingers. ''One, he went to a registered adoption agency. Two, you were both subjected to several interviews with medical and psychological experts who put you under intense scrutiny to make sure you'd measure up as parents. Three, having passed all those tests with flying colors, you appeared before a judge or some other legal bigwig who approved your taking a baby, subject to a six month probationary period during which time a social worker dropped by without warning to see how things were going. How am I doing so far?''

She couldn't look at him. She glanced down at her hands, clasped tightly in her lap. Her lashes, their shadow stretched to ridiculous length by the candlelight, flared across the high arc of her cheekbones. Her mouth trembled. And he, damned fool that he was, wanted nothing so much as to take her in his arms and apologize for haranguing her.

If only she were just some woman he'd met socially...!

He left the thought unfinished, ticked off to discover that his body was already ten steps ahead of his brain. Just as well the waiter loomed up out of nowhere, somber as a black-clad angel, his head bald as a billiard ball decked out in a halo of white fluff. "Are you ready to order, sir?"

Michael shot an inquiring glance at Camille. She seemed on the verge of tears. "We'll both have the filet mignon," he decided, latching onto the first thing that came into his head. "Medium rare. And a bottle of your best Shiraz."

"Very good, sir." The waiter disappeared, leaving behind a cloud of silence, thick as the air before a thunderstorm.

Realizing he was drumming furiously on the table with the pads of his fingers, Michael clenched his fist and said, "Steak okay with you, Camille?"

She shook her head.

"You want me to cancel and order something else?"

She cast about the room, looking for all the world like a trapped doe. Finding no help on the inside, she fastened her gaze on the floodlit gardens outside. "Why are you doing this, Michael?"

"Doing what?"

He knew exactly what. And the pitying look she leveled at him told him *she* knew he was just playing for time. "Why are you cross-examining me as if I've committed a crime? Why do you care how we came to adopt Jeremy?"

"Maybe because I care about you."

"I'd like to think so, but the way you're acting...."

"I just find it strange that Todd's problems didn't raise a red flag with whoever looked into your family background. I don't pretend to be an expert on adoption rulings in California, but I know that in Canada, pretty stringent guidelines are laid down to protect children from the kind of home situation Jeremy fell into.''

She stroked her thumb over her pale pink nail polish. Twisted the pearl ring on the third finger of her right hand. And said in a voice so hushed he had to strain to hear it, ''Nobody interviewed us. Todd heard through a colleague that there was a woman in Los Angeles desperate to find a home for her unborn child. We went to meet her, and the three of us worked out an arrangement.''

''*Worked out an arrangement?*''

''There was nothing fishy about it, if that's what you're implying,'' she said sharply. ''We undertook to pay her medical expenses and help her make a fresh start after the birth, and she agreed to let us take her baby. Todd drew up the necessary documents and the three of us signed them with two of his law firm partners acting as witnesses. You already know all this, Michael, so I don't know why you're bringing the subject up again.''

''Yes. And I still have a hard time believing it never occurred to you that there should have been more to it than that.''

''Why should it have, when everything was perfectly in order?''

He threw up his hands in disbelief. ''Because from what you've told me, it's plain that the only thing you signed was an agreement for sale. You bought a black market baby, Camille.''

A delicate flush rode over her face. ''That's absurd! I did no such thing. And what gives you the right to sit in judgment of my actions, anyway? Just who do you think you are?''

Oh, sweetheart, if you only knew! But he couldn't tell

her now. He'd put her on the defensive and there was no way he'd get her to receive the truth kindly at this point. Furthermore, he was too steamed to try.

Biting down on the urge to pound his fist on the table and bellow, *That commodity you bought happened to be my son and I'd have seen you all in hell before I'd have let you have him, if I'd known,* he mustered the dregs of his composure and said, "I'm trying to be your friend, Camille."

"I fail to see how."

"Then that makes us equal, because I fail to understand how a woman as educated and sophisticated as you appear to be can take at face value everything that's handed to her."

"Maybe because I'm too trusting and a little bit naive."

"You adopt a baby knowing your husband's a lush and your marriage is on the skids. You swallow wholesale his story of just happening to find a pregnant woman living in a flea-pit motel in L.A. and—"

"How did you know he found her in a motel? I never told you that."

"If she'd been living in luxury, she wouldn't have needed rescuing," he said, breaking out in a fine sweat. Many more slips like that, and he wouldn't have to admit a thing. She'd figure the whole story out for herself. "It could have been a mansion, for all I care. The point I'm making is, he comes up with a woman conveniently waiting for a couple with money to pick her up, clean her off, pay her bills and buy her baby for a princely sum. And you don't raise a peep of protest when neither a judge nor a social worker is involved in the arrangement. You never once ask to see *both* parents' consent to the adoption." He shook his head in disgust. "I don't call that trusting and naive, Camille, I call it stupid. And perhaps a little too self-serving. I think you used an innocent baby to try to shore up your sinking marriage.''

Her eyes gleamed with unshed tears, but they stemmed as much from anger as hurt. Spots of color burned on her cheeks. Her breasts rose and fell in agitation. ''I did nothing of the sort,'' she said, the pulse at her throat racing so hard he could see it. ''I thought my marriage was back on track. And we didn't just go shopping one day and come home with a baby, you know! We spent the last four months of the pregnancy with the birth mother, in part to give her the chance to be sure adoption was the route she wanted to take, but mostly to prepare ourselves to become parents.''

''And a fat lot of good it did you! The so-called father takes off within weeks of the kid's birth, leaving you to do double duty as a single parent. Not what you'd call an *ideal* arrangement, is it?''

The hurt won out over the anger. ''Don't you think I already know that?'' she cried softly, the tears rolling down her face. ''Don't you think I lie awake at nights, worrying about how much my son's missing by not having a father around—of how much he's been cheated? Of course I do! Maybe I'm every bit the fool you say I am, Michael, but I love my son with my whole heart and I'd give anything— *anything!*—not to have had things turn out the way they did. But I don't know what you expect me to do about it at this late stage. I might have bought a baby, according to the way you see things, but I'll be damned if I'm going to run out and buy a husband, just to fulfill your idea of what a family's all about!''

''Oh, jeez, Camille!'' He shoved his napkin at her. ''Here, dry your eyes. So help me, I didn't bring you here to ream you out and make you miserable. It's just that every time I think about your scheming bastard of an ex-husband,

I see red. It's not just Jeremy who deserved better. You did, too."

She opened her mouth to reply, and let out a sob instead that had half the diners in the room looking their way.

He clapped a hand to his forehead. The way things were going, he'd have a lynch mob after his hide before long. "Please, Camille, stop crying."

To her credit, she tried. She bit her lip until he thought it would bleed. She swallowed as painfully as if she'd got an orange stuck in her throat. She turned to stare out of the window so that he couldn't see her face. But the tears kept coming, sparkling from the ends of her lashes and splashing onto the fancy beadwork on her dress.

The waiter reappeared. "Your wine, sir," he began, then stopped with the bottle poised in midair. Concern furrowed his brow and sent wrinkles chasing up his shiny dome of a head as Camille pressed her napkin to her mouth and pushed away from the table. Strangling on another sob, she made a dash for the open door to the patio.

"We've changed our minds. Maybe later...." Already on his feet, Michael waved the waiter aside and went after her.

By the time he got outside, she'd vanished. There was no sign of her on the steps leading to the gardens, but unless she'd vaulted over the lush flower beds on either side, which seemed unlikely given the cut of her dress, she had to have taken the path winding under trees strung with little white lights.

She had, but even so he might easily have missed her if it hadn't been for her muffled sobs leading him to where she huddled on a bench in a secluded alcove formed by a ten-foot-high hedge with a keyhole entrance carved in it.

Figuring he'd screwed up enough to invalidate his hands-off promise, he dropped next to her on the bench and took her in his arms. Just to comfort her. Just so that he could stroke her back until her shoulders stopped heaving and she was feeling better.

Then he'd confess.

And tell her she had nothing to fear from him because all he wanted was to see his son occasionally and contribute to his life however she'd let him.

And hope she'd believe him and feel inclined to be generous.

CHAPTER SEVEN

SHE huddled in his arms, her heart going a mile a minute like a terrified, injured bird's. And it was all his fault. What the devil was wrong with him? Was he really so unsure of his own claims that he had to trample all over hers before he found the guts to come out with the truth?

Tucking her head beneath his chin, he pressed his hand to the side of her face. Her tears scalded his fingers, but it was her hopeless efforts to get herself under control that damn near broke his heart.

"I'm not worth it, you know," he muttered against her hair. "If you're going to make yourself sick crying over somebody, it shouldn't be for some fool shooting his mouth off on matters he knows nothing about."

Another partial lie, but necessary under the circumstances. Jeremy was his son, regardless of who'd been named father on the birth certificate, but if he was looking to point the finger of blame at someone for the omission, that person was Kay. *She* was the one who'd robbed him of his rights, and he had no business trying to shift responsibility for his loss to the woman whose only sin had been that she wanted his baby a lot more than Kay ever had.

So tell her that, you dumb schmuck! Quit procrastinating and lay it all out for her.

Before he could begin though, Camille drew in a breath that left her slender frame shaking like a leaf caught in the wind, and said in a waterlogged voice, "I knew."

"Knew what, love?" he asked cautiously.

But she'd slipped into a private inner world where he

couldn't follow, and seemed not to hear him. Sitting up a little straighter, she pushed her hair back from her face and stared blindly at the tall hedge surrounding them. "I asked him, and he told me not to interfere. He said it was his job to take care of the legal end of things, and mine to learn to change a diaper. But I knew...it was all too sudden, too easy. I *knew* something wasn't right. I've always known. And it terrifies me."

"Unless you deliberately falsified the facts in order to cheat the mother out of her child, you have no reason to worry," he said, finally cluing in to what she was going on about. "She isn't going to show up at your door and demand her child back."

That much, at least, was the absolute truth.

"But *he* could."

"Todd?" He stroked his knuckles down her cheek to her jaw. "Honey, you said yourself—"

"Not him," she said. "The other one. The *real* father."

"I guarantee he'll never make trouble for you."

Another truth, but pitifully inadequate when stacked up against the mountain of deceit still waiting to be exposed.

She turned her head and regarded him solemnly a moment, then a small dreamy smile flitted across her face. "You sound so sure, I almost believe you."

How many heaven-sent chances was he going to blow before he quit dancing around the subject? Even if she despised him for waiting so long to reveal the whole sad story, telling her would leave him with the satisfaction of knowing he'd put her fears to rest for good.

"Look," he said, bracing himself for her reaction, "a little while ago, you said you wanted to know all about me—about who I really am."

"I've changed my mind." She swivelled in his lap, the better to look at him. The tears were done. Her eyes were big and luminous, and very beautiful. Her words whispered over his mouth, flavored with champagne. The tips of her breasts touched lightly against his shirtfront. When she moved, silky underthings rustled against her skin, and he remembered how she'd felt when he'd run his hands over her naked body.

"Huh?" he croaked, dizzy with the scent and sound and feel of her.

"I said, I've changed my mind."

"How come?"

"Because I already know everything that matters."

"You don't know beans." He touched his finger to her lips to silence her, and was caught completely unprepared when she drew the tip into her mouth. The aftershock flew straight as an arrow to his groin. *Bull's-eye!*

Things were not going according to plan. Not one little bit. He was fast losing his grip. Shoving good intentions aside, his mind was doing what it always seemed to do best whenever he found himself alone with her: taking up residence in his nether regions.

"I know you're honorable and decent and kind," she said, removing her finger and fixing her gaze on his mouth instead. How she managed to talk rationally when he could scarcely breathe stupefied him. "I know you've showered Jeremy with more attention than Todd ever did and certainly brought him more pleasure. That by itself is reason enough for me to be glad I met you."

"I think—"

"That I'm going a bit overboard with the compliments?" She gave another of those distracting little shrugs that left him squirming. "Don't worry, I'm not going to embarrass either of us by pretending we're anything more than the proverbial ships passing in the night. But that doesn't alter the fact that when I'm upset, you make me feel better. You call me sweetheart and honey as if you mean it, and it's been such a long time since anyone did that."

"I—!"

"Let me finish, please, before I lose my nerve." She sketched a tender finger over his eyebrow. "You make me face my demons, something I was unable to do before I met you. Most of all, you're not afraid to tell me the truth."

"Stop it!" he ground out, closing his eyes to avoid having to witness the honesty in hers. "You don't know what the hell you're talking about."

"I know that you've been my friend and that means everything to me." She moved closer. Too close. Her breath tumbled over his face, fresh as a spring morning. "Thank you, Michael," she said softly, and kissed him on the cheek. Then, with another rustling of silk, she slithered off his lap.

How the touch of her lips—bestowed with a guileless sincerity that was almost childlike—could translate into a kiss so loaded with sexual promise that it electrified him, defied explanation.

Nor did he waste time trying to come up with one. "Where are you going?"

"Back to the dining room. I think I've said enough."

He tussled with his conscience, telling himself that if he could do nothing else right, in this instance at least he could live up to her lofty perceptions of him and let her go. To try to keep her there because he couldn't control the hunger raging through him, was indefensible.

"Stay...!" Ignoring his pitiful attempt at nobility, the word tore loose from his throat, half command, half plea.

She paused on the brink of flight, her head tilted in such a way that her profile shone pale and perfect against the dark foliage of the hedge. Helpless to prevent himself, he curved his arm around her hips and turned her to face him again.

Just one more little kiss, he promised himself, all the time knowing that, where she was concerned, a little was never enough.

Even so, scruples still might have won the day had that damnable slit in her skirt not trapped his hand so that, as she pivoted toward him, his palm slid beneath the fabric and closed over her thigh.

If he'd had any sort of moral fiber, he'd have stopped right there and then, instead of groping around blindly, worse than a horny eighteen-year-old making out with a high school cheerleader.

Trouble was, cheerleaders wore tight-fitting drawers and panty hose to keep them decent while they flung themselves around on the football field. But Camille had on silk stockings which left three inches of bare skin at the top of her thighs, and skimpy satin panties which offered no resistance at all to his finger inching past the elasticized lace to caress the fleecy-soft hair between her legs.

He was lost, and he knew it.

And so was she. She crumpled forward and if he hadn't held her pinned between his knees, she'd have collapsed on the gravel at his feet. Instead, she swayed toward him, her head drooping on the slender stem of her neck like a fading flower.

"Ah!" she exclaimed, on a fractured breath.

She was tight and moist and so ready for him that with one touch to the sensitized bud hidden in the sweet folds of her flesh, he brought her to orgasm—and came close to it himself.

He wanted her naked beneath him, on a bed, with candlelight glimmering over her skin. He wanted to kiss every inch of her; to put his mouth where his hand was and taste the honeydew sweetness of her release.

He wanted to remain buried inside her for long, deep minutes at a stretch, and watch her eyes glaze over and her mouth fall softly open just before she came. He wanted to move within her slowly and deliberately, surfing the waves of passion time and again until, at last, with his heart fit to burst, they hammered him into submission.

He could have done all that and more. The lodge offered overnight accommodation. For the price of a room and fifteen minutes of patience, he could have secluded her in privacy and comfort, and taken the rest of the night to pleasure her.

But she, still vibrating helplessly against him, fumbled to open his fly and reached inside to cup him in the palm of her hand. The agony increased a notch, raking through him and threatening imminent destruction.

Fifteen minutes?

The sweat sprang out on his forehead and prickled the length of his spine. The speed with which he was losing ground, he feared he had less than fifteen seconds in which to hike up her skirt and yank down her underwear. Smothering a groan, he skimmed her dainty panties down her legs.

He thought he heard the faint tearing of silk. He hoped not; hoped he hadn't damaged that gorgeous dress. But it was a secondary concern, overshadowed by the certain knowledge that unless he put an end to the exquisite torment she was inflicting, he'd spill into her hands long before he could enter her, and that would be the end of it.

With the slit of her skirt spread wide over her thighs, he cradled her hips and hauled her astride him. Felt the sweet, damp flesh between her parted legs settle snugly against him, and with one mighty thrust, plunged inside her as the perimeter of his control started to crumble.

She closed around him, tight and sleek. Gritting his teeth, he fought to hang on just long enough to reawaken the faint echoes of pleasure still rippling through her frame. The bench was narrow, hard, unaccommodating. Whether by instinct or design, she drew her knees up and hooked her heels behind his waist in a frantic attempt to weld herself more seamlessly against him.

Supporting her with both hands, he tilted his hips up, driving ever deeper in a fruitless attempt to lose all of himself inside her. The move destroyed him. As the distant thunder of release gained strength, relentlessly drowning out everything but the frantic beat of her heart against his, he buried his mouth at her ear and started to tell her he was sorry.

But it was too late. The dam burst and ripped through him, trapping the words in his throat and pummeling him without mercy. Caught in its fury, she clung to him, her fists clenching reflexively at his shoulders, her eyes flying wide in a sightless stare. Painful, staccato breaths puffed from between her parted lips, as if her lungs were squeezing the very life out of her.

For a long moment, she hung suspended on the edge of sanity. He felt the heated flush ride over her, the quiver that ruffled her skin. And then, with a series of inarticulate little cries, she contracted around him, racked by spasm after spasm of splendid anguish.

Crushing her to him, he rode the dying swells to a perfect calm. He had never felt more connected to another, never more complete.

Paradise, though, was short-lived. Too soon, the real world swam back into focus and he had to face what he'd done. Unable to look at her, he eased her off his lap.

She teetered unsteadily a moment, like a sleepwalker rudely awakened. Her hair lay tousled around her face, and her dress was rucked around her hips.

Ashamed at the destruction he'd wrought, he went to ease the skirt into place. As he did so, something pale and flimsy near her right shoe caught his attention and he saw that her panties were hooked around her right ankle like a flag proclaiming his unconscionable behavior.

Stooping, he lifted her other foot and threaded it through the appropriate opening, but stopped short of pulling the garment up her legs. "I think you'd better take care of the rest," he muttered, and turned away to fumble with his own state of undress while she put herself to rights.

Except, there was no putting right what he'd done. He'd let self-indulgence displace caution, not to mention common decency, and treated her with an appalling lack of dignity and respect. Why she didn't haul off and sock him in the jaw he didn't know.

"I shouldn't have let that happen," he finally mumbled, still too ashamed to look her in the eye. "It's a bit late to express regret, I know, but when I'm with you...."

He trailed off, painfully aware of how lame he sounded.

"Don't be sorry, Michael," she said. "I'm not."

"How can you be so forgiving? For Pete's sake, I put my needs first, without any regard for yours."

"You're wrong. You made me feel beautiful and desirable."

"You are desirable, Camille, that's the problem and if, in his more lucid moments, your ex-husband forgot to mention that, he's got one more to add to his list of sins." He shook his head in self-disgust, and started toward the keyhole opening in the hedge. "I don't know about you, but I've lost my appetite for food. I think it's best if I just take you home."

"Walking away isn't going to change anything, you know," she said.

He stopped and swung back to face her, guilt making him surly. "If that's supposed to mean something profound, you've lost me."

"You're afraid, Michael."

"Huh?"

"You're afraid to face your real feelings. You're hoping I'll tell you never to come near me again, then you won't have to deal with what really happened tonight."

"I know exactly what happened tonight, I assure you," he said grimly. "I took advantage of you when your defenses were down. In my book, that makes me lower than dirt."

"Are you at all interested in knowing how I feel?"

"Used?" he suggested, resorting to sarcasm to cover up the fact that he couldn't stand himself. "Abused?"

"Loved."

"Oh, jeez!" He thumped a fist to his forehead. "Don't go glamorizing what we did. Love has nothing to do with it."

"Then what does?" she said. "The way I see it, what we shared adds up to something a bit more momentous than having a bad hair day."

"We had sex."

"Oh, Michael, if you really believed all we'd done was have sex, your conscience wouldn't be bothering you now to the point that you can't wait to get rid of me. You'd play the perfect date, buy me a nice dinner, and consider the score even. No apologies, no remorse, and definitely no regrets."

"I like to think I'm not quite that crass," he said, wincing at the radiance of her smile.

"You're not. You're a very nice man who holds himself

accountable for his actions, and you know how to make a woman feel…good.'' She smoothed her hands down her dress one last time, combed her fingers through her hair, and came toward him. ''But that doesn't mean you owe me anything more than you're able to give, okay? I know you'll be leaving soon, and although I wish you didn't have to go, I'm not fool enough to think you're going to rearrange your life on the strength of a three-week relationship. I'm just saying I'm grateful for what we've had. It's been wonderful, Michael. I'll treasure the memories for the rest of my life. You'll be the summer fling I'll remember with fondness when I'm old and gray. End of story.''

It wasn't often that he was caught at a loss for words, and even rarer that he found himself so moved that his eyes burned with the threat of tears. Quite by accident, he'd come across a jewel of a woman, and like the undeserving boor he undoubtedly was, he'd not recognized her worth until it was too late. And thanks to his stalling tactics, it most certainly was too late.

To tell her now that he was her child's natural father, and expect her to accept that he hadn't deliberately wormed his way into her heart for the sole purpose of getting closer to his son was asking for a miracle he didn't deserve.

Burying a sigh, he left her in the car, went back to settle his bill at the lodge, then took her home. The drive was memorable in that they exchanged not a word the entire time. When they reached her house, he walked her as far as the flight of the steps outside her front door, and no further.

Realizing that as far as he was concerned, the evening was over, she turned to face him one last time. ''Well,'' she said, with an uncertain smile, ''I guess the only thing left to say is thank you for a lovely time and good night.''

He didn't reply. Instead, he gazed at her, committing to

memory her lovely heart-shaped face. He saw her smile fade, and her mouth tremble. He saw how she lowered her eyes so that he wouldn't see how filled with hurt they were. And he saw how she drew on the breeding and class that were her trademark to get herself inside and away from him before her pride collapsed.

Not until the door had closed behind her did he finally speak the only words left to say. "Goodbye, Camille."

Then he climbed back into his car and took off, knowing it all had to end here. If he wanted to retain a shred of self-respect, his only recourse was to leave her in ignorance, and if that meant he'd never see Jeremy again then he had only himself to blame.

She had given so much, and all he'd ever done was take. He couldn't hurt her more than he already had, and he couldn't go on punishing himself, either.

He'd found a son. He'd briefly known the joy of being a father, albeit in secret. But for everyone's sake, he had to leave it at that and walk away before he caused everyone more pain.

She would not cry. She would remember instead how he had loved her—how his kisses had swept aside her inhibitions, how the flush of passion had swept over her body and she'd let it take her where it would. And she would trust the instincts which told her that it wasn't over between them. She'd hold on to the conviction that his feelings for her ran deeper than he was willing to admit and that he'd realize it, once he'd dealt with his guilt. She would not give up on him until he made a clean and final break with her.

It was the only way she could get through the night.

Morning, though, cast the truth in a much harsher light and revealed her instincts for the wishful thinking they really were. She might have been foolish enough to fall in love, but Michael was made of sterner stuff. His life did not coincide with hers, and if she'd been in any doubt about that, her parents, showing up uninvited just after lunch, certainly brought the message home in a way she couldn't ignore.

"I don't imagine you're going to like what you're about to hear, but that can't be helped," her father began. "As you're well aware, your mother and I have been disturbed—deeply disturbed—by your apparent infatuation with Michael D'Alessandro. Camille, you have to put an end to this association. The man is not to be trusted."

"How do you know that?"

"Because I had him investigated."

She stared at her father in scandalized disbelief. "You did *what?*"

"I hired someone to look into his background. I felt I had no choice."

"No *choice?* Dad, you had no *right!*"

"You're my daughter and that gives me the right. Having to watch the hell Todd put you through and knowing I was helpless to do anything about it was bad enough. If you think I'm going to stand idly by and let it happen a second time, you greatly underestimate the power of a father's love, Camille."

"Michael is as different from Todd as night is from day."

"In one respect he certainly is," her mother put in. "Whatever Todd's faults, he always managed to look after his investments. He never let anything, not even his...ahem, little problem, interfere with his work. The same can hardly be said of your latest admirer. Less than two years ago, a series of bad business decisions left Michael D'Alessandro on the brink of financial ruin."

"Are you saying he's bankrupt, Mother? Is that what you

were trying to tell me the other day, when you warned me the only reason he could possibly be interested in me is for my money?''

"What we're telling you," her father said flatly, "is that although he's made a remarkable comeback, he's in no position to be frittering away his time on your doorstep because he's in the mood for a month of fun in the sun. He has business obligations in Vancouver requiring his attention—matters the foreman he left in charge is not qualified to handle, which begs the question why, just when he's poised for considerable success on his own turf, he's setting up camp at your front door.''

"Maybe because I've made it clear he's welcome here.''

"I'm afraid, my dear, we've uncovered another reason which has nothing at all to do with you.''

Until then, her parents' suspicions had struck her as preposterous, largely because nothing they had said countered what she already knew. But her father's smug certainty that he'd found a rattlesnake in her bed and that she was too stupid to recognize its danger roused her to a rash, defensive anger. "Before either of you says another word, you should be aware that I'm in love with Michael and if he were to ask me to move to Canada to be with him, I'd be gone in a shot. *That's* how much I believe in him.''

Her mother let out a yelp and pressed a hand to her heart. "You cannot be serious, Camille!''

But her father merely sighed and said grimly, "I was hoping matters hadn't progressed quite that far. I hoped you would show more sense than to throw in your lot with a stranger. Dare I ask if he returns your feelings?''

To tell them the truth was more than she could bear, but lying was not an option either, so she struck a middle ground. "I haven't asked him.''

Her father removed a slip of paper from his pocket. "Before you do, my dear, you might want to do a little investigating of your own based on this.''

Glad that he couldn't see how her heart had started to race, she took the paper and read the information printed on it. *Room 4, 7 West, St. Mary's Hospital, San Francisco.*

''Is this supposed to mean something to me?''

''It will, once you discover who it is he's been spending most of his time with. I think it will prove conclusively that he's been lying to you from the minute he walked into your life.''

The morning after the dinner fiasco, he drove into San Francisco and checked into a small hotel near the hospital. Kay's time had dwindled to a matter of days, if not hours, and it made more sense to be close by. Or so he told himself, and that was the story he was sticking to, because to acknowledge the other reason—that he was voluntarily walking out of Jeremy's life without so much as a goodbye—was just too damned painful to deal with.

Kay seemed brighter when he visited her that afternoon. ''I didn't think you'd come until later,'' she said, reaching for his hand.

''I wanted to be sure I caught you before you went to sleep. I've got something to show you.''

He'd been carrying the photos with him for days, but he'd held out showing them to her for fear that seeing them would upset her too much. But the clock was winding down and he didn't have to be a doctor to know it. Pretty soon, she'd be past caring.

He cranked up the bed a little and spread the pictures on the fold of the sheet in front of her. ''This is our boy, Kay. What do you think of him?''

Her eyes, already huge in her sunken face, glowed like coals, but it was the smile transforming her face that choked him. "Oh, my baby!" she whispered, running her fingers over the face of the child she'd given away. "Oh, my precious little angel! Look at him, Mike. He reminds me of you."

"Nah," he said, doing his damnedest not to lose it. "He's the living image of you when I first met you. Remember that day?"

"You were playing basketball at U.B.C."

"And you were the cheerleader whose lap I landed in when I tried to keep the ball in play."

"You said I had great legs."

Oh, honey, he thought, squeezing his eyes shut against the pain of seeing the way she looked now. *You had great everything in those days.*

"I wish we'd been able to make it work, Mike."

He cleared his throat and stroked her arm. No use pointing out that he'd tried. No use, either, pointing out that she'd had her sights set on a career in show business, and there'd been no talking her out of it.

To be fair though, he hadn't put up much resistance when she'd said she wanted a divorce. They'd been college sweethearts who'd married more because they were used to each other than anything else. Once the bloom wore off, they'd shared little more than a bed. The way he'd seen it, when the only thing a man and woman had in common was good sex, there wasn't much hope the relationship was going to last over the long haul, and even the sex hadn't been all that good toward the end.

She thrashed her head from side to side like a trapped animal desperately seeking escape and finding none. Her lips were cracked and dry, her color the ghastly yellow of fading bruises. "I sold my soul to the devil…traded my baby for fame and glamor."

"Hush," he murmured, wiping her face with a damp

cloth. "You made a mistake, honey, but it's time to forgive yourself."

"I was good, you know…the lead dancer in a nightclub, Mike…my name up in lights. Rita Osborne…just like the devil promised…." The rambling drifted into exhaustion and her eyes closed.

Michael believed in God. Growing up in the heart of Vancouver's Italian community, he hadn't known a kid who didn't. Church on Sunday, being an altar boy, singing in the choir—they were as much a part of life as home-made pasta. But it had been years since he'd prayed.

He prayed then, though, because it was all there was left that he could do. *Take her home,* he begged, his eyes misting over as he watched each labored breath leach a little more strength out of her. *She's paid enough.*

She stirred. Plucked restlessly at the sheet. "He said he'd make me a star, you know."

"Who, the devil?"

"No, silly," she said, all at once sounding completely lucid. "My agent. But he didn't. He just took all my money. And when I told him I was pregnant, he told me no one would hire a woman sticking out a mile in front to dance in a chorus line."

So that was why she'd been destitute when Todd Whitfield had found her! Some scam artist had robbed her blind. "Money doesn't really matter much in the overall scheme of things, Kay," he said.

"It does when it's time to pay. A pound of flesh, Mike, right?" Her face contorted into a hideous rictus of amusement. "Except a pound wasn't enough, was it?" Her hands fluttered weakly over her wasted body. "There's nothing left of me."

"Kay…!" *Oh, God, please help her. Help me!*

"When they told me I was going to die, I had to come

back…had to find my baby and see…for myself. But I left it too late…."

"The devil's had his due, Kay," he said. "You're paid up in full. Our boy's in good hands. Loving hands. You can rest easy now."

"Yes," she said on a whisper, her eyes drifting shut once more. "Yes."

For a while longer, he sat with her, watching the slow, steady throb of the pulse in her throat. Wishing it would stop. Afraid that it might.

What a hell of a way for a thirty-five-year-old woman to die—in a ten-by-ten foot hospital room, and no one who gave a damn that she was alone in the world except an ex-husband. No friends to give comfort, no phone calls, no cards to pin to the corkboard above the bed, and the only flowers those he brought in every couple of days. Stargazer lilies, her favorite—but even their exotic scent couldn't overpower the smell of death that clung to her.

The door swished open to admit one of the nurses who regularly looked after Kay. "Why don't you take a break, Mr. D'Alessandro?" she said. "Go get yourself something to eat. Take a walk outside and get some fresh air. It'll do you a world of good."

"I hate to leave her alone."

"She won't be alone. I'll sit with your wife until you come back and if there's any change, I'll have you paged."

"Thanks." He needed to get away for a while and clear his head. He had the feeling it was going to be a very long night. "I'll turn on my phone if I leave the building. They've got my number at the nurses' station."

He was almost at the door when Kay stirred. "Mike?"

"I'm here," he said.

"I love you, Mike."

He paused on the threshold, briefly at a loss. How was he supposed to respond?

The answer came, clean and simple. Whatever she'd done or not done, she didn't deserve to die believing no one cared. She'd been his wife at one time; she'd borne his son. They were reasons enough to keep a special place in his heart just for her. So he told her the only truth that mattered anymore.

"I love you, too, honey."

CHAPTER EIGHT

HE WAS wiping his eyes as he came out into the corridor, and didn't see her lurking a few yards away. Numbly, Camille watched as he turned the corner to the elevators.

Part of her wanted to run after him, and comfort him. He didn't strike her as a man easily given to tears and her heart broke a little at the sadness draped over him like a shroud. But another part of her wanted to shriek in anguish because, without meaning to, she'd overheard too much.

I hate to leave her alone....

I'll sit with your wife....

I love you, too, honey....

He'd told her he was divorced, and she'd believed him. He'd told her the reason he went to the city was that he had business there, and she'd believed that, as well.

He'd come from his sick wife's bedside and within the hour made love to *her.* She'd rolled around without a stitch of clothing on, in the sand down by the river, and let him touch her all over. *Let him have sex.*

She'd listened to him lecture her about adopting a baby when her marriage was on the skids, and been grateful when he'd forgiven her enough to seduce her a second time.

She'd as good as told her parents never to darken her doorstep again, unless they were prepared to take back all the horrible things they'd said about him. She'd invited him into her home, introduced him to her son.

She'd let him make a fool of her, over and over again, and if she had a grain of sense, she'd go home to Jeremy and forget she'd ever met a man called Michael

124

D'Alessandro. She was obviously much better suited to being a mother than she was a lover.

But, like an open wound begging for attention, curiosity pulled at her, drawing her toward the window in the door through which he'd just left. What was she like, that woman on the other side whose adulterous husband had betrayed her all the time he was telling her he loved her? Why was she in a San Francisco hospital? They had hospitals up there in Canada, didn't they? And doctors?

Camille stole closer, intending to sneak a look through the pane of glass when suddenly the door swung open and a nurse came out carrying a water carafe. "I'll be back in a couple of minutes, but it's okay if you want to go in for a visit while I'm gone," she said, hurrying past. "She's sleeping a lot now, but talk to her anyway. Let her know you're there. We think it helps."

She ought not to go in. It wasn't any of her business. But though her conscience told her that, Camille's feet had a mind of their own and dragged her inexorably over the threshold and into the room.

She was aware of nothing but the scent of lilies in the air, and the figure lying so motionless on the bed that, for one horrified moment, she thought the woman was dead. Was backing stealthily toward the door, in fact, when the body gave a spasmodic twitch and gasped, "Mike?"

Camille froze, torn between pity and an irrational terror which urged her to flee the scene. But the woman—Mrs. D'Alessandro—seemed so distressed that in the end, pity won the day. Approaching the foot of the bed, Camille said, "He stepped out for a minute. Is there something I can do for you?"

"Thirsty," the poor thing managed, rolling her head from side to side.

A tumbler of chipped ice stood on a nearby table.

Dropping her bag on a chair, Camille took a tissue from the box by the sink and tipped several slivers of ice into it. "Here," she said, turning the poor, ravaged face toward her so that she could slip the melting ice between the dry, colorless lips. "This will help."

Her eyes were closed. The skin was drawn so tautly over her features that they'd shrunk to the size of a child's. But she'd been a beauty in her day, the high cheekbones and delicate jaw attested to that, and she'd been a redhead although little was left of her hair.

She was without question a stranger, her body wasted by disease almost to nothing, yet looking at her, Camille was haunted by a sense of familiarity. "Who is it that you remind me of?" she said softly, more to prod her own memory than because she expected a reply.

But as if she were trying to answer, his wife spoke again, an incoherent muttering this time, and picked weakly at the bedcovers as though searching for something—a slight movement only, but enough to dislodge what appeared to be colorful postcards hidden by a fold in the sheet. They slid between the guard rails and landed facedown on the floor under the chair.

Realizing she'd lost them, she groped for a handhold and tried to sit up, but the effort exhausted her. "My baby!" she cried on a thin wail of distress, sinking back against the pillows.

Camille's heart swelled with fresh pity. Oh, how frail and thin she was, how transparent her skin! "Please, Mrs. D'Alessandro, don't upset yourself," she begged, scooting down and reaching under the chair. "Your postcards are right here. I'll get them for you."

But they weren't postcards at all. They were photographs. Of Jeremy gleefully kicking a football on the lawn in front of her house. Of Jeremy, all dark tousled hair and big brown eyes, posing proudly beside his new red roadster.

"What on earth…?" Hands shaking, Camille picked up the snapshots, telling herself there was a logical explanation for finding them in that stark little hospital room. But the reasons tumbling through her mind made no sense. Why would a man bring pictures of another woman's child to his dying wife's bedside, and why would that poor soul think they were of her baby—unless…?

Time slowed, lumbered back nearly four years, and froze in horrifying detail to the last time Camille had been in a hospital.

December the eleventh, two days after Jeremy was born. She'd dressed him in a pale blue terry-cloth sleeper and a white hooded jacket she'd knitted herself. He'd looked adorable.

"We'll take good care of him," she'd promised his pretty auburn-haired birth mother.

"I know you will," Rita Osborne had said, tucking the envelope Todd have given her into her purse. "He'll have a much better life with you."

Stricken, Camille stared at the photographs and flinched at the clammy dread of certainty closing over her.

"Please…!" Full of yearning and heartbreak, the entreaty floated on a wilting breath from the high bed.

As slowly as if she were a hundred years old, Camille clutched the arm of the chair and pried herself upright. Michael D'Alessandro's dying wife was watching her, her huge, dark eyes wide open and desperate. And Camille knew then what it was that made the woman look so familiar when everything else about her had changed.

The face and body might be ravaged beyond recognition by illness, but the eyes—dear God, the eyes were a replica of Jeremy's. The resemblance was unmistakable. Indisputable.

"Rita?" she gasped, recognition flooding through her just before the floor swam up to meet her, and a world grown suddenly menacing faded into black.

She came to on a gurney in some sort of supply room lined with white cabinets. Her forehead throbbed and a nurse was taking her pulse. "Ugh!" she groaned, squinting against the bright overhead light. "What happened?"

"You fainted," the nurse said, swatting Camille's hand away when she reached up to investigate the weight on her forehead. "Don't mess with the icepack, sweetie. It's there to help reduce the swelling. You took quite a dive and smacked your head on the side of the bed. Good thing we heard the racket, or you'd still be lying on the floor."

"I never faint," she said, with feeble indignation.

"That's what they all say, until it hits home."

"It?" She wished the room would stop spinning. Wished someone would tell her how and why she was there to begin with.

The nurse stroked her cheek kindly. "Watching a loved one die takes a terrible toll on family and friends."

At that, everything came rushing back in ghastly detail, and for a moment Camille was afraid she might pass out again. But she couldn't afford the luxury. "I've got to get out of here," she said, struggling to sit up. "I need to be with my little boy."

"You're in no shape to be going anywhere just yet."

"You don't understand. I *have* to go to him." *Quickly, before Michael D'Alessandro beat her to it.*

"Not a chance, sweetie. Not until we contact someone to come and get you."

"I don't need anyone. I have my car here and can drive myself home."

"Uh-uh!" The nurse shook her head. "There's no way you're getting behind the wheel of a car in your condition. I'll bring in a phone and you can call your husband or a friend to come and pick you up. Hopefully, by the time he gets here, you'll be able to stand up under your own steam without keeling over. Meantime, stay put."

"You don't understand," Camille began again, but she was talking to an empty room. The nurse had bustled out, certain her word was law and no one would dare thwart it.

Much she knew! No one was going to keep Camille there against her will, not when Michael D'Alessandro was on the loose with criminal intent in mind! She might have hit her head when she fainted, but her brain still worked well enough for her to figure out what he was after.

He wanted Jeremy. Her son—*his* son!—was all he'd *ever* wanted, and all the rest—the compliments, the kisses, the sex—had been nothing but a load of calculated hooey designed to distract her from his real agenda.

"Well, over my dead body!" she muttered, flinging aside the icepack.

The door swung open and rubber-soled shoes whispered across the floor. "Stubborn, aren't you?" the nurse remarked, sizing up the situation. "What's it going to take to convince you I know best—another crack on the head?"

"I'm in a hurry."

The nurse pursed her lips and shrugged. "Okay. Feel free to get up and leave."

"Finally!" Heaving a sigh of relief, Camille sat up and swung her legs over the side of the gurney.

Big mistake! The walls tilted, the overhead light swung crazily, and what her stomach was doing didn't bear thinking about. Defeated, she fell back against the pillow.

"Ex…actly!" Cordless telephone flat on her hand, the nurse stood sentinel, a ruthless prison guard disguised as a ministering angel. "Ready to make that call now?"

Refusing to give in to the tears of panic stretching her control to the limit because she knew, once she started crying, she'd never stop, Camille considered the only two options open. She could call her parents, confident that regardless of the harsh words she'd flung at them, they'd rush to her aid, or she could call Fran.

The nurse tapped her foot impatiently. "Well, sweetie, what's it going to be?"

She had a blinding headache, her stomach was queasy, and her life was a mess, all of which, Camille decided, left her with only one real option. Meekly, she took the phone and dialed Fran's number. At least *she* wouldn't say "I told you so."

Nor did she waste time asking questions. Like the good friend she was, she listened to Camille's brief explanation and said only, "Sit tight. I'll be there in half an hour."

"You'll be feeling more like yourself by then," the nurse said, when Camille relayed the message. "Keep the icepack in place, and I'll bring you some hot tea."

In fact, it was nearly an hour before Fran showed up. "The parking's the pits at this hour," she explained. "Then I had trouble finding this room. Sorry, Camille. I know you must be itching to get out of here, but don't worry about Jeremy. I phoned Nori and told her to bring him over to our place for dinner. I didn't think you'd feel up to cooking, so Adam's making barbecued ribs for all of us."

Light-headed again, but from relief this time, Camille eased her feet into her shoes and collected her handbag and jacket from the counter. Apart from being a bit weak at the knees, she felt almost normal again.

"Keep an eye on her," the nurse advised Fran, ushering

them out of the supply room. "She's been checked over by one of our staff doctors and doesn't seem to have suffered any serious concussion, but she did take quite a fall and shouldn't be left alone tonight. Here's a list of things to watch for. If you have any concerns, call her family doctor."

"Will do." Fran tucked the sheet of paper into her purse and turned to Camille. "Ready to go?"

She'd been ready for well over an hour, the need to see her son growing more urgent with each passing second. Not until she could hold his warm, solid little body in her arms and see for herself that he was safe, would she be able to relax. Without waiting for Fran, she started down the corridor, certain there was nothing in the world that could stop her headlong rush to freedom.

Nothing, that was, except finding herself in the middle of another nightmare. As she drew level with Rita Osborne's room, the door opened and Michael came out looking absolutely shattered.

There was no avoiding him, and no pretending he hadn't seen her, so she stood her ground and drew on the last reserves of her pride to get her past this final hurdle. "Hello, Michael," she said.

He stared at her as if he'd seen a ghost, then made a visible effort to pull himself together. "What the devil are you doing here, Camille?"

"I came to see Rita," she said. "Your wife, remember?"

Leaning against the wall, he dragged a weary hand over his face and try though she might to harden her heart, Camille couldn't help feeling sorry for him. He stared at his feet a moment, then lifted his gaze to her face. His blue eyes were bruised dark blue-black with pain and grief. "I can't deal with you right now," he said bleakly. "It'll have to wait."

Her pity evaporated in less time than it took to blink. *He* was giving *her* the brush-off, after all his duplicity? "I can't deal with you at all," she replied, the words chipping out of her mouth as hard as granite. "Not now, not ever."

Fran caught up to her just in time to hear her remark, took one look at her face, another at Michael's, and said, "I don't pretend to understand what's going down between the two of you, but I do suggest that this is not the place to sort it out. Michael, you look very upset. If you need someone to talk to, you know where to reach us. Camille, we're leaving. Now."

And with that she strong-armed Camille the rest of the way down the hall and around the corner to the elevators.

Whenever Camille had needed her, Fran had always been there, loyal and steadfast to the end, but patience wasn't her strongest suit. All the way down to the main floor and out to where she'd left the car, she kept her peace, but her curiosity was nearing boiling point. Camille knew it but she couldn't bring herself to confide in her friend. She huddled in the passenger seat, still too dazed with shock to put her thoughts into any sort of order, let alone share them, even with someone as sympathetic as she knew Fran would be.

They were approaching the Bay Bridge when Fran finally broke the silence. "Okay, Camille, if you're not going to volunteer, I'm going to pry. I didn't raise a peep when you phoned to say you were at St. Mary's and needed a ride home. I simply jumped in my car and came racing to your rescue. The least you can do is explain why. We can skip over the fact that you fainted for no apparent reason and now have a lump on your forehead that leaves you looking a bit like a unicorn, and go straight to the reason you were ready to rip Michael's throat out in full view of hospital staff. What the hell's got you in such a state?"

Camille sifted through all the possible answers: he's married; he's a liar; he's an adulterer. But in the end, only one really mattered. "He's Jeremy's father."

Fran swerved and narrowly missed sideswiping a car in the next lane. "That's insane!"

"But true, nevertheless. He's married to Rita Osborne. He's the abusive husband who abandoned her when she was pregnant."

"Did *he* tell you that?"

"He didn't have to. I caught him red-handed playing the devoted husband to his dying wife." She stared out of the window, the wheels of her mind spinning frantically. "Fran, I need to ask another favor."

"Well, sure." She sounded as if she'd been poleaxed. "Ask away."

"Will you please let Nori and Jeremy stay at your cottage in Bodega Bay for a few days?"

"Camille, all three of you can stay there for as long as you like, you know that."

"I have to stay at home. That's where he'll come looking."

"He? You mean, Michael?"

"Who else? The only reason he came here to begin with was to find his son. Now that he has, it's pretty obvious what his next move will be."

"He doesn't have a snowball's hope in hell of ever getting his hands on Jeremy, if that's what's worrying you."

"Don't be so sure," she said, recalling how persistently he'd quizzed her on the details leading up to Jeremy's adoption, and how artlessly she'd given him the ammunition he'd so obviously been seeking.

There might be, he'd said, that night by the river when she'd told him there was no way Rita Osborne's delinquent husband could ever take Jeremy away from her. *Given the fact that your husband opted out of the responsibilities he deliberately undertook, a court might look very favorably on a natural father's claim to his blood child.*

"You've got every reason to be furious with him, Camille, I grant you that," Fran said, "but don't let your imagination run wild. He might have a lot to answer for, but he doesn't strike me as a kidnapper."

Never trust a stranger, Camille. You're asking for trouble if you do....

"He wants Jeremy, Fran. I know that for a fact."

Fran flung her a startled look. "You mean he actually came out and admitted as much?"

"Yes. I just didn't realize it until now. But everything he's said and done since he first came to town points to that. The evidence was there all the time, if only I'd known what to look for. Instead, I let myself be taken in by his smile and his kisses. I even...."

Despair at how easily she'd fallen into the trap he'd laid dammed the words in her throat and she couldn't finish. Couldn't bring herself to admit what an utter fool she'd been. But she'd said enough to lead Fran to all the right conclusions.

"Are you telling me the two of you made love, Camille?"

"Not quite." She bit her lip and cursed the tears stinging her eyes. "According to him, all we did was have sex. Unfortunately, I chose to read more into it than that. Silly me, huh?"

"Don't be so hard on yourself. I've seen the way he looks at you and I'd bet money that he's not exactly...let's see, how do I put this delicately? He's not exactly *unmoved* by your charms. That ought to bring you some comfort."

"I don't see how."

"Well, add it up for yourself, dearie! You're the adoptive

mother of his son, he wants to play an active role in his son's life, and the pair of you are halfway in love with each other. If that doesn't balance out to the ideal equation for a marriage of convenience, I don't know what does!''

"You seem to forget that one part of the equation is already married to someone else.''

Fran blew out a frustrated breath. "It's not that I've forgotten so much as I'm having a hard time believing it. Are you sure you didn't misunderstand?''

"I know what I heard, and I know what I saw. He's married, and he loves his wife.''

"You're certain of that?''

Caught in the vicious treadmill of memory, the words she'd overheard echoed relentlessly inside her head.

I'll sit with your wife...
I love you, Mike...
I love you, too, honey....

"Absolutely,'' she said.

Three hours before, the sun had rung down the curtain for Kay in a great orange ball of splendor. Now, nothing but a carpet of more stars than he could count in a lifetime filled the sky. No mist crept up from the ocean to shroud him in privacy as he stared emptily out at the view; no sympathetic cloud shadowed the bright moon.

Not that he gave a damn who saw him or what they might think of a man slumped on a park bench, with only a plastic bag containing a dead woman's personal effects for company. He was past caring about anything at all except the wicked waste of a life burnt out long before its time.

It was all very fine for the priest who'd administered the last rites to tell him that she'd found peace at last. *He* hadn't been the one who'd stood by helpless to erase the fear in her eyes before she sank into final unconsciousness. Nor had he been the one she'd turned to at the last and begged, "Take care of my baby, Michael...promise me you will."

He would, of course. But he didn't fool himself that it was going to be easy. No one had been able to tell him how Camille had found her way into Kay's room. Nor did it much matter beside the far greater issue of her having discovered the truth from someone other than himself.

Superimposed over his grief for Kay, the memory of Camille's pained shock when she'd come face-to-face with him in the hospital corridor bedeviled him. What he wouldn't have given for the right to take her in his arms and just hold her without any need for words.

Tomorrow, there were arrangements to be made—the tying off of all the loose ends still connecting Kay to a world where she no longer belonged. He'd take care of them first because there was no one else to do the job. Then, in a few days, when he had himself under better control, he'd go to Camille and find a way to atone for the hurt he'd dealt her, and at the same time try to honor his last promise to Kay.

It was the least he could do. Even though she'd died without his ever discovering why she'd cast him in the role of villainous husband, his anger had long since been swallowed up by pity. Her wrongdoing had caught up with her in the end and exacted a terrible price.

Once Jeremy and Nori were safely stashed in the Knowltons' cottage up the coast, Camille waited, knowing it was a matter of time only before Michael showed up. She kept the gates closed, the security system armed, and for three days paced the house, steeling herself for the showdown. Rehearsing what she'd say. Promising herself she wouldn't be swayed by anything he might throw at her: not by outrage or misery, and most of all not by sweet talk.

Then, just after ten on the morning of the fourth day, the intercom buzzed and her heart rate went into overdrive. But the closed-circuit television screen showed only the maintenance crew come to clean the pool. As soon as they left, she activated the remote lock to secure the gates again.

If there was to be a final confrontation, she intended to take charge of it from the outset and be ready for him. He'd caught her off guard for the last time. Or so she thought.

But he tricked her again, appearing so silently from the shrubbery surrounding the pool deck that she wasn't even aware of his presence until his shadow fell across the open book in her lap.

"Before you raise the alarm, I come in peace," he said, dropping into the chaise next to hers. "And if you're wondering how I got past all that fancy electronic equipment undetected, I parked down the road and slipped through the gates on foot when that van left. I knew you wouldn't let me in otherwise."

He wore black denim jeans and a short-sleeved white shirt unbuttoned at the neck. His face looked thinner, giving cleaner emphasis to the hard line of his jaw. Furrows of fatigue radiated from the corners of his eyes. His mouth was curved with sorrow, and the sun glinted off a few threads of silver in the hair at his temples.

He looked so wretched, so utterly defeated, that she was reminded of a beautiful wounded angel condemned to a hell she couldn't begin to imagine, and it was all she could do to remain impervious to his pain.

"Why wouldn't I let you in?" she said, finding some solace in the fact that she didn't sound a fraction as disconcerted as she felt. "I'm not afraid of you. If anything I pity you. Even a man of your shabby morals deserves a hearing, guilty though you are of the most contemptible deceit."

"I doubt anything I have to say is going to cut much ice with you at this stage, Camille."

"I doubt it, too. But you are the man who once told me confession is good for the soul, are you not?"

He sighed and looked around, his expression so wretched that despite everything he'd done, a twinge of pity stirred the cold ashes of the passion he'd once aroused in her. Before it took too firm a hold, she reminded herself that the hell he was in was of his own making and if she let him draw her into it, too, she deserved all the misery she'd undoubtedly reap.

Affecting an indifference she was far from feeling, she said, "Well? Is there *anything* you have to say, or shall I call the police and have you arrested for trespassing?"

If he'd come back with an apology, or cut to the chase and simply told her the truth, no matter how ugly it might be, she might have been able to hang on to her dignity.

But he did neither. Instead, he cast a searching glance over the garden and said, "Is Jeremy here?"

CHAPTER NINE

HE WASN'T off to the best start.

"No, Jeremy is not here!" she fairly shrieked, bolting out of the chair and flying at him.

Before she could rake her fingernails down his face, he fended her off with one hand and said, "Calm down, for Pete's sake! The only reason I asked was I didn't want to chance him overhearing us again."

"So you say!" she spat. "But we both know that's just a smokescreen to get you what you're really after."

She was petrified, he realized. Her eyes were huge as saucers, their pupils dilated with fear. "Honey, I don't know why you think I'm here—"

"Don't you 'honey' me!" she said, aiming a kick at his shins which he avoided by calling on soccer skills he hadn't used in a long time. "I'm not your 'honey' and I never was. Save it for your wife Rita, though if she's as easily taken in by your endearments as I was, I feel sorry for her."

"In fact she was my ex-wife, but it's a moot point now. She died on Sunday afternoon, moments before I ran into you outside her room."

He conveyed the news less to arouse sympathy than to deflate her anger because, as things now stood, trying to engage in a reasonable conversation was a lost cause.

The ploy worked. The fight went out of her and her voice was hushed when she said, "I'm sorry. I could see how ill she was, poor thing. I'm sure you must be very grieved."

"I am," he admitted. "A lot more than I expected, given

that we've been divorced nearly five years and hadn't been in touch once in all that time until very recently."

"Oh, please!" The fire in her eyes erupted again as quickly as it had died down. "If the only reason you're here is to add another lie to the pile you've already told, I don't want to hear it."

He frowned, puzzled. "What lie? You've known from the beginning that I'd been married, Camille. Why are you making such an issue of it now?"

"Maybe because I heard you tell her you love her. *And* I heard the nurse refer to her as your wife. In my book, neither adds up to your being divorced."

"At the stage she was at, I'd have told her whatever I thought she wanted to hear because, by then, it was *all* I could do for her," he said. "Sure she'd made some mistakes and done some terrible things, but she was already paying for them big time and I didn't see it as my job to add to her load. There comes a time when a guy has to move past all the anger and resentment that's been eating him alive. For me, that time came on Sunday.

"As for the nurse calling her my wife...." He shrugged. "It was a harmless mistake on her part and I'm sorry if it bothered you, but frankly I had bigger things on my mind right then than setting a comparative stranger straight on my marital status. I'd have thought, considering what you'd just learned, that you would have had, too."

"Adultery isn't something I can just brush aside as being of no consequence."

She was sticking to her position of woman wronged, but it was costing her. He could tell by the way her tone lost some of its starch, plus the fact that she couldn't quite meet his gaze.

"We didn't commit adultery, Camille," he said, lessening his hold on her wrist and snagging her fingers in his.

"I know I've kept things from you, but I'm being completely up-front with you on this."

He'd have done better to keep his distance. She snatched her hand away as if he'd stubbed out a burning cigarette on it. "I can't imagine why you think I'd believe anything coming out of your mouth!"

He raised both arms in surrender and backed off a couple of yards. "All right, let me put it to you like this—if a stranger tells you what an adorable kid Jeremy is, do you feel obligated to point out that he's adopted?"

"Don't be ridiculous! Of course I don't."

"You confide it only to people who matter?"

She flushed. "Oh, all right, you've made your point! So you weren't lying about being divorced. Congratulations, I'm sure! But that hardly mitigates your other deceptions."

"I'm aware of that," he said. "And if you think they haven't weighed heavily on my conscience for quite some time now, you don't know me as well as you think you do."

"I don't know you at all!" she said scornfully. "You never intended that I should, or you'd have been open with me from the start."

"How so? By marching up to you the day we met and saying, 'Hi, that's my son you're parking on the merry-go-round, and if it's all the same to you I'd like to get to know him, so how about I come to your house tomorrow and we'll work out a visitation schedule?'"

"At least I'd have known where I stood. We might have been able to arrive at some sort of agreement."

"Come off it, Camille! I'm supposed to be the liar here, not you. You'd have tried to have me thrown in jail, and we both know it. And I can't say I'd have blamed you, given the story Kay had fed you."

She eyed him suspiciously. "Who's Kay?"

"My ex. Until she married me and took my name, she was Rita Kay Osborne, but everyone called her Kay. She didn't start using the name Rita until after the divorce."

"Probably because she wanted to disassociate herself from you as thoroughly as possible. You were a rotten husband."

"I'm sure I made my share of mistakes but contrary to what she might have led you to believe, walking away from my son isn't one of them. If I'd known she was pregnant, I'd have provided for her and the baby."

"And?"

It was pretty clear what else she was asking, and he wasn't about to compromise his integrity any more than he already had, even if this was the one time she'd have preferred him to lie. "And he'd never have been put up for adoption on the black market."

"I *knew* it!" Her voice trembled pitifully and it was all he could do not to haul her close and kiss her fears into oblivion. "This is where you've been headed all along, isn't it? It's why you seduced me—because you thought, if you softened me up, I'd let you…trample roughshod over my entire world."

"That isn't why, Camille," he said. "If you believe nothing else, know that the one thing I've most wanted to avoid is hurting you."

"Well, you didn't succeed!" she cried, her eyes streaming. "You've taken my life and chopped it up into little pieces. And you're not done yet, are you?"

Dealing effectively with a woman's tears was something he'd never mastered. Despite her Irish ancestry, his mother's equable temperament had seldom crumbled in the face of adversity, and Kay's way of retaliation when things hadn't gone her way had been the silent treatment. At his wit's end, he said, "Now what sin have I committed? For

Pete's sake, Camille, it seems I can't do anything right with you, no matter how hard I try.''

"Oh, stop it! *Stop it!* I know why you're here, and it's got nothing to do with trying to make things right. You've come to take my son away from me.''

"Huh?''

He must have looked as stunned as he felt, because she came at him again, all spitting fury. "What's the matter, Michael? Do words escape you for once? My goodness, when someone beats you to the punch, you're not quite as nimble with the glib replies, are you?''

Unless he found a way to calm her down, she was going to tip over the edge into full-blown hysteria, something he *knew* he'd never handle. "Sweetheart,'' he said, trying once again to take her in his arms and placate her, "you've got it all wrong.''

She slapped him away. "Save it, Michael. You're going to have to come up with something a lot more original than a repeat performance of the same old smooth moves if you seriously expect me to hand my child over to you. I'll see you in hell first!''

"I have no intention of trying to take Jeremy away from you.''

"Then why are you here?''

"Because I hoped we could behave like the two mature adults we're supposed to be. I hoped that, instead of leaping to irrational conclusions, you'd at least listen while I offered the explanations I know are long overdue. But given your present frame of mind, it doesn't look as if that's going to happen.''

"No, it isn't,'' she said. "I'm not feeling very rational right now. I'm feeling distinctly threatened because I've come to realize that, with you, there's always a hidden agenda.''

"Not anymore, Camille," he said, his patience at an end. The last few days had been rough; the nights even rougher. Answers he'd hoped to find, Kay had taken to the grave, and the ensuing frustration was wearing him down. "The gloves are off. You're looking at a man who promised a dying woman that he'd take care of her son, and I'm telling you up-front that it's a promise I intend to keep."

"He's not her son!" she cried, her face contorting in pain. "He's mine. And I can look after him without any help from you, so take your promises and choke on them!"

He could have tried persuasion. He could have soothed her ruffled feathers by spelling out his intentions and thus proving that he had nothing diabolical up his sleeve. But when a woman had made up her mind not to listen, no matter how reasonable the idea being presented, a man's best recourse was to keep his answer short and succinct. So he planted his feet apart, folded his arms, and drowned her out with a resounding, "No!"

Her mouth fell open in pure shock, leaving him to suspect that not many people had dared say "no" to her in the past. That she managed to look adorable, whether she was sobbing, raging or gaping, hadn't escaped his notice either, but it was fast losing its charm. He was tired of being manipulated by the women in his life. It had been too late to do much about it by the time he learned what Kay had been up to behind his back, but he was damned if he was going to let Camille lead him around by the nose.

"You don't have any choice," she told him, recovering quickly. "You don't have the right to come charging into his life and taking over. I'm his legal parent, not you. I've got the papers to prove it."

"Don't make me play hardball, Camille," he said softly. "We both know I've got a strong case, should I choose to pursue the matter through the courts. As for your having papers!'' He let out a snort of disgust. ''Hell, we're talking about a child here, not a pedigreed pooch, though I suppose, given that you cut your teeth on the theory that money can buy just about anything you set your heart on, it shouldn't surprise me that you see my son as just another commodity.''

At that, the little witch stepped close and poked him hard in the chest with her finger. Twice. Cripes! ''Well, it certainly didn't take long for you to show your true colors, did it, you great overgrown bully?'' she seethed. ''I can't believe I ever bought your Mr. Nice Guy act.''

''I'm exactly the same person I've always been, Camille. A man cheated out of knowing his own son by my desperate former wife and your sleazy excuse of a husband.''

''*Ex*-husband!''

''Now, perhaps,'' he amended, pretty steamed himself by then. ''But he wasn't when he drew up that shady adoption agreement, was he? He was màrried to you, and you both stood to gain by the arrangement he made. Trouble was, he couldn't live with what he'd done and took refuge in the bottle. But you never had a problem, did you? Even though, by your own admission, you thought the whole deal smelled to high heaven, you just held your nose and kept right on playing the perfect mother and poor, long-suffering wife.''

He was out of line and he knew it. From the way she stiffened in outrage, she knew it, too, and probably would have decked him if the ding-dong tone of the security alarm hadn't warned her that someone had entered the house through one of the perimeter doors.

Flinging him a last poisonous glare, she crossed the pool deck and started up the steps leading to the house. By the time she reached the top with him close behind, the Japanese nanny and Jeremy had appeared on the terrace.

He looked flushed and miserable, and the nanny looked worried.

"So sorry not to wait for your call before we came back," she said, giving a little bow, "but Jeremy's cold grew much worse overnight and this morning he complained of an earache, so I thought it best to bring him home."

Stooping, Camille held out her arms. The little guy stumbled to her and buried his face against her skirt. She brushed a soothing hand down the side of his cheek and under his jaw. "You did the right thing, Nori," she said, nodding reassuringly at the nanny. "He's burning up with fever. Run a cool bath so we can sponge him down, will you, while I place a call to Doctor Hythe?"

The nanny scuttled away.

"Probably an ear infection," Michael said, trying to be helpful.

Camille looked at him as if he were something that had crawled out of the woodwork. "And how would you know?"

"I might not know much about being a father, but I'm a pretty experienced uncle and I've seen this happen before when a kid his age gets a cold that starts acting up. If I'm right, the sooner he's on antibiotics, the sooner he'll start to feel better."

"You think I don't already know that?"

"I'm beginning to wonder. Why else would you be wasting time arguing the point? Here, let me take him while you make that phone call."

"Absolutely not!" Small, perfect breasts heaving, she pulled Jeremy into the shelter of her arm and held him glued to her side as if she feared he might physically tear the boy away from her. "Nori!" she cried, so much terror in her voice that Mike winced.

Cripes, what kind of ogre did she think he was?

The nanny reappeared on silent feet, a huge bath towel draped over one arm. Edging toward the door, Camille gave the child a gentle push. "Go with Nori, darling. Mommy'll be with you in a minute—as soon as she sees Mr. D'Alessandro off the premises."

"Forget it, Camille. I'm not going anywhere," Michael said, as the nanny trotted off with her charge.

"You're not getting your hands on my son, either," Camille informed him. "And just in case you're thinking of resorting to brute force, Nori holds a black belt in karate and don't think for a moment that she'll hesitate to use it if you try to interfere. You'll be flat on your back before you know what hit you."

It was the last and most ridiculous in a tired list of threats. "Will you for Pete's sake stop over-dramatizing and get your priorities straight!" he roared. "I've had it up to here with your nonsense, you hear? Like it or not, that's my boy we're talking about and I'm not about to be shoved aside like an old shoe when he obviously needs medical attention."

"I'm his mother—"

"And making a hopeless mess of the job right now, if you ask me!"

She drew herself up to her full five-feet-five or whatever, aristocratic nostrils flaring. "You really are an insulting boor, aren't you?"

"Honey, you have no idea the depths to which I can sink if I'm pushed far enough. But keep this up, and you'll find out soon enough."

Her gaze flickered, and she gnawed on her lip a moment. "Much though it galls me to admit it, you're right," she finally admitted. "Jeremy comes first. If you want to help, you can drive us to the clinic. We'll take my car. You'll find the keys on a hook in the rear hall, next to the door leading to the garage. I'll meet you at the front entrance in ten minutes.''

She didn't wait to hear his answer. She just left him to find his way through the house to the area in question. She might suffer all kinds of uncertainties in other areas of her life, but put her in mother mode and she dished out orders as if she owned the world.

They were headed home within the hour, complete with prescribed medications for the ear infection he'd predicted, and for all that she tried to hang on to her resentment, Camille couldn't help being grateful that Michael was with her. For so long, she'd had only herself to rely on in a crisis. Having a man take charge, even of something as simple as driving and parking the car so that she was free to devote herself to Jeremy's needs, made such a difference to the load she'd carried for the past three years.

Covertly, she glanced at him, searching for some physical likeness to Jeremy, but she could find nothing in the stern profile of the man behind the wheel which in the least resembled the sweet childish features of her son.

For that matter, there was nothing of the charming lover she'd briefly known, either. A new and disconcerting side of Michael had emerged, along with the truth of his identity. Underneath that sexy, easygoing exterior lurked the toughness of a street fighter. It would not be wise to alienate him, and wiser still not to let him see how afraid he made her.

Wetting her lips nervously, she said, ''Thank you for caring enough to help us out when you already have so much else on your mind.''

''I thought I'd made it clear that nothing takes precedence over my son's well-being.''

She almost cried out, *Don't you dare call him that!* But the shocking reality was, he and Jeremy were genetically linked and no amount of wishing it were otherwise was going to sever the connection. So rather than start another all-out war, she buried her objection in a cough and took a more diplomatic tack. "It might be best," she said, casting a cautious glance over her shoulder to make sure Jeremy couldn't overhear, "if you didn't say that in front of Jeremy."

"He's asleep," Michael informed her curtly. "Has been for the last ten minutes. He can't hear a thing."

"Still, if he should get any inkling of…who you are, it would confuse him terribly. He's already asked why he doesn't have a daddy."

"Well, now you can tell him that he does."

"No, Michael!" Dismayed, she clutched at his arm.

He shrugged her off as if she were as inconsequential as a gnat. "Then I will."

Terror rose up again, and try though she might, she couldn't contain it. "Please don't! He's too little to understand why."

"You mean to say you haven't taught him all about the birds and the bees yet?" A bitter smile touched his mouth. "Shame on you!"

"This isn't a joke."

The glance he flung at her was so weary and disillusioned, she could have wept. "Hell, Camille, right now I'll take my laughs any place I can find them."

"What I meant was, if you tell him you're his father, he'll want to know why you don't live with us. He's just a little boy, Michael. Don't expect him to believe you care about him unless you plan to be around to prove it."

He blinked and looked away. A sigh shook him. "I've

got to tell you, I don't know how I'm going to leave him, Camille. I wish there was a way—''

Had the seed Fran planted taken root without her knowing it, or was it the wretched misery which crossed Michael's face that made her blurt out rashly, "Maybe there is. We could get married—purely for Jeremy's sake, of course. It might not be the ideal arrangement for you and me, but it's what's best for him that matters.''

The silence with which he greeted the suggestion was so lengthy and painful that she wished she could curl up into a ball and disappear. When she could bear the suspense of waiting for his reply not a second longer, she closed her eyes in an anguish of humiliation and mumbled, "On second thought, it's a stupid idea. It would never work.''

Just as swiftly as her heart had sunk, it soared again when he said thoughtfully, "Hold your horses. I haven't turned you down yet.''

She sucked in a breath, hardly daring to contemplate what it might mean if he were to say yes. Could they make a marriage work?

She could! She could do whatever it took to keep Jeremy with her and make him happy, including turning a blind eye to the fact that Michael probably wouldn't have looked at her twice if it weren't that she had something he desperately wanted.

So what if he wasn't in love with her? He was decent and kind and dependable. He didn't buckle in the face of adversity. He'd never put his own interests ahead of Jeremy's. And she'd lived with a weakling long enough to know that *they* were the qualities that really mattered, not how often he showered her with compliments or toasted her with champagne.

But to her disappointment, when he spoke again it had nothing to do with marriage or Jeremy. "Strange," he said, slowing down to make the turn into her driveway. "I could have sworn I closed the gates when we left."

"You did," she said. "I distinctly remember it."

"But they're open now. Guess you must have company."

He was right. As they rounded the last curve in the drive, a gray Mercedes-Benz, one she recognized with sinking dismay, loomed into view at the far end of the guest parking area next to the house.

The minute Michael brought the car to a stop, she leapt out and without waiting for him to lift Jeremy from the back seat, raced up the steps to the front door just as Nori, who must have heard their arrival, pulled it open. "They phoned," she said, anticipating the question before Camille could ask, "and although I tried to put them off, when they heard you'd taken Jeremy to the doctor, they insisted on coming over."

They would! Taking orders from a nanny, even one as impeccably polite and respectful as Nori, wasn't in their nature.

"It can't be helped. As long as they don't know Michael was with me—"

Nori looked distressed. "They already do. They saw his car on the side of the road and recognized it."

So the troops were in place, waiting to mount another offensive. And Michael, with a sleepy Jeremy in his arms, was climbing the steps and about to walk into the line of fire.

"Where are they now?"

"Having coffee on the terrace."

Desperate to avoid what would undoubtedly be a disastrous confrontation, Camille said, "Okay, here's what we'll do. You get Michael to take Jeremy upstairs to bed and ask him to stay with him until I come up, and I'll get rid of my parents.''

It wasn't an ideal solution, but it was the best she could come up with at such short notice because she knew without bothering to ask that Michael wouldn't just deposit Jeremy on the doorstep, then leave. Nor did she want him to, not with the question of marriage still hanging in the balance.

"We heard," her mother started in, the second Camille stepped out to the terrace. "And it goes without saying that we are horrified."

"Don't be," Camille said, deliberately misunderstanding. "It's just a mild ear infection—nothing serious. He'll be back to his usual self in no time at all."

"We aren't talking about Jeremy," her father said. "Camille, we hoped that when you discovered the extent of that man's mischief, you'd have the good sense to send him packing."

"*That man* happens to be Jeremy's father, Dad. Even if I wanted to, I doubt I could keep him away from his son."

From the thunderstruck expressions on both their faces, it was obvious that their private investigator hadn't done quite as thorough a job as her parents thought.

"That's preposterous!" her father exclaimed.

"Nevertheless, it's the truth."

"He's no such thing and if he told you he is, it's just to cover up the fact that he's had another woman on the side all the time he's been inveigling himself into your life. The man is an outright liar."

"And a money-grubbing opportunist," her mother put in.

Her father waved that observation aside as if it went without saying that *of course* money was at the root of the whole problem. "What I don't understand, Camille, is why a woman of your intelligence would swallow such an implausible story.''

''Because I found irrefutable proof that it's true, that's why. The woman he was visiting in St. Mary's was Rita Osborne and if the name doesn't ring a bell, it should. She was Jeremy's birth mother.''

''So? What's that got to do with anything?''

''Michael was her ex-husband.''

Her father turned faintly purple and swung his head like a wild animal sniffing out a hidden enemy. ''Are you telling us he's the lout who left her on the street with nothing but the clothes on her back?''

''No, because that never happened. It was just one of many in Rita's web of lies. I'm telling you he was denied the knowledge that he'd fathered Jeremy and only recently discovered the truth. Unless we can come to some sort of amicable agreement, I'm terrified he'll try to have Jeremy's adoption rendered invalid.'' She paused to let that information sink in before delivering what she knew they'd find the most shocking news of all. ''Which is why I've asked him to marry me. I can think of no other way to protect my son from an ugly and damaging custody battle.''

''Dear heaven!'' her mother squeaked, falling into the nearest chair. ''Camille, you've lost your mind. You need professional help!''

''Because I'm prepared to do whatever it takes to prevent my son's life from being turned upside down? I don't think so, Mother.''

''Have you no understanding of the ramifications involved if you go ahead with this harebrained scheme?'' her father bellowed. ''At present, Michael D'Alessandro owns nothing but a two-bit construction operation somewhere in Canada. But throw in your lot with him, and *your* assets become *his* assets. He marries you, he takes you away from us—to a foreign country where the law will favor him. And once he's established parental rights to Jeremy, he can divorce you and *you*'ll be the one left with nothing worth having.''

"Not necessarily. We could draw up a prenuptial agreement." She flung out her hands. "It's not ideal, I agree, but it's something I can live with, and it's a lot better than spending the rest of my life looking over my shoulder and afraid to let Jeremy out of my sight."

"So he gets a rich wife, and a son he doesn't deserve—"

"And I get peace of mind. You can't put a price tag on that, Dad."

"You'll be selling yourself into bondage," her mother said, "and I think you'll find that to be quite a hefty price tag in the long run."

"I'm prepared to make whatever sacrifice is necessary to keep my son, including selling my soul to the devil if I have to."

"You don't have to go to that extreme," her father insisted. "I'll hire the best lawyers in the city to make sure you don't lose him. And if that vagabond tries to take my grandson out of the state, I'll have him arrested for kidnapping and thrown in jail."

"Your father's right, Camille," her mother said. "Forget this crazy idea. Michael D'Alessandro will never make you happy." She shuddered fastidiously. "He's too commonplace. Too…earthy."

"Better listen to Mommy, Camille," Michael said from the doorway behind her. "I'm all of that and more. It'd be a real step down for a princess like you to wind up married to a peasant like me. You'd be sacrificing everything your little heart's been trained to hold dear."

CHAPTER TEN

THE fact that he'd snuck up on them unobserved did nothing to increase his stock with Glenda Younge. Lurching out of her chair as if she'd found a viper in her drawers, she squawked, "And how long have you been listening in?"

"Long enough," he said, dismissing her and addressing his next remark to Camille. "Not that I'd dream of deflecting you from more important issues, but just in case you're interested, Jeremy's medication is taking effect already. His temperature's down and he's fallen asleep again."

She had the grace to look somewhat sheepish. "Of course I'm interested. Thank you for keeping an eye on him for me."

"You left him alone with Jeremy?" the dragon lady cried. "My heavens, Camille, you've just finished telling us you're afraid the man might kidnap the child! What were you thinking?"

"I never said that, Mother. What I said was—"

"That you're prepared to do whatever it takes to protect your place in his life, including marrying me if you have to." Mike grimaced. "I'm overwhelmed! The lengths to which you'll go and the sacrifices you're prepared to make, all in the name of maternal dedication, are admirable, Camille."

"Well, there's no use pretending it would be a love match, is there?" she said, turning pink. "We've both been down that road before and ended precisely nowhere, so we might as well call a spade a spade and admit it would be purely a marriage of convenience."

155

"You're missing the point, my dear. In common with every other contract, a marriage of convenience requires one essential component to make it work. How many divorces is it going to take, Camille, before you figure out that trust between the parties involved is the glue that holds a partnership together?"

"If I didn't trust you, do you really think I'd have suggested we share responsibility for Jeremy?"

"Sure I do. Your history speaks for itself. You used Todd to get Jeremy and now you're willing to use me to keep him. And just in case there's a loophole you've overlooked, you'll get me to sign a prenup agreement to protect all your other interests. Talk about covering your ass!"

"Look here, Mr. D'Alessandro," the father cut in. "It's unfortunate that you overheard things not intended for your ears, but you do yourself no favors by browbeating my daughter, particularly not since she is disposed to be generous in allowing you some access to her son."

"*My* son, Mr. Younge."

"You gave him up."

"I did no such thing, nor am I about to now."

"Be reasonable, man! Whether or not you knowingly rescinded your parental rights is immaterial after all this time. You don't have a prayer of getting the adoption order overturned."

"I'm not sure he knows what 'rescind' means," the mother whispered ostentatiously.

"I know what it means," Mike informed her. "Now let me ask you a question. Do you know what I mean when I tell you I'm tired of having to listen to you quacking on about something which is none of your bloody business?"

She looked so scandalized, anyone would have thought he'd just ripped open a raincoat and exposed himself.

"Camille is our daughter," she gasped, fanning herself with her outsize purse. "That makes her our business."

"She's a grown woman, even if she doesn't always act like one. She's got a mind of her own and it's about time you let her use it."

"She's too distraught to think straight, and it's all your fault. I knew you were trouble the minute I laid eyes on you, insinuating yourself into our lives and pretending you were someone of consequence when the truth is, you barely have two cents to rub together."

"Be quiet, Mother," Camille said, with a lot more command than he'd expected. "Michael's right. This is none of your business."

Her father jumped in again then, with another two bits worth of unasked-for advice. "Perhaps not, but you'd do well to look at the product before you rush to put money down on your purchase. You heard the way he spoke to your mother just now, and you've seen for yourself how he managed to bamboozle you with his lies. You'd still be believing every word he says if we hadn't opened your eyes to the truth. Well, a leopard doesn't change his spots, Camille. If you don't think he'll subject you to the same verbal abuse he flung at your mother, or continue to prevaricate whenever it suits his purpose, then you deserve all the trouble you'll be buying."

"Better listen to the old man," Mike advised her mockingly. "He's so sure he knows better than anyone else about everything from soup to nuts that if creating the world had been left to him, he'd probably have had it finished in half the time it took God to do the job."

"I certainly know all about men like you," her father snapped. "Ill-bred, uneducated, posing as an entrepreneur when all you're really looking for is a free ride to easy street."

"I don't know where you got your information—"

"I had you investigated."

"Then you didn't get your money's worth. I'm not interested in getting into a spitting match with you, but if the man you hired had done his job properly, you'd know that I'm a university honors graduate with a degree in structural engineering, and my entrepreneurial skills have just landed me a contract worth a cool six point five million dollars— not enough to match the Younge fortune, perhaps, but more than enough to buy the help I need to reclaim my son."

That knocked some of the wind out of the old man's sails. He hemmed and hawed, adjusted the knot in his tie, and exchanged a glance with his wife whose mental calculator was practically clicking aloud. "They're accomplishments worthy of note, certainly—assuming, of course, that you're speaking the truth for once."

"You can verify it easily enough with a phone call to the University of British Columbia. As for my being ill-bred, my father might have been a working man and my mother a housewife, but I can promise you that if you'd ever been invited into their home, as I was invited into this one today, you'd have been treated with the utmost courtesy and respect—not because you've got money coming out of your keister and think that makes you better than everyone else, but because that's the way they always treated guests. Not that I expect you to appreciate such a foreign concept."

"There's no need to be sarcastic, young man. If we've misjudged you, we're sorry. It's possible you're more deserving than we originally thought."

His tone suggested it was probable pigs would fly before he'd make such a gross error in judgment, and swallowing cyanide a hell of a lot more palatable than having to admit he might be wrong.

If he hadn't been so ticked off, Mike might have laughed at the man's discomfiture. "Let's not go overboard with the compliments," he said. "We both know you think I'm pond scum."

"At last we agree on something. Sadly, the conferring of a university degree does not, of itself, endow a man with breeding."

"Well, heaven forbid I should prove you wrong yet again, so here's one more thing for you to chew on. I'm also a bulldog when it comes to protecting what's mine."

"That sounds like a threat, Mr. D'Alessandro."

"Read it any way you like, but know this—from where I stand, leaving my boy to fall under your kind of influence and doing nothing to counteract it, marks me as a negligent father, and that's not a label I care to have hanging around my neck."

"What are you saying, Michael?" Camille asked, her voice brimming with alarm.

He daren't look at her because he knew if he did, he'd cave in. She reminded him of a lovely, fragile butterfly batting its wings frantically against the net closing over it. His every instinct was to rescue her, to spare her injury, to let her fly free without let or hindrance. But doing that would mean more than breaking his promise to Kay; it would mean corrupting the principles which formed the lodestar of his existence. And if he did that, he'd never be able to live with himself.

"Your parents don't want me breathing the same rarified air as you, Camille. And I don't think you've got the moral fiber to go against their wishes. So I'm turning down your proposal. You might be desperate but I'm not, and I sure don't need the in-laws from hell playing vigilante on your behalf. If I ever marry again, it'll be to a woman able to stand on her own two feet and who sees me as something other than a monster who has to be appeased at any price.''

He was at the front door before she caught up with him. ''I've never thought of you that way,'' she cried, hanging on to his arm. ''Please don't punish me for my parents' mistakes.''

''I might be a trusting schmuck who got taken to the cleaners once, but it isn't going to happen a second time. You're cut from the same cloth they are, Camille, and you want to know what clinched it for me? That you were a party to a private investigation all the time you were kissing up to me.''

''I wasn't a party to it,'' she whispered hollowly. ''Not until the end, and only then because my curiosity got the better of me. When I went to the hospital, all I had to go on was a floor and room number, nothing else. I had no idea I'd find Rita, or that she was your ex-wife. I'd never have made the connection if it hadn't been for the photos of Jeremy.''

He wiped his hand down his face, all the weeks of sub-terfuge combined with the misery of the last week leaving him suddenly weary. ''You know what, it really doesn't matter anymore. The cat's out of the bag and nothing you or your parents can do is going to stuff it back in again. I have a son and there's no way I'm letting you or anyone else cut me out of his life. I've already missed too much of it.''

''So you're going to tear him away from everything dear and familiar, just to satisfy your need for revenge? My goodness, whatever happened to sweet reason and rational discussion, Michael?''

''It went the way of trust.''

She shifted from one foot to the other and made a con-certed effort to hang on to her control, but she was close to breaking point and he knew he had to get away. He could be as merciless as the next guy when it came to fighting for what he believed in and defending his rights, but driving Camille over the edge—hell, that was more than he could handle.

"You'll be hearing from me," he said, yanking the door open, "but if, before then, you need to get in touch, I'm staying at the Portland. I expect to be kept informed of Jeremy's progress. If he gets worse, let me know immediately."

He made his tone intentionally brusque and it seemed to do the trick. She wrestled her emotions into line and glared at him from eyes brilliant with unshed tears. "You're certainly showing your true colors now, aren't you? Whatever happened to that nice man who—"

"Haven't you heard, Camille? Nice guys finish last. And I don't like losing so from now on, you'll be playing by my rules."

"And exactly what will that involve?"

"I'll call later on tonight and let you know. I'll tell you this much, though. Do yourself a favor and get rid of your folks before then because I've had about as much of their interference as I can stomach. This is between you and me, and if you persist in involving them, I can promise you you aren't going to be happy with the outcome."

He phoned at half past eight and foregoing any social discourse, leapt straight to the point. "I assume you're alone?"

Not a trace of warmth or humanity colored his words. This was the voice of a man well used to emerging the winner in the dog-eat-dog world of business.

"I'm alone," she said, grateful that he couldn't see the pain she knew was written all over her face.

She wanted the other Michael back; the one she'd known before. Why couldn't they have fallen in love at first sight and eloped to the Dominican Republic before her parents' well-meant interference threw everything out of kilter? His being Jeremy's father wouldn't have mattered then. The three of them would've been one big happy family regardless.

"How is Jeremy?"

"Much better. Asleep."

"Good. I'll be flying home tomorrow, but I'll leave a number where I can be reached any time, night or day. Keep me posted. I want to know how he's doing."

"You're leaving so soon?" A gaping sense of loss swallowed any relief she might have felt at the news.

"Yes," he said, "but before you start dancing on the ceiling to celebrate, don't take that to mean I'm walking out on my son. Here is what is going to happen. First, I'm going to set up a trust fund for him."

"Michael, that really isn't necessary. I have money enough to support him."

"I don't care what you have. It's what Kay has to give that matters here. Sooner or later, he's going to ask about his birth mother—what she was like, why she gave him up. For his sake, I intend to paint as positive a picture as possible. For him to learn the uglier aspects of his adoption can only hurt him."

"I agree," she said. "And if that's all you meant by your promise to take care of him, I can certainly live with it."

"Oh, there's more," he informed her, with the same brutal candor. "I intend to phone every Sunday evening before he goes to bed. You will see to it that he's available to take my calls uninterrupted by anyone else, most particularly your parents. He and I will talk for as long as it pleases us, and you will not listen in because you have my word that nothing I say will in any way disturb or confuse him. To all intents and purposes, I will remain for now the family friend he met for the first time this summer. *For now,* Camille.''

Although he'd said nothing which directly threatened her custodial rights, the implication that the worst was yet to come left her palms slippery with sweat. ''And later?''

''That's where you come in, my dear. You are going to tell him I'm his father. Exactly how you go about that is up to you, although I strongly suggest you exercise due caution, and control any inclination you might have to portray me as the villain of the piece. If that means putting a gag order on your parents, do that as well, because I won't tolerate their negative input.''

''I see,'' she said, the chill emanating from the telephone invading her bones. ''Have you also circled the date when all this is to occur?''

''I'm prepared to be flexible on that. You have until the beginning of December to get him used to the idea that he has a father with whom he'll be spending his birthday and Christmas.''

''You expect me to let you take him to Canada for Christmas?''

''Not this year. We'll start out with small changes. I'll come to California on both occasions. But I *will* see him every day that I'm there. I'll watch him blow out his birthday candles. At Christmas, I'll take him to see the sights, we'll go shopping together to buy a tree, I'll be the one to set it up and help him hang his stocking. And I'll be there Christmas morning when it's time to open gifts. I've missed playing Santa Claus for his first three years. I'm not about to be shut out of the fourth.''

''But what about us, Michael?'' she said.

"We'll be civil to one another," he told her, misunderstanding, deliberately or otherwise, what she was really asking. "I'll give you a bottle of perfume, you can buy me a pair of socks—we'll go through all the proper festive motions. But there is no 'us'. We're not even friends, Camille. Not anymore. But because we both care about Jeremy, we'll put on a convincing show."

"I'm not sure that I can do that," she said, her heart breaking.

"Then go spend Christmas and his birthday with your parents. But don't even think about inviting them over to your place or I'll take Jeremy somewhere else both days."

"Is this all I have to look forward from now on—just one ultimatum after another, or else?"

"More or less. When he's a bit older, we'll arrange to share holiday visits. You'll put him on a plane for the two-hour flight to Vancouver, and I'll be there at the other end to meet him. Divorced couples do that all the time and it seems to work well enough."

"We aren't divorced."

"No. And never will be because—"

"Because we'll never be married. I already know that, Michael. You don't have to keep rubbing it in. I just wish we could have found a way—"

"Wishing isn't enough, Camille," he said, just the slightest hint of regret shading his tone. "We've got too many things going against us and we both know cobbling together a marriage for Jeremy's sake does him no favors at all if, in the end, it blows up in his face. And it would, because although you might be ready to—how did you so charmingly put it? *Sell your soul to the devil if you had to?*—I'm not interested in buying."

"You're never going to forgive me for that, are you?"

"I already have, sweet thing. It's part of the past—just like you."

"So why keep bringing it up?"

"Because it showed a side of you I could never live with, no matter what perks might come with such an arrangement. Marriage is an adult undertaking, Camille, and I realized this afternoon that, at heart, you're still just a spoiled little girl playing with her doll and all her other fancy toys. If you ever decide to grow up, give me a call and we'll see where things go. In the meantime, I'll have my lawyers draw up a binding agreement for visitation rights."

There was a click and the line went dead. Phone in hand, she stared at the luxury surrounding her: the thick Chinese rugs, the white lacquered baby grand piano, the original oil paintings on the silk-paneled walls, and the plump cushioned sofas upholstered in fabric imported from France. And for the first time in her life, she felt poor. Because he was right. She was a thirty-year-old juvenile posing as a woman, and she was pathetic. *Pathetic!*

But she was a fighter, too. And he'd left the door to the future open just a crack. It wasn't much on which to pin her hopes, but it was enough. She'd show him she was worth a second chance!

"Are you telling me you'd proposed to the man and he was considering accepting, but you let him wriggle off the hook, and here you are, nearly a month later, and you've done nothing to try to lure him back?" Fran didn't bother to contain her disgust. "Honestly, Camille, you deserve all the grief you get! Why in heaven's name didn't you tell your parents to put a sock in it and show them the door, instead of wasting your breath attempting to justify something so far beyond their understanding that if you try for the next fifty years, you'll never convince them you're capable of making your own decisions?"

"I realize I didn't handle things well."

"Obviously you don't, or you'd have done something about it by now."

"I have. That is, I've come up with a plan." Camille ran her finger over the rim of her teacup, debating how to broach the subject which had brought her to the Knowlton house at a time when she'd normally have been reading Jeremy a bedtime story.

"Sitting here confiding your misery to me doesn't count," Fran told her. "I'm not the one you have to convince to give you a second chance, Michael is."

"I know, but I hardly expect him to believe in an overnight miracle. He's been gone only a month, Fran."

"Do you love the guy?"

"Oh…!" She scrunched her eyes shut and bit her lip against the sharp ache of missing him which stalked her night and day. "*Yes,* I love him!"

"So tell him so."

"I can't. Not yet."

"Why not? I'd have thought, given that you've had it up to your ears with subterfuge and lies, that the truth might be an attractive option for a change."

"I don't want him to think I'm desperate."

"Why would he, when you've gone along with everything he's asked for regarding access to Jeremy?"

"Because I'm pregnant."

There, the suspicion she'd harbored for over a week, and which a doctor in the city had confirmed that afternoon, was out! "It's true," she said, laughing despite herself at the stunned expression on her friend's face. "I'm going to have a baby."

"*A* baby?" Fran echoed. "How about *his* baby?"

"Of course *his* baby! I'm insulted you'd think otherwise."

"No, you're not," Fran said. "You're so pleased with yourself you can hardly sit still. When are you going to tell him?"

"Not until I've cleaned up the mess I made of everything before he left."

"Hmm. Probably a wise choice. Because of course, once he knows he's going to be a father again, he'll marry you regardless and that's not good enough, is it?"

"No," she said. "It has to be because he believes in me."

"Does anyone else know you're pregnant?"

"If you mean, have I told my parents, no, I haven't. Michael deserves to hear before they do. I wouldn't have told you, Fran, except that…well, I had to tell someone, or I'd have burst!"

"I guess!" Fran came to sit beside her on the sofa and hugged her. "Imagine, after all those years of trying and not succeeding, you got pregnant just like that! Who'd have thought it?"

"I know." She folded her hands over her womb. "And we only did it twice!"

Fran collapsed into giggles. "With a guy like Michael, once was probably enough!" Then, sobering, she said, "So, what comes next?"

"I want to hold off saying anything to him until I'm past the first trimester because I don't know that he could weather the disappointment if I were to miscarry."

"You're not going to miscarry," Fran said firmly. "You're going to sail through this pregnancy without any problems and present him with a beautiful new son or daughter, and you're all going to live happily ever after."

"I hope so. But there's also something else. I have to

tell Jeremy that Michael's his father. It's the only way I can prove I'm living up to my side of the agreement. But I think it's important to give them enough time to cement their relationship through their weekly phone calls before I say anything.''

''Although you're probably right, I feel compelled to point out that if you put it off too long, you won't have to worry about telling your parents or anyone else around here that you're expecting. They'll be able to see it for themselves.''

''I know. So I thought I'd fly up to Vancouver around the end of October. I'll be almost eighteen weeks along by then.''

''And definitely pushing your luck!''

''It can't be helped. I'll just have to wear loose clothes and stay out of the pool when anyone's around.''

But that would be easy compared to the patience she'd need to see her through the eleven weeks before she'd see him again.

CHAPTER ELEVEN

FALL came early that year, with a series of October wind storms and rain which pretty much matched Mike's uncertain temper. He'd thought throwing himself into the multimillion dollar town home project would take his mind off Camille. It hadn't.

He'd thought strengthening his ties to his son would make up for his failed relationship with her. It didn't. If anything, hearing her answer the phone when he made his Sunday calls intensified the wrenching sense of loss he couldn't shake, no matter how many times he told himself he was better off without her.

He had to curb the urge to try to engage her in conversation, but she made that part easy by wasting no time putting Jeremy on the line. In fact, the sum total of her words to him each week were a nauseatingly cheerful, "Hello, Michael. Here's Jeremy."

The December deadline he'd given her was still over a month away, and how he was going to last that long without seeing her was reason enough to put a permanent scowl on his face. So when he arrived at the construction site on the morning of Friday the twenty-fifth and the first thing he learned was that some clown had put his steel-toed boot through the etched glass panel of an expensive front door, he was not disposed to be lenient.

Neither the man nor the boot was hurt, but the door was a write-off. Normally, he'd have chalked up the incident to the price of doing business, but that particular employee had been careless before and this latest episode was enough to send Mike into a towering rage. "You're a liability to yourself and everyone else on this site," he exploded. "Pull one more stunt like this, and you'll be history, you hear?"

"Half the neighborhood heard, boss," his foreman Doug Russell advised him as the man slunk off. "Including the prospective client who's been waiting over an hour to see you."

"I'm in no mood to speak to clients, prospective or otherwise. Refer him to the sales team."

"It's a 'her,' and I already went that route, but she's adamant. She wants you."

He cursed, something he was doing a lot of these days.

"Yeah," Doug cracked. "I tried telling her that as well, but she's not the type to take a hint."

"As if I don't have enough on my plate!" He stomped into the display unit and flung a tube of blueprints on the granite kitchen counter. "All right, let's get it over with. Where is she?"

"Last I saw, she was wandering around the Greenwood model."

"*What?*" He thumped his fist on the counter. "Has everyone around here gone nuts? That's a hard-hat area and you of all people know what'll happen if she trips over a ladder and breaks an ankle! I'll be up to my keister in a lawsuit I don't need."

"No, you won't, and please don't take out your annoyance on Mr. Russell. He warned me of the danger and I assured him I wouldn't hold anyone to blame if I got hurt."

That voice…he'd heard it in his dreams so often of late that at first he thought it was just his imagination playing another cruel trick on him. But when he wheeled around, there she was in the flesh, stepping in her dainty little boots over the roll of carpet blocking the foyer, and looking totally absurd in a bright yellow hard hat which clashed horribly with her rose pink raincoat.

"Uh...." he grunted, giving a fair imitation of a trained ape having a tough time deciding which banana he wanted for lunch.

By contrast, she was the epitome of calm self-assurance. "Is there someplace we can talk privately, Michael?"

He snapped his mouth shut before he grunted again, and tried to look intelligent.

"I'll make myself scarce, *Michael!*" Doug snickered.

She bathed him in a smile. "Oh, please, Mr. Russell, don't let me chase you away."

"*Go!*" Mike muttered, jabbing him in the ribs with his elbow.

With a last knowing smirk, Doug clumped out. Desperate to fill the cavernous silence he left behind, Mike said, "Is something wrong with Jeremy? Is that what's brought you here?"

He came across like a prison warden who hated his job, but if she noticed his tone was less than welcoming, she gave no indication. She picked her way past a pile of drop cloths the painters had dumped in the middle of the kitchen floor, and went to inspect the built-in china closet in the butler's pantry.

"Jeremy's perfectly fine. Growing like a weed, of course, but that's to be expected."

"Then why? And don't bother giving me the line about being a prospective client because I'm not buying it."

"If I *were* in the market for a town house, I'd certainly be interested in what you're offering here. This is lovely, Michael." She ran an appraising finger over the felt-lined silverware drawer then, when he was just about ready to rap his knuckles on her hard hat and force her to give him a straight answer, turned and said, "I have some rather momentous news, and I wanted to give it to you in person."

His stomach lurched and came to rest somewhere in the vicinity of his knees. Cripes, she'd met someone! She was getting married again to some blue-chip Californian, he just knew it! "I see," he said, sounding as if he'd got a three-inch rusty nail lodged in his windpipe. "Well? I'm listening."

"Not here, Michael. Isn't there a coffee shop close by, where we can talk without being overheard?"

"No," he said. "The nearest one is a ten minute drive away in Crescent Beach and I can't see you being comfortable in a pickup truck."

"As long as you do the driving, it won't be a problem."

"I'm a busy man. Time's money, and I can't afford to waste it."

She shifted the bag slung over her shoulder and marched across the floor to trap him between her and the kitchen island. "I'm asking for half an hour, Michael. You can spare me that, surely?"

Hell, he might as well get it over with! "Okay. My truck's in the driveway."

"I know," she said. "I saw you drive up. Dark blue with a gray stripe, right?"

"Right. Not quite the deluxe transportation you're used to, is it?"

"A lot of things I'm not used to have happened to me since I saw you last," she said cryptically, setting her hard hat on the counter, "and I don't mind admitting I'm finding the changes rather refreshing."

The fragrance of her shampoo, mingling with the smell of new paint and freshly sawn wood, formed a powerful aphrodisiac. Before he did something stupid, like pulling her into his arms, he jammed his hands in the pockets of his jean jacket and brushed past her. "I bet! Well, let's get moving. I don't have all day."

The coffee shop was half empty and they were able to seclude themselves in a booth near the back. "No thanks," she said, when he asked her if she wanted anything to eat with her coffee. "And I'd prefer tea. Lapsang souchong, if they have it."

Not everything about you has changed, sweetheart, he thought, burying a grin. "Camille, this is a mom-and-pop café, not the Ritz-Carlton. I doubt the couple who run the joint have ever heard of Lapsang souchong."

She blushed and he realized how much he'd missed seeing her do that. As much as he'd missed looking at her…kissing her…making love to her and feeling her clench around him just before she came. "Of course. What was I thinking? I'll just have tea, please."

What the hell was *he* thinking! Cripes, he was as hard as a rock! "Okay, what's so important that you had to come all the way up here to tell me about it?" he asked brusquely, once their tea and coffee had arrived.

"I'm planning to leave California. To leave the U.S. altogether, as a matter of fact."

It was even worse than he'd first thought. She was marrying some guy who lived in northern Tibet or some other far-flung spot on the map, and he'd never see her again. "Why?"

"Well, I'm hoping to get married."

He wasn't hard anymore. Hearing her confirm his worst fear left him feeling as if someone had swung a mallet at his delicate parts.

Even though he usually drank it straight, he made a big production of pouring sugar into his coffee because he couldn't bring himself to look at her. "Kind of a sudden decision, isn't it?"

"Not really."

He tipped another spoonful of sugar into his mug. "How do he and Jeremy get along?"

"Famously. Just like father and son."

The canister slipped out of his hand and sent a spray of sugar skittering across the fake wood tabletop. "In case you've forgotten, Camille," he said, barely able to control the fury and jealousy roaring through him, "Jeremy already has a father."

"I know, Michael," she said, not sounding nearly as sure of herself as she had before. "And I'm rather hoping, if I ask very nicely this time, that he'll agree to make an honest woman of me."

"Huh?" Sad to say, he was back to the trained ape bit again, but his brain was too busy scrambling to make sense of what she'd just said to come up with much in the way of witty repartee.

She leaned on the table and sent another drift of shampoo and perfume floating toward him. "You turned me down the last time I proposed, because you said, quite rightly, that I needed to grow up. Well, I've tried hard to do that in the months since you left and I hope, when you hear of the changes I've made, that you'll reconsider your decision."

He cut her off with a slash of his hand. "Hold on a minute and let me be sure I've got this straight."

She sat very erect and folded her hands primly in her lap. Her face was blindingly beautiful, from the radiant bloom of her skin to her huge, serious eyes and sweetly compressed mouth. Her hair, even on a day as gray as this, gleamed like spun gold caught in the rays of an April sunrise.

"You came all this way to propose?"

She nodded.

"It couldn't have waited until Christmas?"

She shook her head.

He leaned back in the booth and stared at the ceiling, the No Smoking sign, the plastic roses in a vase on the glass-fronted display case in the corner—*anywhere* but at her. "Well, it's something to consider, I suppose."

"I won't ask if that's a yes," she said, finding her tongue again, "because I don't want your answer yet."

He shot her a glance from beneath his lashes. "Setting out conditions already, Camille?"

"Just one." She clasped her hands earnestly. "I want you to hear me out and then take the rest of the day to mull over what I've said, before you make up your mind. I've given this a great deal of thought, Michael, and it wouldn't be fair of me to expect you to commit one way or the other until you've had time to digest the pros and cons."

"Name some of the cons."

She lifted one shoulder in a tiny shrug. "I'm used to being a single parent and having the final say on how I want things done. It might take a while for me to 'get used to sharing my toys', as you once put it—although I hasten to add that I've never regarded Jeremy as a toy. Also, I'm very well off, and I don't know how you'll handle that. Some men find it difficult having a rich wife." She lowered her eyes and hesitated before finishing, "And last, it's possible you're involved with someone else."

"And the pros?"

"It would be wonderful for Jeremy to have two parents living under the same roof, and I'd do my very best never to make you regret being my husband."

"Is that all, Camille?" he goaded her. "You can't think of a more *intimate* reason for us to tie the knot?"

She blushed again and refused to meet his gaze. "Well, we are...compatible."

"Compatible how?"

She bit her lip, but couldn't stop the smile tugging at her mouth. "You know! Sex."

"Ah, yes," he said. "Sex. I'd hate to overlook *that* as I weigh my options."

"But there's more, Michael," she said, sobering. "I want you to know that no matter what you decide, I do intend to leave California, and I am resolved to move here. I've looked into it, and because Jeremy has a Canadian father, that won't be a problem with the authorities."

It was a shame that he had to prick such a tantalizing bubble of fantasy, but the probable obstacles weren't something he could ignore, even if she could. "And what do your parents have to say about all this?"

"They don't know yet."

"Aha! Enter major stumbling block number one! Once they find out, they'll never let you get away with it."

"It isn't up to them," she said flatly. "This is my decision. Jeremy's the one who needs to live close to both his parents, not I. And as you so succinctly pointed out, it's long past time I severed the apron strings with my mother and father. I love them, but I don't need them telling me how to run my life and I'm afraid they're going to have to accept that."

He made a tunnel with his hands and blew down it. "You'll find it's easier said than done. When you actually get right down to—"

"I've already sold my house, Michael. The new owners take possession at the end of November. You might turn me down, but you're not going to get rid of me. I'll look for a place near where you live so that Jeremy can visit you every day. Next door, if I can swing it!"

"Whew!" He shook his head. "Talk about tearing up roots and starting over in a big way!"

"Well, it's time I showed a little backbone, don't you think? And you must admit it'll simplify everything if we're close by. Next year, Jeremy will start school. Before long, he'll want to play soccer and basketball and all those other boy things that I know nothing about. And he'll want his daddy to be there to coach him and cheer him on."

Touched more than he cared to admit, he said, "You don't have to sell me on fatherhood, Camille."

"I know," she said. "But I am hoping I can sell you on marriage. I'm hoping you'll believe me when I say that I would be honored to be your wife, but if you decide to turn me down, I'm not going to pack up my toys and go running back home to sulk. I've grown up enough to handle disappointment without falling apart, Michael."

"Let me get back to you later," he said, afraid if he didn't shut her up, he'd lose it and start bawling. She was offering him the world—and talking as if he'd be doing her a favor by accepting it. It was more than he'd dared hope for; more than he deserved. "Where are you staying?"

"At the Pan Pacific. I wondered, if you don't have other plans, if you'd like to meet me there for dinner tonight?"

"Yeah," he said. "I'd like that very much."

"Then I'll make a reservation as soon as I get back. Is seven too early?"

"Uh-uh. Seven's fine." He pulled back his sleeve and checked his watch. "Look, I really have to get back to the job site. I'm expecting building inspectors in another twenty minutes."

She swept up her bag and slithered out from the booth. "I understand. Thank you for taking the time to meet with me."

"You're welcome."

He followed her out to the sidewalk and unlocked the truck. She smiled and thanked him as he helped her into the passenger seat. He said "You're welcome," again, went around to the driver's door, and climbed in.

"This is a very comfortable vehicle," she said.

"Yeah," he said, rolling his eyes and wondering how he could tactfully put an end to an exchange growing more stilted by the minute. But it was a delicate situation. She'd put her pride on the line and he'd been caught by surprise. It wouldn't do to rush things. They were talking big decisions here—decisions that would affect the rest of their lives, and Jeremy's, too. They both needed to be sure they understood exactly what they were getting themselves into because once done, there'd be no undoing it.

She perched in her seat, her pink raincoat wrapped around her, her outsize bag clutched in her lap, her eyes on the road ahead. "Oh, look!" she exclaimed, with painfully manufactured enthusiasm, as he turned the truck around and headed back the way they'd come. "A train!"

She'd been spending so much time with a three-year-old, she was starting to sound like one. And he wasn't much better, hedging his bets and dithering like somebody's maiden aunt. Caution be damned!

He cruised to a stop a yard or so short of the level crossing. "Yeah," he said again, cupping his hand around her neck and weaving his fingers through her silky hair. "A train. And just in the nick of time, too. It saves me having to find a place to park and do this."

He pulled her toward him and she didn't resist. She leaned across the console, her mouth trembling, her eyes glassy with tears, and lifted her face to his. Heart nearly bursting with pent-up emotion, he bent his head and kissed her. Then he kissed her again. And all the stress and tension he'd been carrying around for weeks flew out the window along with caution, and got swept away on the southwest gale thundering across the bay.

''Oh, thank you!'' she whispered, when he stopped to let them both draw breath. ''I'd just about given up hope that you were ever going to do that again.''

''You might have come a long way since the last time we were together,'' he told her thickly, shaping the curve of her lip with his thumb, ''but, honey, you've still got miles to go if you couldn't figure out I've been itching to kiss you from the minute I saw you modeling that hard hat.''

She was at the table by a quarter to seven, just to be sure she'd be seated before he arrived. ''He'll never suspect,'' Nori had assured her, when she'd asked if the peacock blue outfit made her look pregnant.

She sipped from her water glass. Rearranged the accordion pleats flowing from the nipped-in empire waist of her dress, and wondered if the fluttering in the pit of her stomach was the baby making its first tentative moves, or just sheer nerves.

The wall of windows next to the table showed the glimmering outline of watercraft bobbing at anchor in the harbor, and beyond, above the lantern-chain draping the hills on the other side of the Lion's Gate Bridge, the misty aura of floodlights piercing the rain clouds hanging over a mountain where, when the snow came, people could ski at night.

Superimposed over the spectacle, the reflection of the room behind her was flung back in perfect reproduction. The flash of silver caught her attention, the flicker of candles, and then, rising above the small crowd waiting to be seated, Michael's tall figure coming toward her.

Briefly, she closed her eyes and crossed her fingers. *Let it be a perfect evening!*

He bent over the back of her chair. Dropped a kiss on the crown of her head. "Am I late?"

"No," she said, savoring the sight of him all freshly shaved and sparkling in a navy suit and white shirt, with a burgundy silk tie. "I'm early."

"You look lovely, as always."

"So do you."

"Me, lovely?" He laughed and took a seat across from her. "That's a first—but then, there've been a number of those today." He raised his brows and gestured. "Are you expecting…?"

Her eyes flew wide in shock. She gulped and tried to stem the flush of guilt sweeping up from her feet to envelop her entire body. *He'd noticed!*

"…someone else to join us? I see we're at a table for three."

"Oh!" Relief gusted from her lungs and set the candle flame in the middle of the table to flickering. "Well, yes. Just for a short while."

Right on cue, Nori came into the restaurant with Jeremy, adorable in dark blue corduroy vest and pants, and a red striped shirt, at her side. He'd been so proud of his clothes, so excited about his part in the evening. Now, though, he was dragging his feet and looked ready to turn tail and run.

Camille knew how he felt. She was on pins and needles herself.

"Anyone I know?" Michael asked.

She nodded. "Mmm-hmm."

He inclined a taut smile her way. "Are we playing twenty questions, Camille?"

"No," she said, and held out her hand.

Jeremy ran the last few yards and flung himself at her, all the time peeking out at Michael whose face was a study. For once in his life, he was speechless.

Prying Jeremy loose, she steered him toward his father. "Go on, darling. Don't be shy. You know what to say."

"Hello, Daddy."

His voice might have been tentative as the cheep of a newly hatched bird, but there was no mistaking his words, or their effect on Michael.

He bounced his fist against his mouth, blinked, and stared fixedly out the window a moment. He cleared his throat once or twice, shook his head as if to dispel ideas too baffling and wonderful to be real then, when he'd wrestled himself under control, looked back at Jeremy and said gravely, "Hello, son."

Because she knew, if she gave in to the tears pressing behind her eyeballs, that Jeremy would start crying, too, Camille buried her nose in her glass and drained half the ice water in one go.

When she dared to look up again, she found Michael watching her from eyes turned nearly purple with emotion. "You," he murmured, "are one tough act to follow."

"I'm not trying to bribe you, you know. There are no strings attached to what just happened."

"Oh, there are strings, Camille, and they're wrapped so tight around my heart it's barely managing to function."

Jeremy leaned against his knee. "Now that you're my daddy, are you coming to live at our house?"

"Er...no, son."

"Can we come to yours?"

Before Michael could answer, Camille said, "Remember what I told you this afternoon, Jeremy, when we went to the aquarium? That if we couldn't live with daddy, we'd live near him? And after, when we went for a drive, remember those lovely houses by the sea that you liked so much?"

He nodded and fixed his attention on Michael again. "Is that where you live?"

"No," Michael said. "I live in an apartment, but I've been thinking I wouldn't mind living by the sea, in a house with a big garden where a boy and his daddy could kick a ball around."

"With a dog, right?"

"A dog sounds like a fine idea to me."

"And I could bring my racing car and drive all over the garden?"

"Sure."

"And Mommy can come, too?"

Michael's gaze met hers. "Oh, yes. Mommy is definitely part of the deal."

Jeremy heaved a sigh of contentment. "I think I'll like living here."

"And I think this calls for champagne." Michael signaled the waiter. "It's not every day a man gets to have dinner with his son."

He ordered sparkling apple juice served in champagne flutes. "To the future," he said, raising his glass. "And to the three of us."

"Cheers!" Jeremy piped up, clearly delighted with all the pomp and ceremony.

It was just as well Nori came to collect him a short time later, before the excitement became too much for him.

He watched as his son trotted off with the nanny, then swung back to face her. "I never thought I'd say this but, just this once, I'm glad to see him leave. Because you and I have business to discuss."

"Oh dear!" She dabbed the corner of her mouth with her napkin. "That sounds ominous."

"First, I have to tell you I've never seen you look more

beautiful. You're glowing, Camille, in a way you never were before. You light up this entire room.''

''I'm happy.'' She lowered her eyes almost shyly. ''Happy to be here. Happy to be with you.''

''Me, too. And it's been a long time since I've been able to say that.'' He reached into his inside pocket and took out the velvet bag he'd stashed there. ''I thought, when I went shopping for a ring this afternoon, that giving it to you would be the highlight of the evening, but you up-staged me with Jeremy. Nothing will ever equal that. But at least you know the reason I'm accepting your proposal has nothing to do with what you've given me tonight.''

She gasped a little and covered her mouth with both hands. Her eyes were big as saucers and suspiciously bright. ''Oh, Michael, that's the nicest thing you've ever said to me!''

''But telling you I love you is the most important. I can't promise I'll always be nice because I'm not always a very nice person, but I swear to you, I'll love you for the rest of my life.''

A tear fell down her face, bright as a shooting star. ''You don't have to say that, you know.''

''I wouldn't, if I didn't mean it. 'I love you' aren't words I toss around lightly. So believe me when I say, I do love you. Very much.''

She sniffed, and still managed to look beautiful. ''I wanted to be the first to say that to you. Because I love you, too, with all my heart.''

''Too bad, spoilt little rich girl,'' he said. ''I beat you to it and I'm never going to let you forget it.'' He loosened the cord at the neck of the bag and tipped the ring into the palm of his hand. ''Will wearing this help you get over the disappointment?''

He took the third finger of her left hand and slipped the

ring into place. It was at least two sizes too big, but the diamond solitaire was perfect. Elegant and classic and matchless, just like her. "If you don't like it, we can return it and choose something else."

"I absolutely love it," she cried softly, and patted the chair next to hers. "Come and sit beside me, Michael. I have something to give to you, too."

He didn't need to be asked twice. He'd been waiting all night to get close to her. But, "I've already got more than any man could want," he said. "I've got you and Jeremy. I don't need anything else."

"Oh, I hope you don't mean that." Her smile, shining through the tears, was tremulous. "Because this is *not* something that can be returned or exchanged."

She took his hand and placed it at her waist. At least, it used to be her waist. But underneath the yards of silk, or whatever her dress was made of, he felt something round and solid. Like a little football. Or a basketball.

He snatched his hand away and jumped up from the table. "What have you got hidden under there, Camille?"

"I'm not sure yet," she said demurely. "It's either a boy or a girl. Congratulations, Michael. You're going to be a daddy again."

He didn't know how it felt to pass out, but the dizzying pattern of black dots dancing before his eyes suggested he might be about to find out. Slumping back into the chair, he eyed her nervously. Now that he knew what to look for, the basketball was pretty hard to miss. "Are you telling me you're pregnant?"

She let out a giggle, something he hated in other women but which rippled out of her mouth like music. "Oh, I hope so, otherwise I'm in trouble."

"You're in trouble anyway, you little witch," he

growled. "Why didn't you say something sooner? What if I'd refused to see you? What if I'd turned you down?"

"That's precisely why I didn't tell you. I didn't want you marrying me out of obligation or pity."

His mouth dropped open. "You know what? You're daft!"

"I'm carrying your baby, as well," she said, bold as brass. "So watch your language."

He started shaking with laughter. His mouth split in a mile-wide grin. Grabbing her by the shoulders, he planted a kiss full on her lips and didn't give a rap who saw. "Forget dinner," he said against her mouth. "You're coming with me. This baby and I need to get better acquainted."

He rented a suite overlooking the water. He told her he loved her, that he'd loved her for a long time. He took off all her clothes and laid his face on her bare stomach and told his baby he loved it, too. He held her in his arms and kissed away the happy tears she shed.

And finally, with the moon peeping through the window from between ragged clouds, he made love to her.

In a bed.

At last.

The Greek Millionaire's Marriage
by Sara Wood

DIMITRI ANGELAKI braced his powerful legs as his launch surged forwards, its streamlined hull scything cleanly through the glittering sea towards the little fishing port of Olympos. He sang softly to himself, an old Greek love song, in a throaty voice that conveyed his passion for life and love.

It had been an odd day. One with stark contrasts of delight and anxiety, during which his senses had been utterly sated—and his nerves had been tested to the utmost.

Glancing around, he allowed himself an indulgent moment of pleasure, letting his gaze linger on his wife's incredible body, and enjoying the gleam of her golden-goddess skin against the luxurious cream leather seat. To his approval, her bikini was minimal: three small turquoise triangles barely concealing the essence of her womanhood.

The dazzling light was turning her hair to white fire where it fanned over her slender shoulders and he felt a helpless little jerk in his chest when he recalled just where that hair had been that day, slithering and sliding over the most sensitive parts of his body in an erotic dance that had driven him to paradise and beyond.

His chiselled mouth curved sensually and a throb began yet again in his loins. That was the joy of sex with Olivia. First would come the anticipation: the fiery glances that ripped his brain to shreds, the messages of hunger and need clearly projected in her sea-blue eyes.

5

Then, as surely as night followed day, came their un-inhibited lovemaking: inventive, crazy, wild and tender—but always intensely satisfying and releasing the steam valve of their mutual passion.

Finally, he thought, now fully aware of her and with all his senses on high alert, he could enjoy a rerun of every erotic second, from the first glance they'd exchanged to their final sighs of release.

A growl of pleasure rose to his throat and his hands were less than steady when he belatedly turned his attention to steering a straight line again. She got to him, right in the gut, and he loved that because it made him feel alive and utterly male.

Sometimes he wanted to shoot his fist up into the air after their lovemaking, and shout Yes! like a kid who'd just scored a goal. He grinned to himself at the very idea. He, a tycoon whose coolness under pressure was admired the world over! But property deals didn't excite him nearly as much as these exquisite encounters with his wife. It was unfortunate that his work took him away from home so often and that the hectic nature of his breakfast-to-midnight schedules meant that it was pointless for Olivia to travel with him.

Still, the time they were together seemed all the more sweet. That day they had anchored offshore to swim naked in the silken sea. Then they had made love in a lemon grove, the intoxicating scent of a thousand blossoming trees adding to his delirium. Later, she'd fed him lobster and grapes on a hillside overlooking the ruins of an ancient temple dedicated to Aphrodite, the goddess of love.

'Venus,' he'd explained to her. 'A poor second to you, my darling.'

Amazingly, he could still feel the thrilling touch of

Olivia's fingers on his mouth, his throat, his chest...and everywhere else. Each deeply pulsing inch of him bore her imprint. It had been one of the most sensual experiences in all the thirty-two years of his life.

Everything would have been perfect—if it hadn't been for his increasing concern for Athena. A frown creased his sun-bronzed forehead as he willed Athena to ring from the hospital to say she was all right. He felt the tension screwing him up again, ruining the memories of the day. But then it was understandable. He loved Athena with all his heart...

Olivia stiffened when she heard the trill of Dimitri's mobile. It had been ringing far too often that day, but with infuriating stubbornness he'd refused to turn it off.

'Greek moguls,' he'd said with a pretence at pomposity and referring to a standing joke between them, 'need to stay in contact with their minions.'

'Then find a minion you can delegate to,' she'd protested, but had been fatally diverted when his mouth had closed firmly on hers and he'd kissed her complaint away with a breathtaking thoroughness.

Looking back, though, she could be more objective. His obsessive devotion to work had been a problem for some time. When he was away, and she only had her disapproving mother-in-law, Marina, for company, she felt increasingly lonely and unhappy. Her insecurity and doubts over Dimitri's true feelings were painfully reinforced by Marina's sly hints about Dimitri's long absences.

Olivia clenched her fists. From the day of her marriage six months earlier, Marina had taunted her.

'All Greek men have mistresses,' Marina had purred. 'Don't think my son is any different.'

A mistress. Would that explain his lack of consideration? Even this long-anticipated trip today, to the ancient Greek theatre at Epidauros, had been marred by his inattention. She sighed. It could have been deeply romantic. Dimitri had demonstrated the acoustics of the two-thousand-year-old theatre by whispering 'I love you' from the performing area far below. Amazingly, she had heard every impassioned syllable from where she had been sitting, fifty-four rows up.

Quite enchanted, she'd risen to her feet to blow him a kiss. Unfortunately just then he'd received another of his infuriating calls and he had hurried out of the arena so that she couldn't eavesdrop on his conversation.

Recalling how offended she'd been, and with her eyes flashing in anger, she curled up crossly in the luxurious seat of his launch, glaring at Dimitri. He handled the boat expertly with one hand, the other holding the loathed mobile to his ear.

Although his back was to her, she'd seen the tension of his body when the phone had rung. And now that he was engaged in an earnest discussion she wondered at the reason for his relief, which was apparent in the easing of those taut muscles that she knew so well. Something was going on.

Her heart cramped. He was almost cradling the phone, his magnificent body fluid with tenderness. A sense of dread played havoc with her stomach. She sucked it in, not breathing. Perhaps her mother-in-law was right.

Yet…Dimitri couldn't keep his hands off her. Almost from the moment she'd become his secretary two years ago, at the age of twenty-four, they'd been mad for one another. Every moment in public together had been a deliciously tensioned ordeal; every second alone had become a shattering explosion of hunger and raw need. They had been blind to sense, reckless in surrendering to the volcanic passions that had seized them.

Thinking of those blissful stolen moments of abandon caused an instant arousal in her and she shifted her slim thighs, pressing her legs tightly together to control the pulsing heat that had begun to massage her with its irresistible rhythm.

Clouds of helpless longing confused her brain and ruefully she realised that the pressure of her bikini top had become unbearable because of the sudden fullness of her breasts and their tingling tips.

Focusing on him, she noticed that he was laughing now. The honey-gold naked shoulders shook with amusement as he murmured something intimate into the wretched phone.

A fierce stab of jealousy ripped through her. Dimitri was *hers!* Body and soul, heart and mind! Immediately she felt appalled by her irrational suspicion and, contrite, she went over to stand behind him, wrapping her arms around the warm, satin skin of his narrow waist in a gesture of remorse, the jutting peaks of her breasts pressing provocatively into his back.

Dimitri jumped as if she'd ambushed him, muttered into the phone something incomprehensible in Greek— which *might* have been 'see you tomorrow', though her Greek was still minimal—and with a hasty *'Adio!'* he broke the connection.

Beneath her hand, his heart thudded fast and loud. In fear? she wondered, alarmed. Maybe he did have a mistress. Business took him away so often he could even be serving a whole harem of women for all she knew!

Yet when he swung around, his eyes were smouldering with intent. Hauling her slender body against his, flesh to flesh, he kissed her with slow deliberation, one deft hand killing the engine, the other untying her bikini straps.

He was fully aroused. Magnificently, thrillingly, urgently. Whilst she revelled in the hardness of him, she couldn't help but wish she knew if it was for her, or the woman on the phone.

'Who was that?' she demanded, an ominous frown flattening her arched brows.

He was intent on an erotic stroking of her hair, the pale ash-blonde strands slithering over her sun-kissed shoulders. He disturbed the sprigs of lemon blossom, which he'd arranged around her head like a crown, and they drifted to the ground in a generous waft of intense perfume.

Dimitri's marauding mouth savaged the golden skin of her throat before he answered lazily and with a satisfying huskiness.

'A friend.'

To her suspicious mind, that sounded a shade too casual. And he hadn't looked at her, his inky lashes dropping to hide his eyes.

'Do I know him?' she asked with even more studied carelessness.

There was a very slight hesitation but it was long enough for her to know he was about to be economical with the truth.

'No. Forget it, my darling. Concentrate on what I'm intending to do to you, mm?'

She firmed her mouth but he teased it open easily

with his tongue. The magic of his fingers, tantalisingly laborious as they undid the ties of her briefs, ensured that she did forget. The glorious surrender of her body began. Throatily whispering outrageous things to her, describing in detail what he had in mind, Dimitri eased her gently to the warm teak deck.

Her hands clutched at the waistband of his swimming trunks and slid them from his body. Beneath her avid fingers, the muscles of his small buttocks contracted and she ran her hands lovingly over the firm curves.

As a lover he was insatiable. Sometimes his hunger startled her, but she, too, could be as wild and demanding. Then there were times, like now, when his tenderness made her heart contract and his thought for her pleasure knew no bounds.

Olivia began to lose control as Dimitri's wicked fingers slipped with unnerving accuracy to the swollen bud of sensation that lay close to her liquefying core. He did love her, she thought in an ecstatic haze. He'd married her, hadn't he?

Celebrate 100 years
of pure reading pleasure
with Mills & Boon®

To mark our centenary, each month we're
publishing a special 100th Birthday Edition.
These celebratory editions are packed with extra
features and include a FREE bonus story.

Plus, you have the chance to enter a fabulous
monthly prize draw. See 100th Birthday Edition
books for details.

Now that's worth celebrating!

September 2008

Crazy about her Spanish Boss by Rebecca Winters
Includes FREE bonus story
Rafael's Convenient Proposal

November 2008

**The Rancher's Christmas Baby
by Cathy Gillen Thacker**
Includes FREE bonus story *Baby's First Christmas*

December 2008

One Magical Christmas by Carol Marinelli
Includes FREE bonus story *Emergency at Bayside*

Look for Mills & Boon® 100th Birthday Editions at
your favourite bookseller or visit
www.millsandboon.co.uk